WINGLESS VICTORY

"A blessed companion is a book"—JERROLD

WINGLESS VICTORY

THE STORY OF

SIR BASIL EMBRY'S ESCAPE

FROM OCCUPIED FRANCE IN THE SUMMER OF 1940

RELATED BY

ANTHONY RICHARDSON

*

THE COMPANION BOOK CLUB

LONDON

*Made and printed in Great Britain
for The Companion Book Club (Odhams Press Ltd.)
by Odhams (Watford) Limited,
Watford, Herts*
S.853.Y

PREFACE

ALTHOUGH it all happened ten years ago, I have never before told the full story of my escape from Occupied France to anyone at all.

The suggestion that I should tell it came from Anthony Richardson, whom I first met when he and a number of other officers foregathered at Ipswich railway station, on 2nd August, 1940, to welcome me back on my return to my unit after the travels described in this book. In my absence, Richardson had been appointed as Adjutant to the Squadron which I had the honour to command for the first nine months of the war.

As things worked out, we never served together—but I felt that he was very close to the aircrew of that great Squadron in mind and heart. He shared their anxieties, their sorrows and their joys in those tremendous days, and I believe he suffered as much strain as any of those who flew against the enemy. He understands human nature and the things of the heart.

So when, all these years after, he urged me to recall my adventures in the escape from France, I think that one of the reasons I allowed myself to be persuaded was that I knew he would understand my story and be able to capture the spirit of the times. There was a do-or-die feeling in the flying air in 1940, which only those who lived through it, could fully understand.

Richardson has related everything that happened to me and brought it to life again exactly as I told it to him. For over four months, we worked together for one or two evenings a week, going over every moment of my experiences, checking and re-checking, building up the full picture from my own recollections and from the notes I had made in 1940, immediately after my return home. The story is true and correct in every detail, with the exception only of the names of non-R.A.F. characters, which are not their real names.

BASIL EMBRY

ILLUSTRATIONS

The photographs in the text have been specially
taken in France with the co-operation of Air
Marshal Embry on the scene of events described
in the narrative.

CHAPTER ONE

EMBRY didn't want to leave. It was useless attempting to evade the issue any longer. He didn't want to leave the Station. He didn't want to leave the Squadron. He didn't want to leave the chaps. A copy of the posting signal was still in his pocket:

From H.Q. No. 2 Group to Royal Air Force Station, Wattisham. Wing Commander B. E. Embry is appointed to command R.A.F. Station West Raynham with rank of Acting Group Captain with effect from 28/5/40. He is to hand over command of his Squadron to Squadron Leader Acting Wing Commander L. R. Stokes on 27/5/40.

That was all the paper work needed to change a form of life almost completely. He was gratified at the promotion because anyone would be. He realized that it was quite reasonable, that he needed a rest from operational flying. It should be in every sense a relief from the strain of leading a Blenheim bomber Squadron into battle against the heaviest odds at any hour of the day. To a degree he would not know the long daily drag and responsibility of the apprehensive hours when the Squadron was stood-to. He ought to be glad—but he wasn't.

He had led the Squadron out over the Forest of d'Hesdin that afternoon, and he had returned with an aeroplane full of holes, but with all his crew intact. And there, in his office in Number Three Hangar at Wattisham, Stokes had been waiting for him as he knew he would be. And Oswald Gayford, the Station Commander, benign and florid, had been there as well. And they'd handed over with the Adjutant, like a cat on hot bricks, prancing about in the adjoining office with an armful of files and confidential documents, in case the new C.O. wanted any of the "gen."

The new C.O. hadn't wanted any of it. Embry could carry it all in his head and pass it on to him. It was then, perhaps, that he experienced the first pang.

So much had been contrived as the occasion had demanded. So many expedients in tactics or modifications had been rearranged at a moment's notice. The war, in dark and fearful flood, was in full spate beneath the bright May skies. Over the Channel the battle for Dunkirk was raging.

The letters in his own personal files, and the jottings in his notebook, the memoranda of his memories, were more vital than anything academically sorted and annotated. That sort of work was fundamentally for the professors: his job was to fight. Therefore, a mere scrawled pencilled comment could be imperative, because its import was so vital. And there had been a great many memories, not of the long period of his service life, but of the last few thunderous months, when all the past years had been concentrated into the justification of his profession by war.

He knew Stokes of old. He could remember his long white face, lank figure and enormous hands, as far back as 1934, when they had been in India together. Stokes had once been a farmer and farmers were reputably men of integrity and thoroughness. They had to be practical and hardworking to make the land fulfil its promise. And that was what was wanted now. Hard work and common sense and courage. He had no doubt that Stokes had all these virtues. But he still resented parting with the Squadron.

He was still being unreasonably resentful now in the Mess, though the official handing over had been completed an hour ago down at the Flights. It was a very deep sort of resentment because his mind wasn't anywhere continuously in contact with the general flow of conversation. They were all there, Stokes and Gayford, Tubby and Flash, and all the others, all grouped round the fireplace, with their tankards of beer in their hands. He was joining in their reminiscences all right, but at the back of his mind was this nagging. There were so many hundreds of details that he should have passed on to his successor, that he must have forgotten scores of them. And it was not permissible to forget, because these were all practical things won by bitter experience, and they could save men's lives. This wasn't the kind of war where you wanted to charge round waving swords and blowing brass bugles. It was a cold and cunning and deliberate business, where the battle went to the man who kept his head.

But Stokes' eagerness to learn was disarming. Later in the evening when they were together and alone, the unjustifiable resentment disappeared as quickly as it had arisen, when Stokes said simply:

"I expect you'll miss the chaps."

And then Embry saw exactly what was the issue at stake. All the training in the world even couldn't really compare with this present business. This was a colossal show and it would need every ounce of resource, of intelligence and courage to see it through; and everybody who was experienced and fully trained realized it, so that the last few months had blended service people together in such a way that comradeship and brotherhood were only terms of speech to be interpreted into action. It was something which couldn't be explained in mere words. It was something which all the squadrons must have gained by now; and so his plight was no worse than

11

many another commander who was to be moved on for promotion, and the essential thing was to make certain he had given Stokes every help that was humanly possible before he left. Given the chance, of course. And then again, the pang.

Nor was there much comfort to be found still later on in his own room, with all the signs of his coming departure in the morning. The strapped valise and packed uniform case were a reminder of the end of a phase. He'd have liked the opportunity for one last crack at the Hun and to show Stokes the way it went. But it wouldn't go that way and he knew it. So he went to bed.

The Squadron was handed over. Or was it?

The following morning, 27th May, was bright and clear. It was expected that in view of the change-over of command, and the great activities of the Squadron during the last two months, that it would be rested for that day, and the sister Squadron would alone stand-to. But during the morning the signal came through from Group that a general stand-to was ordered, due to the rapidity of the enemy's advance towards Dunkirk.

It was quiet and calm in all that countryside around the aerodrome, and in the neighbouring fields labourers worked peacefully, and down the Suffolk lanes, farm carts trundled, and away behind a distant wind-break would sound the familiar barking of a dog. It was the strangest thought that forty minutes in the sky could bring a man into deadly conflict above the blood-stained cornfields of France. But those were the kind of soft thoughts for the "ground-lubbers" as Stokes called them, since his mind was bent on the signal that had come through at nine o'clock on the "tie-line."

Headquarters No. 2 Group. The following Squadrons are to stand-by to attack advancing enemy columns of all arms in the district of St. Omer.

12

Embry's mind was concerned with the signal as well. He didn't allow it to concern him for long.

He said to Stokes: "That's just as it should be. I'll have time to do this last job and get to Raynham on time as well. So I'll brief the chaps, and then we'll just wait for the whistle to go. And after it's all over, then I'll really say goodbye."

There's no use arguing with that sort of statement, when it comes from that sort of man, and Stokes knew it. Nor would Gayford, whatever he may have thought, have raised any serious objection to such a proposal, realizing the intrinsic value of such a trip led by so experienced a commander with his potential successor at his side. So maybe even by the afternoon of 27th May the Squadron hadn't been handed over completely.

Embry briefed his Squadron for the last time. He described the nature of the target and how they would go about their business, and he emphasized with his customary incisiveness the absolute necessity of keeping close formation, and at all costs to follow him completely in any and every evolution. This all-important point he repeated.

At four o'clock the Squadron of twelve aircraft took off in two flights, formated in "vic" formations with Stokes flying at the apex of the second "vic" immediately behind Embry's "box" of three. The aircraft were Blenheim Mark IV, and each carried a crew of Pilot, Navigator/Bomb-aimer, and Wireless Operator/Air-gunner. The Navigator, who also released the bombs, after guiding the aircraft over its target, occupied a space ahead and on the right of the Pilot. The Air-gunner sat in a Bristol power-operated turret amidships over the fuselage. The bomb-load was four bombs to each aeroplane. The Squadron routed out over Kent and flew across the Channel. The Suffolk fields and hedgerows slumbered in the late afternoon sun far behind. Ahead over the gradually approaching enemy coastline hung a sinister pall of smoke. The whistle had sounded.

As they crossed the coast, Calais lay six thousand feet below. Embry could see the sunken ships in the harbour, while part of the town was already in flames. With Pilot Officer Tom Whiting as his Navigator and Corporal Lang as his Air-gunner, he flew on, straight and level.

The old exhilaration was still there. Behind him, close-packed, his Squadron followed. Down below, the stricken countryside wheeled beneath his wing. Very soon now the area pin-pointed in the briefing room should be drawing near. He called to Whiting on the "inter-comm".

"How are we doing, Tom?"

"Okay. Fine."

"Are we coming along?"

"Getting nearer."

There wasn't any resentment now. They were still with him, as they'd always been with him. "One fight more, the best and the last!" That was Browning, wasn't it?

"With death at my throat. . . ." How did it go?

Whiting called him back.

"We're over the area now."

"Keep your eyes skinned."

He peered over the side through the bulge in the perspex. Somewhere, six thousand feet below, German columns were moving. At sections down their route the mobile anti-aircraft guns would be covering the advance. Then, with the target picked up, the responsibility of bombing would be his.

Tom called again on the "inter-comm":

"Dust cloud to port. There's a wood."

Embry stared out again on his port side. Beneath was a dark-green patch of a wood and a road running through it. A very white road contrasted to the heavy green of the trees, under the bright May evening sun, and there was dust rising from it, drifting over the fringe of the foliage till it formed a low semi-transparent cloud over the green fields beyond. Then he saw, through the mist of dust, a brown square speck, and then another. Seconds later the head of a transport column crawled out from the edge of the grey cloud.

He called to Tom: "This is it."

Tom was lying on his stomach, his hands and eyes at his bomb-sight. He raised his left hand in recognition of the message. He was too intent to talk.

Embry settled deeper into his seat. It was up to Tom now. He glanced over his shoulder, first left, then right. They were there. And immediately behind them Stokes was tucked in, just twenty feet below his own tail. And behind Stokes were the rest of them, and every Jack man of them one of his. He hadn't left them yet. "One fight more. . . ."

He was glad he'd been allowed to come. Gayford had demurred and "Hugh Pugh" (Air Marshal Sir Hugh Pugh Lloyd, present Commander-in-Chief Bomber Command), the Senior Air Staff Officer at Group Headquarters, hadn't thought there was much future in it. What did they know? What did anybody know but himself? He could feel the chaps following him; it was just as if they had their hands on his shoulders. Close-packed, follow my leader. . . . Leader! That was the word . . . leadership and the joy of comradeship, with all the chaps together. And when they got back they'd have a party before he left for Raynham. Oh, a wizard party! . . .

"Stand by for bombing," Tom said.

Embry peered out. The target was clearly visible. Excellent. Now for the run in. He called through to the Squadron racing at his heels.

"Stand by for bombing."

Tom would have got the target on the drift-lines of his bomb-sight by now. Embry called up to his gunner:

"Captain to gunner. You, okay?"

15

"Fine, sir."

And then Tom, once more:

"Stand by for bombing run."

Any moment now. Embry settled into his seat. Pressing against the small sheet of armour plate was reassuring. Merely a habit, quite silly. And then on the "intercomm":

"A little to starboard . . . hold it . . . steady."

There was a thumping sensation in the neighbouring air. He glanced out. Ahead three black ugly patches of smoke knotted and curled into the sky.

"Take her to port—*port* . . . hold it . . ."

Thump. And then thud again. And quickly on top of it, another. Then of a sudden the wind whipping into his face, as the side window was blown in. Too close together.

When he'd got back and was making his "quick report" to Intelligence, he'd describe the enemy fire as "moderately intense." And accurate. For a mobile column, very accurate. Something was hurting his leg. The tip of a red-hot needle.

"Steady . . . hold it . . . fine."

A second's pause, and then the long-drawn shout:

"Bombs . . . *off*!"

He felt the aircraft kick as its load fell from it, and then he swung the control column delicately to swerve to port, to circle and wheel away. And so for home.

He called to his gunner: "All right?"

"Okay, sir. They're all here, six. All tight on us."

"Good lads."

The air around them was vibrant. He could only just hear. He must remember to tell Stokes before he left to help him to follow up Corporal Lang's future movements, when they'd screened him. When he himself came back for his second tour in six months' time or so, he'd have Lang back in his crew. And Tom Whiting, of course.

The sky around him was like a stormy sea. Somebody

was banging a vast pair of clappers just to his right. He could feel his aircraft shy away from the blast, as a colt would shy at a gunshot. Well, any minute now, and they would be out of range. As long as the rest of the chaps were all right. And then the aeroplane bucked like a sun-bellying broncho.

It was as if it had received a punch in the solar-plexus. A swift, destroying, winding punch, doubling its body up in sudden anguish and helplessness. He knew immediately that they had received a direct hit amidships directly under the gunner's turret.

He shouted down his "inter-comm." There was no reply. The control column went slack, limp, useless in his hands. He was climbing steadily. He was out of control.

Tom was still on his belly, his eyes glued to the ground reeling beneath him. He was signalling with his right hand frantically. More and more frantically. Embry shouted. Tom signalled again, hearing nothing. It seemed there was a tornado raging in the Blenheim, but no fire—yet. "What sort of a half-wit does he think I am?" said Embry. He snatched off his tin hat and flung it at Tom's back. It hit him between the shoulders. He rolled over, an expression of amazement on his face.

Embry gestured towards the control column, flung up his hands, shouted to no purpose, and made his gesture of helplessness, and then, with a jabbing forefinger, in-dicated the escape-hatch at Tom's side. Tom grinned as if there was something funny about it all, and then he groped for his parachute hung behind him. The aircraft stalled and slowly turned on its side. Its nose went down. The hatch had been jettisoned by now, and Tom was peering out. Embry got up, staggered and clutched his way the few feet forward. Then he put his right foot against Tom's bottom and Tom went head-first through the hatch.

There was time to clamber back and look along the

fuselage to the gun-turret. The air-gunner lay huddled across his controls. There would be no need now to argue the future of Corporal Lang.

Embry went forward again. The Blenheim was in a slow spiral spin, circling towards the ground. He knelt by the open hatch. Somewhere outside, clear of this falling death-trap, was Tom. Perhaps his bottom was sore. Embry went out head first, counted "three" and pulled his rip-cord.

He was floating in the air. There wasn't anything like a wounded aeroplane nearby, and he wasn't trying to claw his way to safety. If he remembered rightly it was Tubby's brand-new aeroplane that he'd borrowed. What a thing!

He swung gently, blissfully. It was like waking to warm, sweet sunlight after a noisome nightmare. Swing on, swing down. Perfectly peaceful. Then he heard the growl of battle beneath him. It was like awakening from a dream within a dream and back into reality. He gazed down. The ground was slowly coming up. Then he saw his own falling aircraft. It hit the ground about half a mile away. It stood perched on its nose for a second, then there was a sudden red glow. A vast and oily cloud of smoke enveloped it. He looked away.

Below was a road and the roofs of German transport. He could see the camouflage markings by now. He spilt some of the wind from his parachute, tugging at the support cords. He swung gently to the right, drifted across the head of the column, and the next moment rolled over in the close-cropped grass of a field, three hundred yards away. A turn of the wrist and he was free of his parachute. He slipped off his flying kit, scrambled to his feet and ran swiftly to the neighbouring hedge, and, panting, flung himself beneath its scanty shelter. His parachute lay like a giant's crumpled handkerchief carelessly discarded in a field.

18

Five thousand feet above and several miles away, Wing Commander L. R. Stokes, with two of his crews lost, gathered his brothers round him in mid-sky, fought off the swarming German fighters, and led the remnant of his Squadron safely home.

The hand-over had been completed.

CHAPTER TWO

THE ditch by the hedge was shallow, the hedge itself low, and though spring was upon it, twig and leaf were sparse. Immediately beyond lay a rough track running off at right-angles from the main road, where the German convoys still rumbled relentlessly forward. Peering through a gap he saw fleetingly a distant group of farm buildings to his left, what appeared to be a group of peasants near its outer fencing, and beyond, high corn. Fleeting enough the glance, because almost immediately sounded the moan and growl of a heavy motor-cycle combination in low gear approaching down the track.

It was a German motor-cycle combination, driven by one young German soldier and the sidecar manned by another. Their automatic rifles were slung across their shoulders. The combination groaned and rattled along the ruts of the tracks, and as it passed, the occupant of the sidecar turned his head and looked directly in Embry's direction, where he crouched on the far side of the hedge. And it seemed to Embry that they stared directly and unmistakably into each other's eyes and the leafy barrier between them was no more than a veil of gauze. But the pair passed, as his reason had told him they would, but the incident left its immediate mark.

These were Germans, armed, his enemies. The men almost impersonally he had sought to destroy from the air. But now he was no longer in the air. He was on the ground, hatless, in uniform and slacks, without any weapon of any kind but his native wit, and it would be their turn to do the killing, face to face, should the opportunity arise. Instinctively, at once, he recognized the challenge, and should he have spoken aloud, doubtless he would have said:

"Catch me then, if you ruddy well can!"

Just that and no more. No long deliberation, no moments of uncertainty, no hesitation. He would not be taken, and if he were taken, then he would escape. It was all going to be as simple as that. His mind was made up from the very start. But maybe, the very moment he flung the gauntlet down, Fate snatched it up.

The German combination had passed, but the ditch and the hedge were insufficient cover for a man in a Wing Commander's uniform of the Royal Air Force, with a discarded parachute and flying kit barely a hundred yards away. He scrambled through the hedge. Distantly the noise of battle continued.

He could see the farm clearly now. A small grey building, with a small barn and an outhouse. A hiding-place? And then he saw again the group of peasants, three men and two women, huddled together by the fence. In the open country he could at least run, but four enclosing walls could make a prison, should there be any intention of betrayal. He crossed the track and made his way swiftly and boldly towards the group.

They were chattering and gesticulating amongst themselves, but at the sight of him they fell into startled silence, and their hands dropped to their sides. There was sullen suspicion on their faces. A man with a grizzled grey beard spat upon the ground and wiped his mouth with the back of his hand. His two companions, in almost one simultaneous movement, thrust their fists truculently into their trouser pockets. One of the women edged behind the older man.

"*Les Allemands*," said Embry. "They are all around?"

He gesticulated, a circling movement of an arm.

The members of the group stared at one another, bewildered, suspicious. The woman in the rear whimpered.

He tried again: *"Où sont les Allemands? Ici? Là?"*

He said to himself: "Why didn't I learn my French decently at school? Oh, hell!"

The man with the beard broke into a rapid patois.

"Je suis votre ami . . ." said Embry. *"Mais les Allemands . . ."*

The flood of the other's speech continued, but its import was clear enough. They were everywhere, these Germans. Behind, in front, advancing on either side. All around; all around. The gestures were unmistakable. And then that sullen silence again.

Embry knew at once that these people were no use to him. They were stunned and beaten. What wits they might ever have possessed had been shocked out of them, and he was still in the open. But beyond lay the cornfields with their high corn. Without another word, he turned from them and made his way swiftly towards the friendly promise of concealment in the crops.

It was then he saw Tom Whiting. There wasn't any doubt at all that it was Tom. He was walking towards him through the corn, scarcely seventy yards away. They caught sight of one another, recognized one another, on the instant. Embry made the infantry signal to "close," whipping up his right hand to the crown of his head. Tom raised his hand in immediate acknowledgment. Slowly, deliberately, they began to walk towards one another. As Embry reached the fringe of the cornfield, he heard again the unmistakable roar of a motor-cycle combination.

He gave the signal to drop. Tom flung himself down and the guardian blades of green closed over him. And then Embry himself was flat on his face, with one great stride into the field.

He could see through the stalks, so close was he to the edge. It was like gazing through a miniature forest. The ground was warm beneath him, and the smell of the earth sweet. The combination had drawn up by the farm. The same two German troopers were on their feet, running forward, their automatic rifles at the ready. One took post at the corner of the barn, the other swung open the door and passed in. He was out in a moment. A word to his companion, and then both men were racing towards the group of peasants. Embry hugged the ground, watching. There was a rapid consultation by the fence, then the bearded man pointed. His arm was stretched out directly in the direction where Embry lay. The two Germans were across the intervening space within seconds. They stood ten yards in front of him, weapons levelled. He rose to his feet. The game was up.

He had no intention of raising his hands in obvious surrender, but held his arms apart in a gesture of resignation. He stared at his captors with interest. Young, fair, erect, efficient and brisk. Soldiers, at least. Their actions were calculated and business-like. Far off, the thunder of battle rumbled on.

While one covered him steadily, the other ran his hands down Embry's sides, over his pockets, his hips. There was neither familiarity nor audacity in his manner; cool efficiency only; men detailed for a job, which they had successfully accomplished. The one nodded to the other; then, indicating the combination, they led Embry towards it. There was nothing to do but comply. He took his seat in the side-car. The driver stood before him.

"English," he said. "Hah! Who?"

"English," said Embry. "A Colonel."

"A Colonel?"

Embry nodded.

23

The driver's companion straddled the bracket seat behind his prisoner. He unslung a water bottle from his belt and passed it forward. Embry drank deeply, passed it back.

The driver fumbled in his pocket, held out a small package.

"British NAAFI. Hah!"

He grinned and made the gesture of smoking. The package he offered was a packet of twenty Players cigarettes.

"Thanks," said Embry, and dropped them in his pocket.

"Wounded? Hurt?"

Embry shook his head.

The driver swung into his seat, turned to his companion spoke rapidly. A pair of goggles appeared at Embry's side from the bracket seat behind. The driver tapped his eyes, blew through his mouth, stooped and picked up a fingerful of dust, flicked it into the air.

"Thanks," said Embry again, and put the goggles on. The combination started off.

They passed down the track, jolting their way towards the main road, and turned in the direction of the wood which had been, so short a time ago, pinpointed as the Squadron's target. They drove steadily, close to the roadside ditch and skirting along the flank of the German convoy which was still advancing. Half a mile later a tap on his arm attracted Embry's attention. Then a hand pointed. To their right, three hundred yards away, rose a column of oily smoke.

"Your aeroplane?"

"Ja," said Embry. "My crew . . . bad . . . bad!"

"Hah!"

"With me . . . my men . . . bad."

"Ja . . . ja."

It was well to let them believe he was the sole survivor.

24

Tom Whiting still lay somewhere behind in the corn. They drove steadily on, towards the wood which Embry had bombed.

Everywhere in the wood were German soldiers. They lined the road and were clustered together under the trees. At the roadside, trucks and mechanized vehicles, heavily camouflaged with branches and leaves, waited for the word to advance. The green solitary wood teemed with life and activity. The combination swung from the road into a glade. Here, no doubt, in those days so short a time ago, now seemingly never to have existed, fallow deer and rabbits crossed and recrossed and the jackdaws chattered in the treetops. Now was only a vast, low murmuring of human voices, the grinding of engines, and a sinister restlessness, before the gentle wood should spew forth its mass of armour and destruction.

At the end of the glade stood a group of German officers. The combination drew up beside them. The driver dismounted, saluted, then turned and beckoned Embry. He clambered out, wincing for the instant on the sudden twinge of pain catching him by surprise in his wounded leg. A moment later he was before the senior German officer present.

He was a tall, dark young man, at least six foot two in height; immaculate, erect, clean-shaven. For several seconds they stood apprizing one another, the elegant tall figure and the stocky Irishman, with the out-thrust under-lip and the brilliant eyes. A strange moment: a little battle here, as it was to be for days to come, with the clash of wits on either side.

The German spoke in his own tongue. With his German on a par with the fluency of his French, Embry shrugged his shoulders. Not so much perhaps a gesture of contempt, for it was not in him but to admire a certain quality when he encountered it, but of indifference. Or might there have been there, for a moment, a weariness of strain and shock hitherto unrecognized. But the moment passed.

This imperious young Prussian shouted. He opened his mouth and showed his big white teeth and writhing tongue, and the volley of his oaths was like a volley of pistol shots. The group of officers around him raised their heads momentarily from their maps and field-service notebooks, and one in the uniform of the Luftwaffe stepped forward. A lean, fair boy, a typical airman. He said in perfect English:

"He is telling you to salute!'

"Oh!" said Embry. "I see."

"I am a Luftwaffe officer liaising with the army. Well?"

"What's your fellow-officer's rank?"

"Captain."

"My compliments to the Captain," said Embry. "Tell him *I* am a Colonel in the British service and Colonels do not salute Captains—*first.*"

"You wish me to pass that on?"

"Certainly," said Embry.

The liaison officer turned to the Prussian. He spoke rapidly in German. The Captain stood rigid.

"Bah!" He spat out the epithet of exasperation and disdain, and with a wave of his hand dismissed the matter. There was the momentary shadow of a smile on the Luftwaffe officer's face. He turned to Embry again.

"How were you shot down?"

"Anti-aircraft fire—flak, as you call it."

"Our flak is very good, is it not?"

"Well, it shot *me* down!" said Embry.

"I see," said the liaison officer. And the hint of a smile was again behind his eyes.

"What were you doing when you were shot down?"

"A reconnaissance. Why do you ask?"

There was a pause. When he spoke again, there was no chance of mistaking the implication.

"We have been heavily bombed. They have had heavy casualties. They are rather angry."

"I see," said Embry, and not an eyelid flickered.

"Please to wait. You will be taken shortly to German headquarters where you will be looked after." He rejoined the group of officers behind.

Five minutes later, the Prussian Captain, his tommy-gun slung over his shoulder, led Embry to a car. He sat in the back with the Prussian as escort. A word to the driver and they were sweeping down the glade between the trees and on to the metalled road again. The sun was dropping over the tops of the trees, and the shadows were lengthening as they drove out of the wood.

Embry sat back in the cushioned seat with folded arms. He closed his eyes, for the lids were burning as if he had been staring too long at the sun. The car sped on swiftly along the open road. He had no idea of his bearings now. It didn't matter. Sooner or later he would find out: sooner or later would come his opportunity. One bold dash. Sooner or later. He opened one eye and glanced at the stony, sphinx-like figure beside him. A good thing they couldn't speak each other's language. There might be words. Bad types, Germans, but then, of course, there were good "bad types." And the young Luftwaffe officer. You could spot the flying types every time. People like Flash and Tubby and Stokes. They'd be back by now. Hot baths and then some beer. He hoped there were plenty of them left to have hot baths and beer to follow. His chaps. And probably this arrogant swine on his right felt the same in his own peculiar fashion. Well, well, a funny world, my masters. . . .

The car stopped. He felt a touch on his arm. The Prussian Captain had stepped out. He jerked his head. Embry joined him.

"Commander-in-Chief," said the Captain briefly, and led Embry across the road to where a staff car stood. A click of the heels and a salute. Another touch on the arm and Embry stepped forward. It was approaching twilight now. Only very distantly, very faintly, at intervals, sounded the rumbling of the guns.

There was a driver in the front seat of the car and an armed escort on the running-board. Beside the driver sat the General; in the back seat, a Colonel; the General's staff officers stood in a half-circle around the car.

There was no mistaking the occupant. With his high-peaked hat squarely on his head, sat the Panzer expert, who was to send his cohorts behind the Maginot Line, General Guderian. The air of authority, the perfect poise, the distinguished mien, the arrogance, they were all there.

Embry took another step forward. He had no cap, so he didn't salute, but brought his heels together and his hands to his side at attention. An interpreter joined him. What had Embry been doing; what had been his mission?

The same reply: reconnaissance.

"How many in your aircraft?"

"Two," said Embry, without a moment's hesitation. Tom was still at large, with any luck, and if they found what had been Lang . . .

"You are to go with the General. Please get in."

Embry sat beside the Colonel in the back seat. They drove off into the twilight. A little wind had risen in the east and was blowing gently over the flat, wide land. It was growing chilly and Embry was getting hungry. The feeling came upon him suddenly. Maybe they'd give him food later on. Maybe they wouldn't. One thing he was certain about. He damn well wouldn't ask for it!

They drove on. Once they were held up as a column of German tanks passed by. The turrets were open and the crews erect. As each tank passed, the commander turned his head to "Eyes Left." As each tank passed Guderian's hand flicked to the peak of his cap. It might have been a peace-time review on the evening of a gala day and not a fighting column moving into battle. And Embry thought: "I hate their guts and everything they stand for, but this is the flower of the German army, and God help me, but they've got something here!"

Once again they stopped as darkness fell, for a consultation with a picket at a cross-roads. The escort stayed with Embry, and the easterly wind crept more swiftly over the land and a solitary star twinkled. He shivered and rubbed his hands together. The staff Colonel entered the car again, and the driver opened the door for Guderian. The General took his seat. He glanced behind. Then without a word, he seized his greatcoat which rested on the seat beside him and threw it into Embry's lap.

"Thank you, sir," said Embry, and pulled the coat around his shoulders. Once, he remembered, a popular English novelist of the nineteen-twenties had used a Victorian child's copybook tag as a jesting sub-title to a novel: *When gentle folk meet courtesies are exchanged.* He fell asleep.

He awoke cold and famished from a cat-nap, drowsing where he had struggled in transitory nightmare to heave Tom Whiting through an escape hatch, only to find him continually stuck halfway. His bottom. It was pitch dark, and a moonless night. Only the side-lights of the car were on. They were stationary before the high dark piles of a great building.

"Please." It was the German Colonel at his side. Again the pressure on the arm. Embry began to climb out. He handed the General's overcoat back to him. Guderian sat motionless, indifferent. As Embry waited for further instructions, a door at the head of a wide flight of steps opened and a figure ran swiftly down. With his eyes growing accustomed to the dark, Embry could see the turreted outline of the château against the sky. A voice at his side said in perfect English:

"Be good enough to come with me, if you please."

He heard the General's staff car start up and move away as he entered the house. He saw momentarily a dimly lit and vast hall with a noble staircase before him, and then he was in a small bare room, with a table and two chairs.

"Please take a seat."

As he walked towards the table, the door clicked to behind him and somewhere in the recesses of the house, a bell rang. He sat down and faced about.

"I am arranging some food for you."

"Thank you," said Embry, and took stock of his new companion. A young man, with the rank of Major, rugged, red-headed, genial. He joined Embry at the table.

"What were you up to when we shot you down?"

The same opening gambit and the same reply to the opening move.

"Reconnaissance."

"How many were there in your crew?"

And again with Tom in mind: "Two."

The door opened and an orderly entered. He carried a tray with a loaf of brown bread, a bottle of wine and a plate of tinned meat. He laid out knife and fork and glass. He clicked his heels and went out.

"Help yourself. We can talk while you're eating."

But the fork was already moving towards Embry's mouth. In a little time, he lay back in his chair. He drained off his second glass of wine. There was something strangely untypically German about the man opposite to him. Selected for his task, no doubt, whatever it might be. But now with his hunger appeased, warm and with wine taken, was the hour to be careful.

"Not quite as comfortable as your own mess in England, but better than nothing, no doubt."

Embry made no reply.

"It's colder here, too, than in the south of England. . . ."

"I'm grateful for your hospitality," said Embry, "but you're not going to find out where I come from."

They smiled at one another.

"Oh, I merely surmised that you'd have operated from the south or south-east. I don't know that part myself, but I have relatives in Scotland. Oddly enough, my name's MacLean. I am looking forward to being in Scotland again quite soon."

"I've no doubt you will be," said Embry. "As a prisoner of war."

The German laughed.

"Oh, no! England's lost the war already. Tell me, how much damage have our bombers done to London?"

"London has not been bombed."

"Oh, but it has. Our official sources say so."

"Then your official sources are unreliable."

"And Belgium has capitulated."

"Poppycock," said Embry, though later he was to learn that the latter statement was true.

"You English are crazy," said the German. "You let us build a bridge and bring our guns up, and then attack it, instead of attacking when we are in the course of construction. There was that affair at Maastricht. We were allowed to cross the river, and then your Blenheims attacked. They were brilliant. But it was too late. You may have heard of it?"

"I seem to remember something about it," said Embry, who had led that very sortie on the Maastricht bridge!

The German glanced at his wrist watch.

"I will have them show you where you will sleep. We are using the stables as a guardroom. This is German headquarters."

"Oh!" said Embry. "And where might that be?"

"I'll give you the same answer as you gave me," said the German, and they both laughed again.

But as the German opened the door, he paused and his manner changed. He said brusquely:

"Are you going to try to escape?"

"Would you?" said Embry, not wishing to be tricked into any suggestion of accepting parole. "Would you try to escape if you were in my position?"

"No," said the German called MacLean, "I should not. And the reason I should not is because this place is the best and most closely guarded in France. You would be shot within five seconds of the attempt. Shall we leave it at that?"

CHAPTER THREE

DESPITE the meal, and fatigued though he was, he slept but intermittently. There was little straw on the cobbles of the stable stalls and the stones themselves were still pungent with the sharp smell of ammonia. Some twenty German soldiers lay sprawled nearby, and all night long there was movement, of men entering, unbuckling their equipment and throwing it aside, before they, too, stumbled down and sank into fitful sleep, of the continual starting up and accelerating roar of despatch riders' motor-cycles in the yard outside; and should there for one moment have been any semblance of quiet, then a Germanic snore, of which there is no imitation on earth for magnitude and volume, restored the balance of unrest.

In the early hours, when vitality ebbs low, the first hint of homesickness reached him. Knowing the term to be fatuous, he called it "homesickness" to himself, lying on the cold rubble floor, because any other and stronger phrase might have proved unnerving. It would be quite intolerable even to contemplate that he might never see the chaps again—nor his wife and his sons and daughter. He had long ago so mastered fear, without denying its presence, that he knew how to deal in a very sure way with its ugly consorts of despair and grief and bitterness; to nip it in the bud, as the saying went. He had argued it out with himself. There should never be such a thing as a runaway horse. It should be checked in its first wild pace before it got out of hand. So with these other things.

And with that iron philosophy fear became an ally, making a man doubly careful, doubly cautious, acting not as a soporific on his actions, which was a symptom of "wind-up," but as a spur to his cunning and an incentive to action. But lying in the cold and the dark, alone amongst a myriad enemies, with all the terrible uncertainty of battle and its suspense heavy in the chill night air, didn't make it all that easy, and there were moments, strive though he might, when his wife's face appeared before him so vividly that she might have been beside him, and he heard Flash's laughter and Tom Whiting's chuckle and Corporal Lang's "Okay, sir, okay!" But being himself, he mastered himself, and when morning came, he strolled out into the yard, his hands in his pockets and the inscrutable, quizzical smile on his face.

The yard was wide and spacious with a high wall around it, and a double-door gateway, with a guard mounted on the threshold. The château towered high at the far end, and the stables and harness-room and garages flanked the other three walls. Through a door at the head of a short flight of steps on the château side, a stream of orderlies moved constantly up and down, or trooped in and out through the gateway. Here was all the turmoil and intense activity of a headquarters, and he wondered where it was, and what a tremendous and satisfying miracle it would be if he could only discover and by some magic means bring the Squadron over and lay all the buildings and their inhabitants flat with the earth. No doubt, if such a gift had been granted him, he would, regardless of himself, have waved his magic wand, and, like Samson, torn the temple down. Instead, he became interested in a group of French children who had wandered in, and with whom the German soldiery, scattered about the yard, were sharing their chocolate ration. And it again made him think how strange a world was this, when an enemy could give a friendly hint, as the Luftwaffe officer had done, how two antagonists such as himself and the Prussian captain could share the same views of discipline, how a victorious General could share a coat with a prisoner, and now the presence of children made immediate appeal to men whose training and whole attitude of mind was bent on destruction, death and brutal conquest.

He wandered in the direction of them and watched a while and when one small girl in pigtails had difficulty with her morsel, he took it from her and removed the silver paper, which in her eagerness she had forgotten. She laughed, and Embry laughed at her, and the soldiers laughed as well.

"If you don't take the paper off," said Embry, "you'll get a tummy-ache." He rubbed his midriff, rolled his eyes.

She shook her head, but squealed her delight, and one of the Germans plucked at her pigtail, and the other children clapped their hands.

"She's surely a pretty little girl," said a voice at Embry's elbow.

The fluency of speech, the unmistakable American intonation caused Embry to glance sharply round, almost in the expectancy of facing a fellow prisoner of war. He saw instead a tall German soldier, his steel helmet pushed to the back of his head, and his hands on his hips.

"When were you last in America?" said Embry.

"I was there for several years some way back."

"You liked it?"

"Yeah! Maybe I'll go back there again, when we've finished with this war. Well, it'll be over soon and I'll be glad. I've a family."

"So have I," said Embry.

"That's tough—for you."

"Maybe, it'll be tough for you, too."

"No. No. It's in the bag."

Embry heard them first. The distant low throbbing of

advancing aeroplanes. He listened intently and his ear, tuned to the sound, recognized them immediately as British. Someone from the gateway shouted. The yard began to clear and the children ran towards the stable. A German driver tripped over a pile of rubble and swore. Embry grinned. Then he saw the formation in the space between the surrounding trees. They were flying at about six thousand feet and as he watched he could see the puffs of smoke of the flak exploding behind them.

"So much for your vaunted flak," said Embry. "You ought to teach your people to shoot ahead of their target."

"Yeah! Well, maybe they hit their mark at times. You're a prisoner?"

The formation wheeled out of sight and passed.

"Yes," said Embry. "I was shot down yesterday."

"Well, that's how it goes."

"It's not the first time," said Embry, the lie ready on his lips.

"No?"

"I'm a regular officer and I saw service in Iraq. I had to force land and was taken prisoner."

"How did they treat you? I've heard the Arabs have nasty ways with a knife."

"I escaped."

"You did?"

"I'm a wealthy man. Lucky I am. I had a word with the Arab escort. It cost me five hundred pounds."

"Five hundred pounds. That's a lot of money in dollars."

"Just what I was thinking," said Embry.

There was a pause. Gradually the yard was filling up again. An officer came to the door at the top of the stairs and shouted. His face was purple with rage.

"Well, *I* didn't run," said the German.

"Maybe," said Embry, "you might have been too interested in hearing what I might have to say."

"Maybe I might be. Maybe I might not be. Maybe I might surmise what you're going to suggest. That after the war is over you will deposit a certain sum of money in a certain bank in a certain place, and that I shall collect, provided I help you out of here."

"You must be a thought-reader," said Embry. "Did you learn that during your stay in America?"

"No," said the German. "No, I can't say I learnt that one. But I did learn not to be taken for a sucker." And, shouldering his rifle, he turned abruptly and made his way back to the stables.

The German Field Security Police who came shortly afterwards to collect him in their car wore breastplates held in place by chains around their necks. They went about their business unconcernedly, talking with their friends at the gate, and later lingering for a further story while they wrote out their receipt for their prisoner at the stable guardroom. It was, Embry felt, like being signed for as a piece of rather inferior equipment. Their attitude indeed was one of studied unconcern. In contrast to his late acquaintances, their approach was, if not unfriendly, over-officious. It was, he supposed, the same with Service police the world over. Obeying instructions, he sat beside the driver in the front seat. The second policeman, his tommy gun across his knees, kept watch in the rear.

The country around the château was thickly wooded and the turreted walls were almost immediately lost to view as they drove off. With the German headquarters now a thing of the past, his spirits revived. The rebuff from the trooper in the yard had in no way subdued him, but he could condemn himself for his lack of finesse. It was clearly apparent that that kind of approach would meet with failure. As well attempt a bargain with these two basilisks in whose company he now was. He should have known, he told himself, that all those whom he encountered at this stage would be men completely loyal to their cause. If the war should drag on for years, then maybe in the later phases, with a declining morale, bribery might achieve its object, but not now. A more direct approach was needed. He thought of the woods around them, and the more he contemplated their density, the more the temptation grew to make an attempt to escape.

They had left a better-class road and taken to a rough track with the trees and undergrowth thick on either side. At times the branches almost interlocked overhead, so that they drove through an arboreal tunnel in the subdued light of an early morning, which was already turning to rain. It was ideal country for a break-away. But within two feet of his back was a loaded automatic rifle, and he knew there would be no hesitation in using it.

From time to time, the track became so rough that they were forced to slow down almost to walking pace, and twice the temptation to jump for it and take a chance was well nigh overwhelming; and twice his better judgment kept him in his seat. It was only a matter of yards to the friendly shelter of the trees, and once amongst them he would be able to dodge and zigzag his way between them, so that a burst of fire might be deflected and fail to reach him. That he was prepared to risk. It was the initial couple of yards that offered the supreme difficulty. And the range would be point-blank. The car lurched and he clutched at the side to steady himself.

It was the wicked lurch of the vehicle that gave him the inspiration. And the moment he had made up his mind, he began to suffer that intensity of suspense that only a prisoner of war intent on escape can know. Years later he was to discuss this self-same point with other escapists, and each was to agree on the particular agony of mind of a man, when on the move, preparing to make his attempt, waiting for the precise second, refusing it, missing it, condemning himself for losing an opportunity, and preparing again in an anguish of uncertainty and expectation.

So it was now. He knew what he was going to do. He was going to grab the wheel and wreck the car. In the subsequent confusion he would make his bid for freedom.

As in all things, he considered the project calmly, logically, swiftly. Swiftly because if this thing were to be done, it must be contrived before the woodlands melted into open country. And likely enough that would be soon, since the very roughness of the track indicated a short-cut. He thought hard. He would turn the car over, if possible on its left side, in the hope of pinning the driver beneath his wheel and possibly throwing himself clear. The chief danger would be broken bones. Even a sprained ankle would defeat his purpose. He made a rapid calculation of the credit and debit of the risks. Alone on the credit side was the element of surprise in his favour. It appeared to him a fifty-fifty chance. He would have preferred shorter odds. The car rolled again and he fell against the side. Then once more he condemned himself for an opportunity lost. But his mind was made up. He would accept the odds as they stood.

From that moment the whole world was concentrated on the jolting front seat of a car. Nothing else in the universe mattered but the ensuing series of jolts. As each one came, he exaggerated its reaction, throwing himself a little more vigorously, inclining each time first more towards the side of the car and then towards the driver. He prepared himself for the mother and father of all the jolts that Providence could provide. It came!

He flung himself violently against the driver, seized the wheel and made to swing it over.

He knew immediately that he had failed and that his failure was not due to lack of resolution or any fear of the unpredictable. It was due to the simple fact that he hadn't thought the project out thoroughly enough. He had not taken into consideration the strength which was obviously needed to keep any car on its course on a passage so irregular as the one they were on. The driver's hands had been too fast on the wheel.

The car swerved dangerously, but immediately resumed its course. Driver and escort shouted at the same time. He had no doubt of the nature of the words they used. Minutes later they were clear of the woods and in open country. When he looked down he saw the nozzle of the tommy-gun resting on the back of the seat between him and the driver. It remained there till they reached their destination.

It was approaching ten o'clock in the morning when they arrived at the little town of Desvres. The rain was now falling heavily. He was hungry again and cold. And it seemed to him that no doubt hunger and cold would be part of the policy to keep truculent prisoners subdued. It was to be proved true. His failure to escape was humiliating. Twice in one morning. Twice at the very outset. It wasn't going to be as easy as all that. Courage wasn't enough. He must use his brains more thoroughly. He thought grimly, maybe he'd have time enough on his hands for that!

It was ironic that the football stadium at Desvres should have been selected as a prisoners' cage. As a football ground it was full, but with a sadly unfamiliar crowd. Here were the prisoners taken at Calais; Dutch, French, Belgians, and amongst the British, members of the Queen's Westminsters, the Rifle Brigade, the Royal Artillery and the 60th Rifles. Embry was handed over at the gates and directed to the grandstand, which had been reserved for officers.

It was a dismal sight upon which he stared. The mass of the prisoners, exhausted from fighting before Calais and from their long march, lay on the rain-sodden turf, now churned by many feet into mud. Once he saw a British private approach a small company of officers who had been newly brought in, and were being escorted towards the grandstand. The sudden shouting of the German guards attracted Embry's attention. He saw them seize the offender and rapidly disengage him from conversation with an officer, whom he must have recognized as one of his own. They made their objections clear by the use of rifle-butts and boots. It was a spectacle that sent the blood tingling to Embry's finger-tips. He turned his back on the scene and saw immediately in his rear, several steps up, amongst a group of three Army Colonels and a Chaplain, two Royal Air Force officers. He made his way towards them.

"My name's Embry," he said.

"Mine is Treacy, sir. And this is Flying Officer Casenova."

They shook hands.

Treacy said: "You must be careful what you say." He glanced around him. "You never know."

And Embry said to himself: this is a good lad. He has the gen. He suspects the Jerry has put a fifth column among us already. This is the lad for me. We'll work something out together. And I've learnt my lesson this morning, too. I'll really learn to use my brains.

At noon of the same day, they all fell-in for marching. Men at the head of the column, officers in the rear. No food or drink of any kind had been provided. The rain fell in torrents, as they left Desvres.

He marched with Treacy in his file with two other officers, and a gunner who was lame from the march from Calais. They helped him along with one of his arms around Embry's shoulder, and the other round Flight Lieutenant Treacy's. The gunner's groundsheet, which he had miraculously preserved, could scarcely cover the three of them.

They trudged on mostly in silence, but when anyone spoke it was never to complain. In marked comparison with the other nationals, the morale of the British troops was magnificent.

The column was closely guarded. The formation of files of fours in column of route was preserved in an orderly fashion, but every fifty yards, intersectioned into the column, was a German lorry with machine guns mounted fore and aft with their crews to cover the length of trailing men in both directions. Armed German sentries on bicycles patrolled the column, ceaselessly riding from its head to the rear, turning about when they had reached the far end and passing to the front again. With the weight of the gunner officer on his shoulder, Embry wondered what distance, for each of his own weary steps forward, the bicycle guard was forced to ride. But the rain and hunger made even that small joke thinner still.

Within the hour, with Treacy's help, Embry managed to work their way to the nearest lorry, and after fierce argument contrived to get their companion a lift. Thereafter, under the uncertain shelter of the Army officer's groundsheet, which they had retained in fair exchange for their assistance, they marched on.

The rain never ceased. It fell with a soul-destroying deliberation. It seemed to wash all coherent thought from the mind and reduce it to its lowest common denominator of one of mere functional activity to shut out the long, slow misery of the march. So it was only when they reached the large village of Hucqueliers at seven o'clock in the evening that, shivering and gasping, halted at last in the *place,* Embry realized that he might all these hours ago have made a dash for it.

And again he experienced that sense of frustration and exasperation with his own ineptitude which he had already experienced with the Field Security Police, and he felt with an instinctive certainty that he must act swiftly before the shrewd German treatment of exposure and exhaustion dimmed a spirit even as exuberant as he knew his own to be. Then almost before he knew what they were about, the guards had separated the officer prisoners from the men, and they were in the village church. This, then, was where they were to spend the night. With Treacy at his side he made his way up the aisle and took possession of a choir-stall.

The hard wooden seat seemed in his relief like his favourite chair in the mess. He rested for a little while, his head on his hands, while the rain-water ran down his legs and rapidly made a pool beneath him. It was like draining a dripping sponge. All around was the movement of shuffling feet and bodies struggling against one another to find any kind of resting-place. When he looked up the air was misty with the sweaty steam of his fellow prisoners, but very soon the heaving mass of men had settled down. He thought: so this is the house of God; has God forgotten us? Then he was aware that a priest was among them and in his train a score of villagers, with bundles of straw and buckets of hot potatoes. They passed amongst the prisoners and while Treacy managed to obtain an armful of bedding, he himself was lucky enough to seize a potato. They shared both potato and bedding between them.

The evening deepened. The oil lamps of the church had been lit and a pale, ghastly light lit the strange, fantastic scene of half naked men, stripped of their streaming clothes, sprawled across chancel, aisle and pew. Embry removed his uniform and wrung out his shirt, spreading it to dry as well as it might over the back of the carven seat. So, huddled close to Treacy, he prepared to spend the hopeless night.

After a while he said: "I am going to escape. What about you?"

Treacy said: "Yes. When?"

43

"I don't know," said Embry. "I've already tried twice and pretty poor efforts they were. It'll have to be somewhere on the march, I think. We must stick together."

"Can't we break out of here?"

"There are guards inside, and they'll be posted outside as well."

"Let's take a look round."

"Wait." Embry laid his hand on the other's wrist.

It was dark now outside. The wind had risen and was moaning softly round the eaves. The kindly priest and his followers had departed long ago. Men lay in their half-sleep, rolling restlessly, heaving themselves from one side to another. Someone was snoring and nearby another moaned. The air was thick. By the church door several prisoners were chatting with the guard.

"Let's go over. We might learn something."

"No," said Embry. "There are only three Air Force Officers in this column. We don't want to make ourselves conspicuous."

The guards by the door were showing photos. A Fräulein with yellow hair, no doubt; a Haus-Frau, with her little Nazi children. When the dawn came photographs and mementoes would be exchanged for rifle butts and jackboots.

"We could stay behind. Hide."

"Too obvious," said Embry. "They're bound to search the church thoroughly after they've fallen us in in the morning. And I think they'd make short work of us if we were found. No, it will have to be on the march. I'll think out a way, and this time I'll put the old brain-box into nine-pound boost!"

Then for a little time they slept.

An hour after midnight Embry woke, chilled through. His teeth were chattering and his bare skin was goose-fleshed. He thought to himself: every step forward we make tomorrow is another step forward to the prison

camp at the end of the trail. There mustn't be many more
steps. Rather death in the open than the high barbed-
wire of the prison cage and the long, grey years of waiting
and despair. He woke Treacy, who was already stirring,
and made a tour of the church, stepping over the recum-
bent figures, threading their way through the throng.
Every possible exit was closely guarded. They went back
to their seat and Treacy leant against Embry for warmth,
and when he was drowsing again, Embry wrapped the
gunner's groundsheet round his young friend's shoulders.

He wondered how long this intolerable night would
continue. Minutes were like hours. In this place the
words of promise, of hope, of happiness had been said
and chanted down the sunny years. . . . Now in the half-
dark, over this fantastic scene of stripped and sprawling
men of every kind and class, a great misery sought to
descend. Here in a realistic and quite appalling phantas-
magoria was the sacrilege of universal sorrow and despair.
He raised his head and saw, dimly, upon the high altar,
cleared of its crucifix and candelabra, the naked figure of
an exhausted man. His arm trailed whitely grey against
the crimson altar-cloth. He was deep in sleep. And Embry
thought: "In my Father's house are many mansions," and
wondered if he had, of a strange suddenness, discovered
something which in a vague and troubled way he had
often sought to find before. He put his arm round young
Treacy's shoulder.

They were roused at four o'clock in the morning by
the guards shouting to them to dress. At five o'clock they
were marshalled in the *place* and fell in with the British
officers in the rear of the column and just ahead of the
last armed lorry. The rain had ceased and the sun was
breaking through.

Embry took his place in a file of four with two
Lieutenant-Colonels and with Treacy in the file immediately ahead. They moved off as the early shadows began

to shorten across the square. Two hours later, at the first halt, Embry told the senior Colonel that he intended to escape. They discussed their position and where the line might now be in relation to the salient gap. As they moved off again, one of the Army officers who had a compass with him came to the conclusion that they were travelling in a south-easterly direction, and that the Germans had probably decided to escort the column to the Somme, and then to double back along and within the salient. They marched on.

As the sun rose, an extraordinary state of tension became apparent within the column. It apparently originated somewhere in the foremost files where trouble may have broken out, and the rumour circulated down to the rear that there was no destination in sight, but merely an execution ground where the column would be liquidated. The apprehension around him only served to quicken Embry's wits. He watched carefully.

When the column moved through wooded or hilly country, the guards became doubly alert. The sentries stood up in their lorries and the machine-gun crews took post. Embry wondered if there had been an attempt at a break-away previously somewhere ahead.

He said to Treacy: "We take our chance when the country's open. The guards relax then. I'll arrange it and let you know what I've done and am about to do."

Checking by the Army officer's compass, he noticed at midday that the column changed direction. Glancing to his right at a crossroads, he saw to his amazement on the signpost:

"To Embry: 3 kilometres."

He broke out laughing, touched Treacy on the shoulder, pointed out the sign, and said: "There's your omen for you."

Thereafter he acted quickly. It was no difficult matter to reshuffle the files immediately in his rear so that the tallest prisoners marched between himself and the armed truck. Short in stature, he was reasonably confident that he would only be partially visible to the sentry in the lorry. They were now in open country with a ditch on either side of the road. The guards were relaxed. He asked the senior Colonel to whom he had reported his intention to keep an eye on the lorry sentry, and when his head was turned away, to say "Go." He himself would watch the cyclist patrol.

They marched on.

Five minutes later the voice behind him said : "Go."

Before he could move, the armed cyclist patrol pedalled by.

"Keep on watching," said Embry tensely.

He could feel his finger nails biting into the palms of his hands. His lips were dry and he wanted to swallow. The cyclist patrol returned, pedalled steadily down the left of the column. He passed. A minute passed.

"Go," said the Colonel's voice.

Embry tapped Treacy's shoulder for the signal and went—headlong. He dived under the nozzles of the German machine-guns as he had dived for an inside three-quarter's ankles on the Rugger field. He went through the air head and shoulders first, hit the side of the ditch, rolled in and down to the bottom. He lay in half a foot of water and the green, grassy sides of the ditch rose around him. He lay utterly still, waiting for the warning shout, the sound of running feet on the metalled road, above the clicking of safety catch and bolt. There was no sound at all. He lay in the bottom of the ditch and he felt there would never be any breath in his body again. Then he counted sixty. It was all very quiet. Then another sixty. He got to his hands and knees. His heart was thumping in his chest. Then he crawled up the bank and peered over.

The tail of the column, with the armed lorry unconcernedly jolting along immediately behind the rear file, was two hundred yards away. The train of prisoners marched slowly, steadily on. There was no sign of a guard or cyclist patrol doubling back. They hadn't seen him! The distance between the column and himself increased...

They hadn't seen him!

The column slowly disappeared from view round a winding bend of the road. He waited for several breathless minutes, staring in the direction it had taken. Nobody returned.

His heart was still wildly beating with excitement and exultation. But he'd made it. He'd got away. He turned and looked over his shoulder across the far side of the ditch. What he saw filled him with sudden bewilderment and dismay.

CHAPTER FOUR

LESS than a hundred yards away, at the crest of a rise in the ground, a French peasant woman was milking a cow. Her right cheek was pressed against the animal's muddy flank and her right hand was busy at its task, but her face was turned towards Embry and her left hand was frantically signalling him to take cover again. He dropped flat, but he had taken in the situation with one swift glance.

Three-quarters of a mile ahead, the road wound past a wood. From her position on the knoll of ground near the ditch, this unexpected ally could command a view of the column now rapidly passing from view. She had become on the instant a second pair of eyes for him with a far more effective range of vision. Even at such a moment and with the position still fraught with uncertainty and peril, he could afford a moment's wonderment at her swift appreciation of the circumstances. He watched intently for any further movement on her part, but she had returned wholeheartedly to her milking with complete indifference and unconcern. He lay close to the side of the ditch and waited.

She might never have seen him, so completely was she absorbed in her work, and the wonderment of a moment before changed to a disturbing thought that this very indifference could only indicate the presence of approaching danger. Doubtless from where she was she could see across the tree-tops of the distant wood, for which he would make when the opportunity arose. When the opportunity arose! Had she already seen, detached from the long column now coming into the far-off straight of the road, an armed patrol racing back towards him, their automatic rifles at the ready, while an N.C.O. swept the countryside with his binoculars. It was unnerving to rely on eyes other than his own. Then on the sudden, she had turned on her three-legged stool and was waving him on once more. He sprang from the ditch, exulting.

A mile before him lay the copse. Two hundred yards to his right a thorn thicket grew on the rising ground. He ran quickly towards the friendly welcome of the wood. Behind him sounded the retreating drone of a passing motor patrol. He ran on.

It was quite a unique experience to run across open ground towards possible sanctuary under the guidance of a stranger. There was, moreover, a distressing sensation of stark exposure as if he were some hunted creature flood-lit under the glare of a million searching eyes. It seemed quite impossible that any living creature could cover the intervening distance unseen and undiscovered. He wondered if the whine of a bullet would be the first indication of pursuit. Or would it be the typical shouting?

Then he heard, from the road below, the rumbling of a convoy. He half halted in his paces, looked round and saw the Frenchwoman signalling again. He threw himself down on his face.

Once more she became absorbed in her task, but now there was no sheltering ditch in which to hide, but only between him and whoever passed below the convexibility of the ground. He wondered if, even with the greatest of luck, he would reach the wood, and as he lay there again had the time to wonder if Treacy had broken the column nearer the trees and was already within their shelter.

The convoy rumbled on, a seemingly interminable passage of vehicles that seemed to occupy minutes that had already turned to hours. At the time the feeling of help-lessness and nakedness increased, so that in an unaccountable way his temper rose with his exasperation and fear of discovery, and he found himself saying out loudly as if he were again exhorting Tom Whiting to get out of a falling aeroplane: "For God's sake, woman, get on with it!" As if, he told himself, the poor clot could do more magnificently than she was already doing! Then again she signalled.

The wood seemed very far off. It was already as if a century had been on its way since he'd left the ditch. He had not been on his feet for another score of paces when he was warned again. This time there sounded from the shallow valley behind the unmistakable crackling of small-arms firing. He thought: this is getting too warm altogether. Sooner or later she'll make a mistake or I shall blunder. As she signalled him on for the fourth time, relinquishing his idea of the sanctuary of the wood, he turned sharply to his right and plunged into the small and isolated thorn thicket on the edge of the rising ground.

It didn't seem possible that anyone could have combined so many brambles with so many thorns in such a small space. The briars were like wires and the trailers slashed across his wrists and cheeks. But the clump was well over the height of a man's head, and the mesh of thorn and stem closed in behind him as he ripped his way through. Then he was in the centre of the clump and was down in the thick slush of mud that surrounded the thumb-thick stems.

He lay there panting, his head on his folded arms, while the greasy mud soaked into his chest and thighs. There was more shooting going on outside and it was nearer. A fiercer burst sounded and then there was silence. He glanced down at his watch, rubbed the mud-smeared glass clear with his finger-tip. He had broken from the Calais column at thirteen-fifteen hours. It was now thirteen-thirty hours.

The seemingly century-long, interminable passage from the roadside ditch to the hillside thicket, with its almost unendurable delays, had taken just fifteen minutes!

He lay in the thicket and for a long time listened only to the beating of his own heart as he rested, head on hands. Now in the comparative security of the brambles, he had an opportunity to think. It seemed that a very great deal had happened in a very short time, but in a confusion of first thoughts, the foremost were that he was parched with thirst, ravenously hungry, and utterly lost, and that his leg hurt. He attempted to assuage his thirst with water scooped from an oozy pool by his side, but it caked almost immediately in his mouth and revolted him, so that he rubbed his lips till they were sore. Thereafter he knew he must endure till fairer opportunity arose.

His first thoughts were for Treacy. He was deeply concerned as to what might have happened to his young comrade, so shortly acquainted, but so profoundly associated. Had he taken his chance, when he himself had parted company with the column, only to have betrayed himself immediately? He tried to think back with accuracy over the past short period of time, so brimming with incidents. Had there been any sound of shooting shortly after he himself had found himself in his ditch? He couldn't remember with exactitude, but he thought not. Anyway there were other ways of stopping an escaping prisoner of war than a bullet in the back. He dismissed the unpleasant thought.

Where, then, might Treacy be? Might he have reached the wood by the bend in the road, or could he be still in the ditch, though a quarter of a mile or so on? If that were so it was not improbable that he had already broken cover and the watchful peasant woman, still no doubt at her animal's flank, might be able to direct him to the thicket where his late companion lay. Much as Embry might long for a friend at his side in a state of extreme emergency such as this, he could only pray that neither their unknown ally nor Treacy himself would be rash enough to attempt even the mildest exploration before daylight fell, so disclosing their position; and on that pious hope he realized that he must not move to search for his friend till night, and longed immediately that night could come.

Meanwhile he must evolve a plan. There should be nothing haphazard about this escape. He had already proved to himself the virtue of clear thinking. Service training told him that he must always have an answer ready at a moment's notice. What, then, was the answer to this? Well, what, then, was the problem?

The problem consisted in reaching the British lines on the bulge of the salient of the Somme, as discussed with the British Colonel in the column; the alternative would be to strike out towards the Channel ports. Then, remembering Calais was taken, he decided on the Somme.

Travelling only by night it would, he felt, take one or two days to catch up with the British lines. He had a shrewd idea of the terrain, having bombed Abbeville, but there his knowledge ended. He had neither map nor compass nor any really precise idea of where he was, no papers of identification, no food or money to procure it, and he was wounded in the leg. And he was unarmed and alone.

The sudden realization of his loneliness was momentarily quite unnerving. All around, beyond the confines of the thicket the broad land rolled away to the sea and in between myriads of men teemed, working, battling, struggling, and only he himself was alone, separate, isolated. He wanted Treacy with him beyond the feeling of responsibility which a senior officer, who had suggested escape to a junior, would rightly have. He wanted companionship, someone with whom to discuss his plan, to argue with, to share confidences. And the very thought of the word confidence seemed at once to illumine the situation.

Confidence was what they taught in the service. The confidence the officer had in his men and N.C.O.s; the confidence he had in his senior officers, and they in him; the confidence in himself. There lay the crux of the matter. Hunger and thirst, peril and physical discomfort were the enemies of confidence. They nagged and nattered, so that a man began to distrust himself. And fear was their ally.

This is how it would go. This is how these enemies of the spirit could argue, if they were permitted:

"You don't stand a chance. You're lost. You're liable to be shot on sight. Until you're in the British lines—and they are miles away and still moving—you can trust no one. You were betrayed as soon as you'd landed. How do you know the woman with the cow isn't playing some crafty game for reward. *She knows* where you are! If you had Treacy with you, you might stand a chance, because you'd have two sets of eyes to watch with, four ears to bring to the alert, four fists to fight with, two brains to think with. But you're alone. You're alone! And you won't be able to stand the pace physically. Sooner or later mere hunger and thirst will get you down. This isn't the world you know, the world of ordinary daily detail and routine, even of war. The little, simple things you've been accustomed to take for granted don't exist any more. You never thought you'd have given, if you could, a month's pay for a cup of tea, but now you'd give six months! Your clothes are soaked through and they'll be soaked through again. They'll rot. And already they're torn. There's no wardrobe to go to now. There are just three

54

necessities a man needs to live—food, clothing, shelter. A very fine shelter you're in now! So it's quite crazy to go on, isn't it? It's like throwing your own wicket down. Go down to the road and wait till the next convoy passes and give yourself up. No war can last for ever. Better a living prisoner of war than a dead heroic line-shooter! Go and give yourself up and play safe. Now be sensible."

That was how the argument could go if anyone lost confidence. And then later there would be a process of rationalizing the craving that every man had to fight within himself, arguing with that other self, persuading the sensible and grey familiar that sense was finer than sentiment. And very soon a man would believe it. And nobody would know. Nobody would know.

So the Embry who had flown silver planes in times of peace and dressed for a King's levée, or saluted at the head of his Squadron at the raising of the standard, or a colour-hoisting parade, said in the fashion of his own, no doubt, to this mud-stained fugitive in a thicket of thorns:

"What the hell are you thinking about? It's part of the job to escape. It's laid down as a duty. And what's more, it has to be a whole-hog job. And you'll fight your way out like a mad dog, if need be. And that's that."

Then he peered out through a gap in the branches and saw the open German car draw up on the roadway, scarcely two hundred yards away. There was a driver and three troopers. The car had come from the direction the column had taken. The woman and her cow were gone. The three steel-helmeted troopers got out. One of them pointed up the hill to the thicket of thorns.

Embry thought: "Shall I bolt or lie doggo?" Then he remembered what he had heard of World War One, when men were caught at night in No Man's Land, in the light of a sudden star-shell. They had stood utterly still.

He peered out again. The three Germans were gesticulating in strident discussion. He seized a piece of broken stick and tore at the slush and oozy mud beside him. He worked rapidly, sometimes with his bare hands. And in a short time he had dug a little shallow grave. He rolled into it, pulling foliage and briar over him. Now, even if they fired a burst through the thicket, for mere curiosity's sake, he stood, at ground-level, a better chance.

But the rain-soaked earth around, like the sodden sands of a seashore, filtered its water into the small, slimy pit. The smell of the weedy soil was sour and the half-rotted foliage was rank. He heard voices, guttural, German. He pressed himself deeper into his trench. He wondered if nearby a helmeted head was thrust into the thicket, if hands were widening a gap in the briar, if the stub barrel of a tommy gun were nosing its way in, smelling, sniffing almost for the scent of its victim. He waited, tense, rigid, for the sudden shattering blast.

There was silence. Not even from below came the rumbling of the convoys. Then he heard a car starting up. It was fully five minutes before he attempted to move, then he cautiously raised his head and looked out. The road was empty.

Sunset gave him his first opportunity of orientating his position. In the intervening hours he had given careful thought to every conceivable detail as it had arisen. Foremost, he was completely resolute; at whatever cost to himself or to anyone else, he would win through. Once a decision as ruthless as this was made, it was remarkable how clearly he could consider essentials. He was going to the Somme to rejoin his countrymen. Very well.

He left his hiding-place just before dusk carrying with him half a dozen little sticks. The sun slowly began to drop behind a range of low hills. He scratched a line on the soft ground, scraping through the grass with a stick. The line, drawn from the setting sun, marked his position east and west. He had already decided that the Somme would be lying in a south-easterly direction. With the little sticks stuck at intervals in the grass and leading off from the east-west line in an angle, which he had approximately judged, he made a "track-line." He had set course in the direction of his row of sticks. All that remained then was to start walking. But first of all, if possible, Treacy must be found. He crossed the open space of the rising ground and made for the ditch by the road.

The traffic had become desultory. All the afternoon convoys had lumbered past with all the material of war, often enough with lorry-loads of prisoners amongst the tanks. But now there was comparative peace. Only occasionally a car or cyclist despatch-rider would roar past. The sun had gone down by now, the darkness was over the countryside.

He made his way along the bottom of the ditch, often enough knee-deep in water, but there was no sign of Treacy. His anxiety increased as his sense of responsibility deepened. It was he who had suggested escape to the young man. And anything might have happened. It was possible that Treacy might have decided that that particular moment had not been propitious. More likely, if he had not taken that opportunity, it could have been because he would have spoilt his senior's chance. That would have been typical. Always the other man first. But if Treacy had broken from the column he must be within striking distance. Besides the thorn thicket, there was only the wood which he himself had failed to reach. He trudged slowly on.

It took the better part of half an hour to complete the search of the ditch. The dusk had rapidly deepened, and there was still no sign of the missing man. Only the wood remained, but how to search there successfully in the dark? There was only one thing to do. If Treacy were in the wood, he would, almost certainly, be keeping a look-out, as he himself had done in his own hiding-place. Therefore he would take the chance and expose himself. He climbed out of the ditch.

The wood was immediately before him, dark and forbidding. Its leaves rustled slightly in the evening breeze, and rabbits startled at Embry's sudden appearance scampered into the trees. He caught sight of the white flash of their tails as they disappeared among the boles. But there was no other sign of life. He stepped softly into the wood.

It was as silent as death itself. He was tempted to whistle, thought better of it, and snapped a branch of a tree instead. The sound was like the crack of a whip. He listened intently. The quietness crept in around him. Nowhere was there the sudden rustling of undergrowth or the answering snapping of twigs, as a man might make in progress towards him through the trees. He waited for several minutes and then stepped out into the open again. He grew bolder after a little time and made a brief circuit of the wood, keeping well away from the edge, but still with no success. Reluctantly he turned his back on the trees and now that it was dark, made his way directly towards the thorn thicket and his precious "track-line." He had searched in vain for nearly an hour.

By the starlight which was now bright, he picked up his row of sticks easily. He searched the sky for the North Star and found it. In relation to his "track-line" and the star, he picked up the next immediate landmark, a small clump of trees. So in this way he would make his journey in a dead straight line over the countryside, moving from mark to mark and re-checking by the star, through and over any obstacle, without deviating from his course. And so the trail indicated by a row of little sticks by a thorn thicket in the north of France would lead through the nights ahead to the Somme, and the Somme would lead to the British lines, and the lines would lead eventually by air to base in England, and he would be fit and ready to fly and fight again. Dismissing further thoughts of Treacy from his mind, he set off. It was just after midnight.

He made his way at the rate of approximately three hundred yards at a time. His first lap was the easiest. He walked across a meadow, climbed a fence and was beside the first clump of trees which he had selected. Before him beneath the starlit, glittering sky lay the broad, flat lands, with their isolated copses, their heavy crops and meadows of high, lush grass. There were no lights visible anywhere directly before him, but a low and distant lighting of the sky, that flashed faintly and intermittently along the line of the land, hinted of gunfire far off, where the rival armies must be converging.

He chose for the next forward step another smaller cluster of trees ahead of him, checked again by the North Star and went on again.

He was almost at once in trouble. A vast field of corn lay immediately in his path. He hesitated for a moment, wondering if it would be practical to walk round and pick up the new mark without going through the crops. Then he realized that the risk of deviation might be too great. A degree misplaced in each individual lap could make a difference of as much as twenty miles or more to the right or left of his ultimate objective, and though the Somme itself, despite its meanders, offered a broad enough objective, it was not by any means beyond the bounds of reason that continued deviation could lead to him walking in a complete circle. He had no ambition whatsoever to revisit that part of France which he had recently left. He must march straight all the time, come what might. He plunged into the corn.

It was drenched with dew, and he was at once wet through to his thighs, with the corn as high as his armpits. But he could draw his hands along the dripping stems and stalks and gather a teaspoonful of water time and again, so lapping like a dog he quenched his thirst. But even so that was small compensation for the battle with the field.

It was like being half-drowned in vegetation. The ground in places was uneven beneath his feet, so that the heads of corn on their stems closed in about him, as small waves might have done in the sea. And the force necessary to thrust his way forward was surprisingly great. It was like struggling against a cotton-wool adversary, who never came to the violence and satisfaction of an exchange of blows, but employed a defence of unrelenting passive resistance. When he reached the second mark he was exhausted and his wounded leg was beginning to trouble him again.

But not only were the crops his enemies. The high grass of the meadows was also wringing wet. He had not troubled to put on his flying-boots on that last fatal trip, and his thin-soled walking shoes were soon limp and pulped. But he kept to his course, plodding steadily on and now far ahead gunfire sounded together with the intermittent lightning on the lower levels of the sky.

Between the fifth and sixth marks he fell, tripping over a tangle of wire from a broken fence. He fell heavily. For a moment he thought he had broken an ankle, and he lay still, fearful of investigation, for this would have been the end. But at length he rose, and hobbled on.

Ground mist began to gather in patches, and he fancied that the stars were not so bright. He had, as an airman, an acute weather sense, and he became apprehensive lest the weather should close in, so that he would lose his guiding star and his course. There seemed no end to the simplest elements of Nature which could become antagonistic and he thought again how all his life and way of living had been transformed in so short a time. When he got back— he had no hesitation in considering that eventuality as decided—he would bring to the notice of higher authority the necessity for preparing for this kind of thing. Personnel should be trained in the arts of escape. He found himself on the edge of a deep ditch and slithered down. When he emerged he was waist deep in a black and odorous mud.

He rested for a while at the next mark, a white gate in a fenced field, and tried to wipe off some of the filth from his legs with handfuls of grass, but the task seemed hopeless, and he had no doubt that very soon a similar mistake would plaster him from head to foot. As he leant against the gate he heard the guns again, and though it was in a sense a heartening sound, since where the battle was, so were the British lines, yet they sounded very far off. He watched the sky flashes intently, wondering if he could count the seconds between flash and sound, and so determine how many miles lay between himself and relative safety, but he realized almost at once the inadequacy of such a form of reckoning and marvelled at himself for thinking so foolishly. It was, he told himself, because he was slipping, losing his grip. It was time to take a pull at himself. But his leg was very painful and the night was growing darker. All around the quiet night lay and it was full of terrors and enemies. And he was alone. He had never been alone like this before in an unfamiliar world, which had once been so friendly. Now even the stars were against him because a haze had crept between them and him and one by one they were going out. Yet how did it go—the old tag remembered from boyhood—"Yea, though I walk through the valley of the shadow of death, I will fear no evil. . . ." He raised his face to the sky and saw the North Star fading. He went on his way again.

But the sky clouded over, and by three o'clock in the morning he lost direction. In less than an hour it would be dawn and then he would have to take cover again. He could see on his left a wood, a ragged outline in the night. He made his way towards it, aware that he was limping now, and he found himself thinking that rejoining the British lines on the Somme wasn't going to be as easy as all that! He had only just started out and now he was lame and famished and lost. But the wood lay ahead, and there, at least for a little while, he could relax and rest. When day came he would take stock of his surroundings. And on the instant he knew that his immediate path was barred.

He heard the indrawn breath and the sound of the heaving body, he could feel the living presence immediately before him. He flung out an arm wildly to defend himself. He swore loudly and then found himself lurching and staggering against the withers of a cow. He pushed himself clear.

Then he heard a dog bark.

The sound came again, savage, incessant. He thought: where there's a dog, there's a house. He made up his mind at once. The risk must be taken. Better a chance of a German bayonet than slow death in the neighbouring woods from exposure. At least he could go down fighting. He walked in the direction of the barking dog.

CHAPTER FIVE

THE house stood on high ground about a hundred yards from the wood. It was a drab, dour little stone-built house. The barking of the dog was furious. Embry paused for a moment at the gate of the small garden, hesitant, wondering if after all he had allowed exhaustion to blunt his better judgment, and that he was walking into a trap. Then he saw that he had no choice. The window over the porch was open and someone was leaning out.

"Qui va là?"

This was the moment. No hesitation now.

"Anglais," said Embry. *"Un Colonel anglais, aviateur."*

He hoped to high heaven it didn't sound too much like double Dutch. The window went down with a bang. Embry went up the path to the porch and sat on the bench inside.

It was too late for any change of mind now. Whatever was to come must be faced. And if it came to the worst, there was still enough strength in him to account for himself for a short time. A short time—to leave his mark. He heard the sound of footsteps within and the rattling of a bolt. He rose to his feet.

He saw the slit of the opening door and the pale light beyond and then a hand was on his arm in a fast grip above the elbow, and the next moment he was inside the house, and the door was being bolted behind him.

He was in the living-room. A lamp, turned down, was on the table in the centre; beyond, stairs led upward and to the right was a door. He stood, swaying a little on his feet, blinking his eyes in the unaccustomed light. There was a movement overhead, as if in the room above, and then the creaking of the stairs.

"*Alors! Ça va! Mon brave....*"

Embry turned to face his host, whoever he might be! He was an elderly Frenchman, an old coat covering his nightshirt, his cheeks wizened, his forehead lined. But his eyes were as bright as a sparrow's and on his large upper lip he carried a gigantic moustache; a very noble moustache indeed. Embry knew that at once, because it brushed first one cheek and then the other, as the little man kissed him. Then he held Embry at arm's length, gazing at him with parted lips and shining eyes.

"*Vous parlez français?*"

"*Non,*" said Embry. "No gen at all! Hell's bells!"

"*N'importe.*"

He snatched one hand from Embry's shoulder, put his fingers to his lips.

"*Sssh! Les Boches!*"

He tip-toed across the room to the shuttered window, listened. Then he shrugged his shoulders, gesticulated, laughed.

"*Personne. J'étais très inquiet.*"

He came to Embry's side.

"*Colonel?*"

"*Oui,*" said Embry, within the scope of his vocabulary.

"*Moi....*" He tapped his chest. "*Paul.*"

He danced across the room to the fireplace. Over the mantelpiece hung a photo enlargement of a French infantry soldier, the peaked shako, the shoulder epaulettes, the vast moustaches.

"*Moi!*"

He pointed at the date. Scrawled across the right-hand bottom corner was: "June, 1916."

"Good show," said Embry, feeling his legs sagging under him.

64

Air Marshal Sir Basil Edward Embry,
K.C.B., K.B.E., D.S.O., D.F.C., A.F.C.

With Embry outside the church in Hucqueliers are the village priest and his helper Marcel who carried in the straw and potatoes to the prisoners.

"*Ca va bien, eh?*"

"Too true," said Embry.

They were holding hands again.

"*Soldat, eh?*"

"*Oui,*" said Embry.

Paul tapped Embry's chest, then his own.

"*Soldat. Français . . . Anglais. . . .*"

He crooked his right arm, slapped it sharply with his left hand, and made a loud and rude and rasping noise with his lips.

"*Les sales Boches. Merde!*"

It was quite clear what he meant.

"*Ah! Maman,*" said Paul. He waved his arms over his head.

"*Regarde! Regarde ce qui se passe. Un Colonel anglais. Il faut le cacher.*"

She stood at the bottom of the stairs, a little round woman, with close-cropped hair in curlers. She was twisting her fingers together in agitation.

"*Maman. Bouge-toi!*"

"*Il est dangereux d'abriter cet Anglais. Les Allemands fouilleront de nouveau la maison. Si on le trouve ici ils nous abattront.*"

"*Non. Non. C'est notre devoir de l'abriter.*"

He explained to Embry: "*Les Boches . . . dans le village. . . .*" He pointed towards the door. "*Les Boches . . . ici!*" He pointed towards the floor, then to the ceiling. "*Partout.*" He touched his own chest again, touched Embry's, pointed to his wife. Then he made the gesture of shooting. "*Bang! Bang!*"

He gestured again to his wife. "*Maman!*" he said. "*Regarde l'état de monsieur le Colonel. Aide-moi!*"

The old man plucked at the buttons of Embry's uniform jacket, unbuttoned it and helped him off with it. He pulled the braces from his shoulders, while his wife blew with bellows on the charcoal of the stove. And in a little time, Embry stood in his shirt alone with his fouled clothes piled on a chair beside him. There seemed nothing incongruous standing there, while the woman bustled about her kitchen and the old man went upstairs and found a clean shirt for him. When the red charcoal had heated the water, the woman bathed his leg, where the blood was caked with the mud. Very tenderly she washed the wound clean, spread ointment on it and fastened a bandage around.

They gave him a meal of hot stew and bread. There was hot coffee to drink and brandy.

"*Cognac*," said Paul and rolled his eyes.

As the food and the liquor went into Embry, his spirits rose again. The old man's son and daughter, a boy of thirteen, a girl of sixteen, came down from their room while Embry ate his supper, and stood, eyeing him, curious, interested, till Maman shoo-ed them off to bed again. And at the end of the meal: "*Merci*," said Embry, and knew how hopelessly inadequate any words could be. Maman beamed and Paul waved his arms.

"*Bon*," said Embry, and rubbed his stomach. "*Trés bon. Merci. Merci*."

Paul nodded his satisfaction, but Maman suddenly turned away and dabbed at her eyes with the sleeve of her dressing-gown and then swiftly went upstairs.

"*Alors*," said Paul.

He took Embry by the arm and led him to the adjoining room, carrying the lamp with him. The bed was curtained in an old-fashioned way, but the sheets were white and clean. Embry climbed into bed, while the old man tested the shutters and the lock of the window-sash. Then he returned to the living-room and came back with a single-barrelled twelve-bore sporting gun. He opened the breech and tapped the cartridge.

"*Dormez bien*," he said. He winked enormously.

"*Les Boches . . . ici. . . .*" He flung the gun to his

shoulder, *"Bang . . . bang . . . dormez bien!"*

"God bless you," said Embry, meaning it; and was asleep on the instant.

It was nine o'clock in the morning when he awoke, and for several seconds he lay uncertain in his mind as to where he might be. His sleeping quarters of late had shown variety if nothing else, and sheets were still strangers to him, then with a glow of gratitude he remembered, as Paul came in with a jug of coffee and his guest's clothes, cleaned and dried.

The old man sat on the edge of the bed, while Embry drank. It would not be wise, he explained, for his guest to stay in the house during the day. The Germans were in force in the village of Contes, just half a mile away, and as they had already visited the farm twice, it was not improbable that they might look in again, for milk or eggs or merely because of their suspicious and disgusting habits. He would therefore guide Embry to the neighbouring wood, where he could safely hide and rest. Meanwhile he would think out during the day the best way to help Embry on his way to the Somme, which was twenty miles away. All of which was delivered with a deal of gesture and an excess of enthusiasm.

It was close on ten when they left the house. The old man went ahead. He went very cautiously, going to the garden gate first of all to spy out the land, leaving Embry in the porch.

It was a perfect late-spring morning and the sun was already high in the sky. From his position in the porch, Embry could see the wood where he was to hide and by peering round the corner, he could see the shallow valley where the village lay. Smoke was rising from many of the cottage chimneys and he wondered how many families sat silent and sullen at their own tables while the invaders finished the last of the coffee and eggs in a relayed breakfast which, with the convoys going through, had probably been going on since dawn.

They were going through now, a steady stream of traffic which crawled along the road beneath. He could see armoured vehicles amongst the lorries and while he waited several tanks thundered past and he thought of General Guderian again and the panzer divisions he had seen just after his capture. He thought, too, of Guderian's courtesy, but it all seemed as though such things were the happenings of a year or more ago and not just two days. In this strange new world of fresh and hitherto undiscovered values, time itself, it seemed, could change. But the sun was warm and his clothes were dry; he had eaten and slept deeply and many hazards lay behind; his hopes were as high as his spirits. Paul at the gate beckoned. Embry left the porch.

Though he had complete confidence in the Frenchman's discretion, it was nevertheless a disconcerting sensation walking boldly down the path and on to the track beyond the fence in broad daylight. The memory and experience of the previous night were still fresh in him, but they reached the wood safely.

"Restez ici," said Paul. *"Au revoir."*

He drew from beneath his coat a small leather-bound book. He winked. Then with a twirl of his moustaches, he turned on his heel and went out of the wood. Embry opened the book. It was a French dictionary!

At noon the old man's son, Emil, brought bread and cheese and milk. He sat on his haunches, his back to a tree, while Embry ate. He had all the assurance of youth and was clearly in his father's confidence as regards their guest. He was a bright and pleasant boy with polished cheeks and dark hair. With the help of a dictionary, they conversed.

Yes, he had always lived here and had been going to

68

school in the village till a few weeks ago. Then the Germans had requisitioned the school premises and that had put an end to lessons. He wasn't sorry. He preferred working for his father on the farm. His sister worked on the farm as well. Before the invasion she had bicycled every day to a job as daily help to an old lady who lived some five miles from Contes, but his father had put a stop to that. He hadn't liked the thought of a young girl being on the roads alone of an evening with German soldiery about. "Had there been any trouble?" Embry asked. No. On the whole the Germans had behaved well. They were a barbarous and brutal race, of course, and his father had some terrible stories to tell of World War One, but beyond a certain amount of drunkenness, there had been nothing outrageous. Maybe it was because they were on the move all the time, constantly passing through, so that no man could settle anywhere for any length of time, but it was, he said, his father's view that they had been specially instructed not to terrorize the populace unnecessarily. And to this Embry agreed, knowing how cunning their enemy was, and how France, caught and tricked, would suffer as much from her friends as from her foes.

During the afternoon he slept, but was awakened by a sudden burst of firing which seemed to come from the village, but after a few desultory shots it died away, and, tired of studying his dictionary, he fell asleep.

It was just before dark that Paul awakened him. He brought with him a map of France torn from a child's atlas and a small gilt compass. He explained that the map could well be spared as Emil no longer attended school and the compass came from a watch-chain which had been his grandfather's. He brought, moreover, a packet of bread and cheese. Embry was now finding that though his own French had made little progress, he could now understand his friend almost completely. He stood at his side at the edge of the wood while Paul explained the difficulties ahead.

"Below," he said, "is the Forêt d'Hesdin and one of the main roads to the coast runs through it. It is now being used intensively by the Germans. Beyond, roughly parallel, is a railway line, beyond again, another road. Both are carrying heavy traffic. If you wish to make the Somme in the direction you have chosen you will have to cross these three obstacles."

"It ought to be a piece of cake," said Embry.

"Comment?"

"Pas difficile, eh?"

Paul shrugged his shoulders.

"Nor must you forget that curfew is from eleven o'clock at night to five in the morning. Anyone found abroad during those hours is liable to be shot on sight. And now —*au revoir et bon voyage.*"

Embry undid the top button of his uniform and drew forth the red and green identity discs which hung on a cord around his neck. He detached the green one and gave it to the Frenchman. He pointed to the name and number, indicated himself. *"Moi!"*

Paul pocketed the disc.

"One day I hope I shall be able to return this to you, but if we do not meet again, I shall remember. And if anyone should ever ask if I knew you, I shall show them your little medallion and tell them what of your story I know. *Au revoir, mon Colonel.* May the Holy Mother light your way."

Then again the magnificent moustaches brushed Embry's cheeks as the little Frenchman kissed him good-bye and wrung his hand. Then, without another word, Paul left him.

At ten-thirty that night 30th May, 1940, Embry left his hiding-place to begin the next stage of his journey. He was full of confidence. He had rested. His wound had been dressed. He had been fed and he carried a supply of food. He had a map and compass. He had, moreover, so great a sense of gratitude to Paul and his family that the very thought of their loving kindness and the risk they had taken buoyed him up. The burden of his loneliness seemed lessened. There was still virtue in the world.

He descended the long slope that lay before him and entered the Forêt d'Hesdin at dusk.

He made his way lightheartedly through the forest. Though he kept a straight course with his compass, he could now avoid awkward obstacles, being able to pick up his bearings at any time; so he skirted the tall thick clumps of bramble that grew in patches round the trunks of the trees and sometimes could avail himself of a passage down one of the long rides that ran through the wood. It was a still night and starlit, but he could hear the rumble of transport an hour before he reached the obstacle of the first road. At midnight he was standing concealed on the fringe of the forest, with the road some fifty yards away running through a shallow cutting.

The road was packed with traffic. It was one of the most astonishing spectacles he had ever seen. The lorries ran nose to tailboard, with scarcely a gap between them. A line of tanks would follow with lighter armed vehicles in their rear. Then would come a detachment of cyclist infantry, pedalling slowly and painfully in a column of fours. Then another convoy and another.

There seemed no end to them. Slowly, relentlessly, the great snake of traffic was crawling westwards, in support of the triumphant enemy forces, and though at that time Embry had little information as to the progress of the war, he was deeply impressed by the implacable onward movement, crushing and grinding its way forward. He lay down at the top of the bank and watched for an opening in the chain of vehicles beneath.

It never came. He watched for over an hour and still

the snake crawled on with never a chink in the iron armour of its scales. But it would come, he told himself— one ill-regulated section of spacing and then he would dash down and through and across before anyone could scarcely notice him. But he had not accounted for German efficiency and the miraculous accuracy of their timing. The night was full of the grinding of engines, changing down into second and third gears, of the clanking of the tank tracks, and the jingle and clatter of the cyclists, and often enough a despatch rider would rattle past, but the moving obstacles of men and iron beneath was impassable. He grew vexed with this interruption to his carefully conceived plans. Everything had promised so well. Now his opening gambit had been countered unexpectedly at the very start. He rose to his feet, and moving along the fringe of the wood, about a hundred yards from the road, followed its path in a direction lateral to that at which he had reached it, but the road swung on a sudden in a north-easterly direction, in the opposite way he wished to go, and though he was several miles from his original position, the traffic was as heavy as ever. At a quarter past three in the morning, with dawn approaching, he was forced to relinquish the attempt to cross. He returned, disappointed, to his former hiding-place in the wood near Contes.

At nine o'clock of the following morning he heard, on awakening from a half slumber that had followed a wakeful unhappy night, the sound of horse's hooves coming down the stony track that ran past the wood from Paul's farm; and approaching the edge of the wood, he saw Paul himself, his hands deep in his trousers' pockets, with the halter rope wound round one arm, leading his cart-horse to work. He had a straw in his mouth and his stained felt hat was on the back of his head. So it was not without a sense of guilt and reluctance, that Embry whistled. But

Paul blew the straw out of the corner of his fine moustaches with never a quiver of an eyelid and with a jerk of his halter stopped his horse precisely opposite the spot where Embry stood amongst the trees.

"You are back? You could not cross? As I thought!"

"I shall try again tonight."

"Make no move until it is quite dark. There are even still more Germans arriving in the district." He gestured with his free arm. "Everywhere . . . everywhere."

He held up his hand with a finger warning silence; he inclined his head, listening. From below distantly sounded a voice, shouting. The short staccato shouts of commands. Paul relaxed again.

"It is growing more difficult every day. I don't like this place for you any more. I have found another better hiding-place. In a little while my son, Emil, will come to you and guide you to it. *Au revoir.*"

Embry stole back into the deeper part of the wood and waited. Paul's news was perturbing. If the Germans were pouring into the district it could only mean that their forward advance was going well, and they were speeding up their reserves and commissariat from their rear; and the further the enemy penetrated into France, the further away would be the British lines. He wondered if in the end he would be chasing a mirage, that lifted and fled every time he approached, only to settle temptingly on the horizon once more. It was not a pleasant thought.

About ten o'clock Emil arrived with his sister. The boy had assumed an important and reassuring air which would have been charmingly humorous in other circumstances, but it was clear he had for the moment borrowed the cloak of responsibility from his father. The girl, on the other hand, flitted round Embry like a butterfly, her eyes bright and her lips parted, a naiad, hero-worshipping. They led Embry across a ride immediately behind him, made a short detour through the trees and reached the edge of the wood a couple of hundred yards down.

"*Voici,*" said Emil.

In the hedge bordering the wood and walled with wattles and half concealed overhead with branches, was a small shooting butt. Here, no doubt in the past days of peace, Paul and maybe his father before him in the self-same favourite spot had waited gun in hand, for the pigeons homing at eventide.

"*Merci,*" said Embry and took the bread and cheese which the boy offered, and entered his new retreat. The last he saw of them as he peered out was the girl looking wistfully back, while her brother shook her by the arm and urged her on. He lay down in his shelter, tired with the night's fruitless efforts and slept uneasily, drowsing in cat-naps till darkness came.

The situation on the road through the Forêt d'Hesdin when he reached it that night was in every way similar to that of the night before, if anything, it might be said that the congestion was greater, as if the column far in advance were racing on, while those in the rear strove feverishly to get ahead, so that those in the middle were compressed closer and closer.

He lay on his stomach, his chin on his hands, regarding the teeming traffic before him with detestation and fury. He expressed his feelings to himself in terms characteristic of the service. He was browned off. He was bound rigid. There was no future in anything and he hadn't got a clue. But above all was the sense of frustration and humiliation. The mere crossing of a road stood between him and the next step.

The simplest thing in the world, yet it couldn't be done. Nor did he wish to return to the farmer. Paul had had a bellyful of him already. Every moment he himself lingered in the vicinity of Contes, his friend and bene-

74

factor was in jeopardy. It would be utterly humiliating to have to return. The Irish blood in him shouted for action.

He got up. The mirage of the British lines was before his eyes. Only in between was this moving barrier of men and steel, a barrier that was only a dozen yards wide. He told himself that he was letting his opportunity slip, that he was letting himself down. If the Germans were checked in their advance, this particular line of communication might be in operation for months. If inversely their advance was speeded up and the traffic thinned out, then the British lines would be farther off again. No! The longer he remained in hiding in the woods, like a felon wanted by the police, the longer he crept out at nights only to return with his mission unaccomplished, the sooner his self-confidence would desert him. Very well then—take the chance!

He heard above the rumbling of the passing vehicles, a shout. He knew instinctively that it was directed towards him. He awoke as if from a trance and found that almost unwittingly his feet had led him down the slope of the verge beneath the trees and towards the road. The shout came again and he realized that it was a challenge. He thought he saw the solitary, stationary figure of a sentry just beside the bank, then with his better judgment once more in control, he turned and fled into the shelter of the trees.

He was not a moment too soon. There was a burst of automatic-rifle firing and a rustling as of leaves as the bullets passed through the thicket and hummed like bees from a ricochet from a tree trunk. He ran on wildly, then, collecting himself, turned and flung himself on the ground.

He waited, breathless, but no one entered the wood. Then, glancing at his watch, he saw that dawn was almost at hand. There was nothing for it, but, disgruntled and discomfited, to return to Paul's wood.

He woke to find Paul staring into the hide-out. He was frowning as Embry sat up, rubbing his eyes. Then Paul tugged at the ends of his moustaches.

He said in his harsh patois: "You couldn't get across?"

"Non," said Embry.

"I will bring you food later. Also a friend with me."

At noon he returned. He was accompanied by a young Frenchman in the late twenties, a thin, small, bitter-looking man, with a faintly blue chin and uneasy eyes. Paul introduced him as the village schoolmaster. He had brought him with him, he explained, because he spoke good English, and now that Embry had failed again to force a passage past the Forêt d'Hesdin, a discussion in detail as to the next move was essential.

Embry held his hand out in greeting. The schoolmaster touched it with hesitant, unfriendly fingers.

"This is kind of you," said Embry, "to help me."

The Frenchman shrugged.

"It is no concern of mine. It is only because of Paul. I don't want to see him in trouble and the sooner you are gone or captured the better."

"I see," said Embry. "Thank you."

"I don't know why I should help you. You are an Englishman and England has brought this trouble upon us."

"Germany is as much an enemy of France as of Britain," said Embry.

"We don't believe that. We think that Britain hates Germany and wants to fight her. But it is my poor country they must choose for a battleground."

"That's not true," said Embry. "Do all Frenchmen think like that?"

"All the ones I know."

"Tell him the news," said Paul in French. "Tell him why I have brought you here."

"The news is bad," said the schoolmaster. "It couldn't

76

be worse. That's why we don't think you stand a chance of escape. Belgium has capitulated. The English Army is defeated and your Highland Division has been flung over the cliffs of St. Valery into the sea. Dunkirk has fallen and the British are evacuating France. I don't think any will get away. As for the countryside around here, it is full of Germans. You are completely surrounded. How can you hope to get away?"

"There's always a way out," said Embry. "If you think hard enough."

"Comment?" asked Paul.

The schoolmaster interpreted.

"Bon," said Paul, and clapped Embry on the shoulder.

"That is all very well," said the schoolmaster. "Bold words. It will need bold deeds as well. I think you have not—what you call it?—a dog's chance."

"Come back this evening," said Embry. "Bring me some food. I'll have a plan by then."

CHAPTER SIX

THE British were leaving France. It seemed incredible, but it appeared to be true. The British Army was defeated. Even the famous Fifty-first Division was destroyed. The Germans had overrun France. God of battles, this was calamity, disaster and defeat!

He sat in his hide-out in the wood near Contes with his head in his hands. The loneliness of the wood surrounded him, crept upon him. He was alone in a world teeming with enemies and there was nowhere to lay his head. The world was his wilderness.

But the mood passed, as it always would, when the emergency called for action. Britain's plight, the fall of her allies, the next obvious threat of invasion of English soil and the menace to her people, demanded a solution to his own personal troubles. He *must* get back. He *would* get back!

He glanced at his watch and found it was two o'clock. He would do a daylight reconnaissance and check up on the schoolmaster's report that the countryside was swarming with Germans.

He left his "little house in the hedge" as Paul had called it and crept stealthily along the hedge in the direction away from the wood and towards the Forêt d'Hesdin. In between lay the open country, beet fields half-hedged sloping down to the forest. It was the first time he had viewed the scene in full daylight.

The ground fell away before him, gently rising again where the forest trees fringed the crest. To his right in the valley lay the village of Contes. Smoke was drifting upwards, trailing gently over the hillside wood. There was the faint grumbling of traffic from below, otherwise the countryside was drenched in sunshine and drowsy with the murmurous quietude of a warm June afternoon. War, bloodshed, and violence seemed unbelievable.

Crossing the open beet field produced again that disconcerting sensation of nakedness which he had experienced just after his break-away from the Calais column. But now the feeling was intensified, insomuch that he had the disturbing information that he was to all intents and purposes surrounded. But the *mauvais quart d'heure* had passed. He was keyed up to action again and the very thought of his jeopardy only increased his vigilance and alertness of mind.

But no raucous shout challenged him as he passed through the beet fields and he reached the trees ahead of him, as far as he knew, unperceived.

This new way of life could, it seemed, change a mood on an instant. If death might trail his footsteps, nevertheless this was living on the crest of life itself. So primitive man must have lived, from moment to dangerous moment, ever watchful, every ready. He wondered, therefore, who might have been lurking in the shelter of the trees, so that as soon as he was in the wood he ran swiftly forward for a little way, doubled his tracks and took cover behind a tangle of briar and lay down.

It was exciting. It was like the boyhood game of cowboys and Indians played all over again but now in deadly earnest. He could hear, as he had expected, the familiar undertones of traffic from the distant road which had proved so formidable a barrier. So the convoys were still going through, rolling onwards to the furious front line near the Somme. He wondered if the British had forced their passage across by now and what manner of rearguard action might be in progress. Then he heard voices.

They were German voices, guttural and harsh, but there was no accompanying sound of crackling twigs which would denote the urgency of pursuit and he imagined that it must be a patrol passing down one of the many rides that ran through the forest. When the sound died away he rose to his feet again.

Thereafter he made progress at a hundred yards a time, walking cautiously, and watching on every side for sudden and unexpected movement and then at the end of each small passage, lying down and listening.

They were everywhere. Sometimes the voices would be startlingly close, at others scarcely audible, but the place seemed alive with small bodies of men. Sooner or later, he told himself, he must inevitably stumble upon one of them. It was time to retire to his retreat. But by this time he found that he had made a detour to his left, reaching again the edge of the forest but a mile or so to the northeast from his first entry and where the fatal road ran out from the trees. And then he saw them.

Rather, first he heard them, wondering why Germans must always shout and if it was a sign of their aggressiveness, or whether it was a self-induced heartiness to cover their own sense of inferiority and fear. But he knew he hated them with a peculiar kind of loathing as one could loathe a savage and ravening beast, magnificent though it might be in its ferocity. And he was glad he could feel that way about them, because it was a spur to his resolution. It was a personal hatred for which somehow he could never find a precise explanation.

He crept to the very last tree of the scattered fringe of trees and saw at the corner of the wood, immediately adjacent to the road, a mobile anti-aircraft battery mounted for action. Their crews were busy around their gun-mountings and the guns were raised skywards. He wondered if the battery had been alerted, and if an air attack were imminent. If that were so, together with the forest infested with enemies, it was time to return to the "Little House in the Hedge."

He reached his hiding-place without incident and crawled in, ready as usual, especially during the first half hour, to spring out at a second's notice should he have been observed and followed, but now the gentle silence was around him again and the afternoon was slumbrous. But his mind was made up.

There was no chance of getting through by the methods which he had been adopting. Travelling by night had been a failure. Not only had his progress been barred, but with the British on the run, his progress was proving too slow. The hope that he might have reached the Somme in two or three days was now gone. Still dressed as he was in his uniform of a Wing Commander, he would stand, in daylight, no chance at all; but if he were to catch up with the British, it must be by daylight he must go. He would, in the future then, make his way in civilian clothes. He must bluff his way through by day.

In some way he must obtain the necessary garments. He would adopt the role of a refugee, one of the many thousands being driven south, another of the lost ones. It was a grim prospect. It would need all his powers of imagination and observation to carry the play-acting through, under the very eyes of the enemy, at all times and at all hours. It would need a constant vigilance not only on others, but essentially on himself. He had no identification papers and his French was scarcely adequate. But somehow, by God's grace, he'd reach the Somme and safety, because he must.

But there was another side to the question. What might be his legal status disguised in such a manner? Could he claim the recognized protection if captured, without his identification badges of rank and the Royal Air Force uniform, of a prisoner of war? No one in the absence of such symbols could possibly accept his word. It was certainly within the bounds of probability that, should certain circumstances arise, he might be shot out of hand.

Yet there must be a solution. There always was a solution if anyone thought hard enough. That was why he had been given a brain; that was why the Service trained that brain to act quickly. It was an elementary principle, which this new world he had entered demanded. It was the jungle law, primitive and basic, eat-or-be-eaten. Very well, he would wear the civilian clothes *over* his uniform. Should he be caught and the game was up, challenged, he could prove his word.

In the early evening Paul and the schoolmaster returned to the hide-out. Embry came to the point at once.

"I had a look round this afternoon," he said. "You were quite right. They're everywhere."

"There was no need to doubt my word," said the schoolmaster, sourly. "I told you it was hopeless. Give yourself up. You are as good as captured already."

"And I told you," said Embry, "that I would have a plan. I have one. Are you prepared to listen?"

"I have little option, it seems."

"I want civilian clothes. I'm going to bluff my way through the German lines in daylight, till I reach our own."

"Impossible."

"*Qu'est-ce qu'il dit?*" demanded Paul.

The schoolmaster interpreted. Paul clapped his hands. He broke into an outburst of patois, voluble, frenziedly delighted.

"What's he say?" said Embry in his turn.

"He thinks it is a good idea," said the other sullenly. "He says he thinks you stand a chance, but only a fool would take the risk."

"Then you will get me some clothes?"

"We shall see."

"But you must." He turned to Paul, explaining his need in broken French.

"We will do our best," said the schoolmaster, and with that they left him.

He made a meal of the food, which they had brought him, and then lay back against the wattle side of the butt, comatose and contented now that he had come to a decision. He would play the part of a tramp, one of the gentlemen of the road, who in England at any rate were persons to be avoided. Indeed, the more unattractive he became the better it would suit his purpose. He ran his fingers over his chin and jowl, and felt a week's growth of beard. It was almost, it seemed, a quarter of an inch long already. He wondered what he looked like.

The evening drew on and night fell. He tried to imagine what sort of clothes Paul and his companion would bring him. He hoped Paul was not going to sacrifice his best "Sunday-go-to-meeting." It wouldn't suit his purpose, but it was just the sort of generous act this extraordinary man would do. Extraordinary because he was risking his own life neither for gain nor for reward with every friendly gesture. If France, indeed, were falling, then it must surely be for lack of men with Paul's spirit. But the hours passed, and though once or twice he thought he heard footsteps, nobody came to visit him. After his elation at solving his problems, the disappointment was severe.

He waited till the early hours of the morning, but still no one came and his anxiety increased with his impatience. What had happened to his friend? Had the Germans discovered something? Was Paul now in their headquarters undergoing interrogation? Embry could imagine the aids to interrogation the Germans might employ with a civilian. Then he told himself that he was expecting too much of the little Frenchman. No man could have done more. Nor was it completely impossible that the schoolmaster, holding the views which he did, had talked Paul out of providing further assistance. He felt he could endure the suspense of waiting no longer. He would assume that he had seen the last of Paul, and, irritated with the inactivity of further waiting, he decided to make one last sortie to the Forêt d'Hesdin and the road.

It was an abortive, half-hearted attempt, and later he was to take himself to task for exposing himself unnecessarily. He reached the road and found the situation much as it had been, though on one occasion there was a definite gap between a lorry convoy and a bicyclist patrol. He knew, had the occasion been one of the previous nights, he would have seized that opportunity, and that it promised success. But he was in two minds now, it seemed, about everything, and the chance was gone almost as soon as it was there. He returned, depressed and tired in spirit to his hiding-place.

There was no sign that Paul had visited him in his absence and again he experienced a pang of disappointment, though he tried to reassure himself that he had expected no such thing. But it was no good, he *had* expected Paul. All the time in the back of his mind there had been the hope that he would discover on his return a tidy bundle, dropped through the opening of the butt.

He sat down on the bracken-covered floor, desolated. The wind had risen and was blowing sharply across the higher ground. It made a tumult in the trees and in that halt and limping hour before dawn when the blood runs sluggishly, it seemed more chilly than a summer night should have been. An unfair chilliness taking advantage of a dispirited man.

He wondered how the battle was going. There had been no tank squadrons on the road tonight, only lorries and heavy transport. The tanks would be in the forward area and their absence in the forest could only suggest that the advance area had moved still further forward. It was very disheartening. Moreover, during the last six hours, he could not remember hearing even the very distant rumbling of guns. And now all the rear area was teeming with the enemy. He felt as if he were in the centre of a vast net which was gradually closing around him. Then he thought to himself: this is no way to look at things. You're tired and disappointed. But the morning's another day and the sun will be up and shining. There's lots of things happened since you left the mess at Wattisham and went down to the hangars for that last briefing. A lot of things, nearly all of which could have meant an end to you, from baling out to the breakaway from the Calais column, to the struggle through the corn to Paul's house. But you've survived all those, and so you can't be meant to give up, by a long chalk, because otherwise it doesn't add up. And that's what people call confidence. Or faith?

And strangely—or perhaps not so strangely—there was comfort in even so illogical an argument, so that he managed to sleep.

The sun was shining when he woke. The air was warm and sweet. He left the "little house in the hedge" because the early morning was inviting, and while surveying the immediate prospects he could make up his mind on the problems which confronted him. He thought it was not improbable that he would have to break into some large house and steal the necessary clothes. It occurred to him as being slightly humorous that an officer holding the King's commission in a high rank could quite calmly decide to become a burglar. It was certainly very odd how values could change. He wondered what lay at the end of such a kind of thinking.

Then as he turned the corner of the wood, he knew that his problem had been solved for him!

It stood in the middle of a field of beet. Its rigid arms were outstretched, as if in a posture of pleading. It sagged a little on its solitary support, pathetically. He was looking at a scarecrow wearing a coat.

He stared for the moment, amazed. It was scarcely conceivable that a solution could be so simple. Then, reckless in his excitement, he ran to the middle of the field, undid the garment from its wooden cross-tree, and ran with his treasure clutched in his arms back to the shelter of the wood.

It was a beautiful coat. It was dark grey, high-buttoned. There was a slit in the back, one pocket was torn off, there were holes in the side, and one sleeve was ragged. But it was the most beautiful coat he'd ever seen. Or was it a jacket? It was hard to tell the difference, so worn was it, so faithfully old. But why bother about that? Manna from Heaven!

He tried it on over his uniform. It fitted. He moved in it, raising and lowering his shoulders to test it, praying that the weather-worn seams would not split, but they held. He buttoned it right up and adjusted his tie. Then he glanced down at the sleeves and saw they were too short, and that two or three blue Royal Air Force sleeve rings of his rank were showing. He took the coat and laid it gently on the ground. Calmly and deliberately he tore up his tunic. He tore one sleeve out and then the other. He ripped the uniform jacket down the back in two pieces. He knew precisely what he was doing. Whatever the international law might have to say in the event of capture, the die was cast.

He buried the four pieces of his tunic in four separate places, scraping out a hollow for each, and pressing back the earth and moss and piling bracken over each place. Then he put the coat on and buttoned it up again, and without a thought of further reconnaissance returned to his hide-out.

He was at the entrance of his hiding-place when Paul and the schoolmaster visited him at nine o'clock. He was gratified to see Paul's astonishment at his garb. The little Frenchman was speechless for a moment, then, snatching a bundle from under the schoolmaster's arm, he broke forth into a flood of words. But this was magnificent! From a scarecrow, eh? *Mon Dieu*, but that was a good one. And see this! What they had brought! A pair of trousers! And a hat!

He handed the articles to Embry. The trousers were of a one-time blue serge, now grey-green with age. The hat was peaked, like a chauffeur's cap, a shapeless affair. Embry put the cap on his head and exchanged his service trousers for the blue serge. Then he buried the former.

"Well," he said, and stood erect.

Paul stared at him and then he began to laugh. He doubled himself up with laughter. He slapped his thighs and shook his head. The schoolmaster joined him.

"Do I look as comic as all that?" asked Embry.

"It is magnificent," said Paul. "It is tremendous."

"I wish my friends at my station in England could see me," said Embry.

"They would not recognize you," said the schoolmaster. "You cannot see yourself, but your beard is well grown and the hat changes the shape of your face with the peak over the forehead. And exposure has no doubt darkened your skin already. You look a vagabond and a scamp."

"And that is just as it should be," said Embry.

"Now walk," said Paul. *"Marchez!"*

He spoke rapidly to the schoolmaster. The latter hastened to explain.

"You are too erect, he says, too straight. You hold yourself too well. Too much of the soldier. You must slouch. He says he would like to see you walk."

"Like this?" asked Embry, and took a dozen steps with dragging feet and hunched shoulders.

"Bravo," said Paul. He addressed the schoolmaster again, gesticulating.

"He says you must learn to gesture like a Frenchman."
Embry flung his arms out.

"Non!" cried Paul. *"Non . . . non . . . comme ça!"*

"He says," interpreted the schoolmaster, "that only people in other countries think a Frenchman gestures with the hands *outwards*. It is not so. It is *inwards*. There! Watch him."

"I see," said Embry, and made the attempt.

"Très bien."

"And there's another thing I must remember," said Embry. "I must keep my hands closed if ever I'm in the company of Germans. My nails will give me away otherwise. They're not the nails of a tramp."

"That is so," said the schoolmaster. "You will need all your wits about you, monsieur. Now I must go. But I wish you luck."

And with no more, he turned away and left them. Embry watched him pass down the lane and disappear over the slope above the village. A strange man, he thought, and perhaps not over-trustworthy. Not that that would affect him himself to any extent, but sharing Paul's secret, and living in the same village, the schoolmaster had Paul in his power. Doubtless Paul appreciated that, but so small a matter could scarcely deter a man of such great-heartedness from his intentions.

"Come," said Paul, and took Embry by the arm. "Come, you must get accustomed to moving about in the presence of Germans. We will do a morning's work together, you and I."

The horse was still standing patiently harnessed to the horse-hoe where Paul had left it half an hour before. He took up the reins while Embry went to the horse's head.

"We hoe between the rows of beet," said Paul. He clicked his tongue. "Gee," he said. "Gee." They moved off.

It was good, Embry felt, to be in the open again without

preparing at every other second to throw himself on to the ground, or plunge into a ditch or a thicket. It was reassuring, too, to have his hand on the horse's bit and to have Paul for company plodding down the furrows just behind. It was like coming out of a dark room into sunlight. The uncanny feeling of nakedness that had pursued him on those several previous occasions when he had moved in the open had departed with his uniform. He knew he looked shameful, a tattered, ill-washed shape of a man; but the ragged coat and the baggy trousers and the unspeakable hat were his armour and his hope.

In mid-morning he changed places with Paul, and a few minutes later he was able to test his new-found confidence. A German staff car passed slowly down a track on the side of the field. The hoe was approaching the track as the car drew level. One of the occupants glanced casually in Embry's direction and as disinterestedly looked away. The mere incident was encouraging.

At noon they tethered the horse, left it with a feed and returned to the cottage. Beyond and below lay the village of Contes, and Embry could see again the smoke drifting from the chimneys over the neighbouring woods. They went down the track quite openly and passed in by the front door. There was no one about.

"I will put you on your way," said Paul.

He had, it appeared, made all the necessary arrangements previously. He took from a vase on the mantelpiece fifty francs. He handed them to Embry.

"You will need a little money."

From the corner by the porch he chose a staff-stick cut from a hickory hedge, handed it to Embry and took another for himself. He unhooked a satchel from a nail.

"Bread and cheese and a bottle of cider."

Embry took the satchel and slung it over his shoulder. "I can never thank you enough," he said. "One day . . ."

Paul dismissed the matter with a wave of his hand.

"*Maintenant!* Off we go! I shall accompany you for a little way."

As they passed through the porch, he laid his hand on Embry's arm.

"We must go through the village of Contes. Remember your walk, your hands. Remember all you've been told. The village is full of Germans."

Always at Wattisham there had been those few moments on the way down to the hangars before setting out on operation, when things hadn't seemed so good. It was only for the briefest space of time, but it always came, a second's cold and terrifying apprehension. It had passed as soon as he'd climbed into his cockpit, but there it was, this almost imperceptible kink in the graph line of courage. And here it was now. "The village is full of Germans." Only there was no aeroplane now to climb into, exerting an instant reassurance. Only now ahead lay this deathly running of the gauntlet to be made on foot.

"Ready to go?" asked Paul, and his bright little eyes were very steady on Embry.

"Yes," said Embry.

He clutched his stick and slouched off with Paul at his side. They took the lane on the left of the house. It dropped steeply, and as they rounded the corner of the hedgerow, the first cluster of houses came into view. Embry drew in his breath deeply, as a diver will do before making his plunge.

CHAPTER SEVEN

THERE were Germans in every doorway and gateway of the grey-stone houses in the straggling haphazard main street of Contes. On either side of the valley the slopes were wooded and the street ran its meandering course towards the river skirting the village. But in the valley bottom, the Germans were there in their hundreds, seated on the ground with their backs to a wall, eating their midday meal; standing in groups, talking amongst themselves and occasionally with the local inhabitants.

The first group that Embry saw consisted of three young soldiers, by the side of a cottage, cramming their mouths full, whilst at the same time they ogled the young French peasant girl who stood before them with a canister of tea in her hands. Though he knew precisely the nature of the ordeal before him, had calculated his chances and had rehearsed in his mind the reactions he should make in whatever circumstances might eventuate, nevertheless the sight of the field-grey uniform at such sudden close quarters was unaccountably startling. It was indeed like walking into an enclosure full of fierce animals and receiving down wind the first whiff of their odorous presence.

The inclination to retreat before it was too late was so strong that he almost flinched. An involuntary, instinctive reaction of self-preservation, that again, and as always, through training and an attitude of mind, only served to quicken his powers of concentration and initiative. But there was no question about the present situation being the real thing. Though a challenge at any moment could be followed by a brief interrogation, to be followed almost immediately with an order for both of them to be shot out of hand, nevertheless there had never been in all his life to date, anything quite to equal the delicious audacity of the moment. He had bombed the Germans and led his Squadron through the "flak" and enemy fighter-planes; he had leapt from the Calais column; he had lain in a thicket and waited for the searching nozzle of an automatic rifle to find him; but now of his own free will and accord, he had come down into the valley and was amongst his enemies. He had only to stretch out a hand and he could have touched one.

As they passed the group by the cottage, the girl with the tea canister, backing away from an amorous lunge of one of the young soldiers, turned, and out of the corner of his eye, Embry thought he saw as Paul passed her a look of recognition on her face, but he could not be sure. All he was certain of was that not one of the Germans, though they glanced casually at the passers-by, took the least interest. So far so good. But the possibility of their scheme being inadvertently wrecked by one of Paul's own friends was a contingency with which he had not reckoned.

And the contingency might easily arrive. In a little village the size of Contes, everyone would know everyone else. A stranger in their midst would be the talk of the hour. What, then, was to prevent one of the local inhabitants, bucolically curious and inquisitive, casually accosting them and passing the time of day? It seemed the most natural thing in the world to happen. Moreover, what might the future hold for his friend? The little Frenchman, in his greatness of heart and high courage, might indeed have put a noose around his own neck. Then as they passed another group of soldiery he realized that Paul had been talking all the time to distract his attention.

"And I said to Maman that is not a little closet, it is a

bidet. You see, it had real taps on it. She would have used it! She had never been in so big a town before, never to stay in a real hotel. It was very droll."

He was laughing all the time he told his story, nudging Embry's arm at the more salacious points, cocking his eye, twisting an end of his moustache. They stood to one side of the narrow street as a heavily loaded lorry passed. A German *unter-offizier* leant over a gate behind them, drawing at a long, curved pipe. The smoke passed pungently under Embry's nostrils.

"And the price he asked for the horses," Paul babbled on. "*Mon Dieu,* the impertinence of the man! One hundred francs, *mon brave.* Imagine it! A bag of skin and bones with a leg at each corner. I told him so. *Attention,* I said, *attention,* my fine fellow. If it's the *dot* of your daughter you are seeking, let her go south to one of the houses in Marseilles. I may be an ignorant country peasant, but I know a thing or two, and she can make her own money in a year or two, as we all know. Better that, than to cheat me with your old bag of bones. *Ma foi!* You should have seen his face. *Alors . . ."*

They were in the centre of the village now, and it seemed to Embry that scores of eyes must be fixed on them, and that behind them a great crowd, malevolent and suspicious, was gathering and that very soon someone would pounce upon them. There was no retreat. And from the sides of the street other enemies would emerge at any moment now, and then still more would appear ahead, so that they would be utterly hemmed in. And that would be the end. But all the time Paul chatted and joked with all the verve and indifference to his surroundings of an accomplished actor. So that Embry told himself that his friend's magnificent play-acting must be something which he, too, must learn and learn quickly. Though the passage through the village of Contes was an agony of apprehension, he could still pick up points and make his own vital mental notes. They reached the bridge over the river outside the town without attracting any attention whatsoever. Paul's superb aplomb had carried them through.

As they crossed the bridge, Paul chuckled. "They are fools, these Germans. They can never see what is beneath their noses."

"Thank God for that," said Embry.

"You did not care for our walk through the village?"

"I didn't," said Embry. "And I'm prepared to admit it."

"I think you may get through. Two days ago, I was not so sure. I think you have a chance now. You did your part well. *Nom de Dieu,* but this will be a story for my grandchildren in days to come."

"I hope to God," said Embry, "that no harm comes to you or yours through this."

"I can look after myself."

"I tried to thank you before, but you wouldn't listen. But now. . . ."

"There is no need, *mon Colonel,* for thanks amongst friends, particularly when they are both soldiers. I do not share the views of my acquaintance the schoolmaster. He only speaks like that because he is afraid. I do not think England is our enemy, or that France is finished. I have fought alongside the British, and that is how you get to know a people, when you are fighting side by side against a common enemy. If I had thought you were running away to escape being a prisoner, I should not have troubled and taken the risk to help you, for that would have been the easy way. But I know in my heart that you are taking this harder way so that you can join your friends once more, and be given another aeroplane, and then fly over again and kill more Germans, because you are a soldier first. So am I, though now I am too old to fight. . . . So that is all there is to be said about the matter. *Ça va?*"

"*Ça va!*" said Embry. "You've got something there."

94

"And now I shall take you to Guisey, the next village."

The ordeal of passing through Guisey was no less than that of Contes, though the village was smaller and the passage therefore took less time. But though the street was thronged with Germans, neither Embry nor Paul were challenged. Indeed they passed through with surprising ease, though once again when they reached the open road beyond, Embry was deeply relieved.

It was, he felt, the knowledge of his own shortcomings that was unnerving; his illiterate French, his assumed walk that could be overdone in a fit of anxiety; his revealing hands that could betray him, so that he told himself he must make a routine check of himself, as it were, pondering all the details of the part he must play at regular intervals. On the moment he realized that Paul had stopped and was saying goodbye.

"On your way," said Paul. "Courage! Your next town is Hesdin. Find the detour and pass round. It might be dangerous to go through the town. It is a bigger place than the others and the Germans may be more strict. Goodbye. Good luck and God be with you." He kissed Embry's cheeks.

"God bless you, Paul," said Embry, and wrung him by the hand.

Without another word, Paul turned and went. Once he looked back, a small dark figure on the dusty road. He waved his stick in farewell and Embry waved back, then Paul walked on again till he was lost to view on the outskirts of Guisey, and Embry wanted to cry out: "Come back, Paul, come back!" because the loneliness now of the dusty road and the cloudless sky was suddenly unbearable, but he gripped his staff and strode on.

He thought as he approached Hesdin that perhaps only war could produce such a fine thing as Paul's friendship, that had flowered on an instant in the night and had lasted unbroken through all the tribulations of the last few days. This was the charity that suffered long and endured. So it had been with his own people bound together with such bonds of comradeship that it seemed unlikely that even death could break them. War was a terrible thing, but it could be a generous giver not only of death but of life, of all the splendid things of life that men couldn't talk about because there were no words great enough to express them but could only understand in the warm silence of their hearts.

He had no difficulty in making a detour round Hesdin. He turned right at a crossroads and took a minor road. There was no traffic and his spirits rose. Half an hour later with the town now left behind, he made good progress. He drank a little of the cider from the bottle Paul had given him, and the sharp taste of the liquor was greatly to his liking. Though he took only a mouthful it was invigorating, and as there was no one in sight, he adopted his usual posture and stepped out with his best foot first.

He was making good progress. After the days of delay in the "little house in the hedge," after the anxiety of the passage through Contes and Guisey, the satisfaction of the open road was very great. He felt elated, and again marvelled within himself how rapidly one mood could change to another now that he was so near to earth and reality. It was as if a whole lifetime could be crowded into a few days, a very quintessence of living. Then he saw the approaching horseman.

At once he dropped into his shambling walk, furious with himself for being caught day-dreaming. No second of any day or night could now, it seemed, be left to look after itself.

The sight of the horseman startled him badly. He could see even from the distance still between them that the rider was a German soldier. For a moment Embry thought wildly of running from the road and taking to the fields

On the right is the signpost Embry saw shortly before his escape and regarded as a good omen.

Below is the spot where Embry dived into the ditch to escape from the column. The woman milking the cows is in the same place as on the original occasion.

Paul, *soldat français*, with Maman and his daughter who was only sixteen at the time of the escape.

which flanked it on either side, only to realize that such an act would be sheer folly, for, with his suspicions aroused, the German could easily overtake him. There was no option left but to face the issue and walk on.

As the distance between them lessened, his anxiety increased. He felt like a dolt, indecisive, witless. The sound of the horse's hooves was clearly audible now. It was chestnut with a white blaze and a white sock on its near fore-leg. He could distinguish the rider now, a young, lean-faced man. He wore a belt with a revolver in its holster. He rode his horse at a walk, easily, casually. Embry could hear the jingling of the bridle bit.

There had been no occasion for him to question himself on the mode of his play-acting because before he was aware of it they were nearly level and he found it impossible not to take stock of what might prove to be an opponent. He found the young German's eyes fixed on him and there was a frown on his forehead. The man reined his horse up, barring the way. He spoke in execrable French.

"Who are you?"

Embry stopped in his tracks. Now that the moment was upon him his brain was cool and clear once more.

"Me?"

"Yes, you. Who are you?"

"A Frenchman," said Embry, realizing his own French was better than his adversary's. "A Frenchman, of course."

"Are you a soldier?"

"Me! A soldier?"

"Are you a soldier in disguise?"

"A soldier," Embry lifted back his head and roared with laughter. "That is excellent. A soldier! Me!!"

He became convulsed with laughter.

"Bah!" said the German and spat with contempt over his horse's withers. He jerked the reins and his horse broke into a trot. He rode out of sight.

Embry leant upon his stick. He glanced down as the sweat splashed on to his hand and saw his wrist-watch.

He gazed at the thing with growing horror. He had been wearing his wrist-watch. He was a French tramp, a down-and-out, and he was sporting a valuable watch on his wrist. Nor was that all. Hadn't he told himself only a short while ago that he must check up on everything? There were links in his cuffs as well; in the cuffs of the shirt he'd put on clean at Wattisham on the day of the sortie over St. Omer. And not only were there links in the cuffs of an officer's shirt, but he was wearing Aertex underpants, and in the back seams of his shirt was the maker's name—Gieves of Bond Street!

He ran from the road, leapt the shallow ditch and ran into the bushes bordering a meadow.

He tore down his trousers and struggled out of his underpants. He thought to himself: "If that blighter comes riding back he will catch me with my pants down in the true sense of the word." But no one returned along the road and he thrust the garment under a bush.

He removed the links from his cuffs and tore the cuffs from the shirt. They joined company with the pants. Then he undid the straps from his wrist-watch, threw them away and pocketed the watch. He felt as if he had been shrived. Then choosing a sheltered corner some distance along the field, he seated himself, undid his satchel and taking out his map, reviewed his general position.

He would, he decided, make for the Somme by minor roads only. The next town would be Tollent and he would leave Abbeville on the right. With good fortune the Somme should not be more than a couple of days off and he was reasonably convinced that the British lines were still somewhere near the far side of the river. He rested a little while recapitulating again all the points of his disguise. He had nearly betrayed himself by thoughtlessness and carelessness. It mustn't happen again. He mightn't be so lucky next time. Even now they might have been lining him up against a wall.

He went over himself mentally, piece by piece. First his feet. The shoes were unmistakably of good quality, but they were so stained and dirty that they would pass. His legs—well, Paul's trousers were satisfactory, and now there was no indication of Bond Street beneath. His body, that was reasonably convincing with the scarecrow's coat, but it would be as well to remove the service-type collar and tie. His head, excellent with this fearsome growth of beard, and the outlandish cap to round it off. There remained then only the danger points of the map, compass, and watch. But these were essentials, and would only be discovered if he were searched. If the worst came to the worst he must eat the map and drop the compass at an opportune moment. For the watch he might be able to find an excuse, now that its straps were gone. Reassured and rested he started on his way again.

He passed through several villages before he reached Cherienne on the road to Tollent. In each instance the streets were filled with German soldiery, but no one took any notice of the unkempt bedraggled figure and his confidence was fully restored to him. But at Cherienne he was accosted.

Two young German soldiers barred his path as he made his way down a side street to avoid the main traffic of the town. There was nothing particularly aggressive in their manner, though he had no doubt as to what the outcome would be should he betray himself. He judged them to be more of the student class, and intent on interrogating him as much for the jest of the occasion than from a sense of duty. But it was a joke which could turn the wrong way quickly enough.

"Where do you come from?"

The taller of the two rapped out the question, in excellent French and in what, no doubt, he considered an excellent sample of the official manner. But Embry knew at once that his French would betray him to anyone who was as good a linguist as this.

"*Moi—je suis Belge.*"

He replied without hesitation, facing his interrogator squarely.

"You come from Belgium?"

"Yes."

"How did you get here?"

"I walked. Or I rode in a lorry sometimes. Sometimes there was a train."

"What do you want to come down here for?"

"I don't like war. So I walk away from it."

"Come along. We're wasting our time." It was the other German speaking, tugging at his companion's arm.

"Very well." The taller of the two turned to Embry. "You don't need to bother about the war," he said, "it's all over."

"I hope so," said Embry.

"It's finished. We have won."

They left Embry on the pavement and crossed the road to a café. He quickened his pace out of the town as much as he dared.

At eight o'clock that evening he arrived at the outskirts of Tollent. He had then travelled sixteen miles from the time he had left Contes. Dusk had fallen and he had grown hungry. He turned off from the road and sat down in the cover of the hedge. He ate half of the rations Paul had provided and drank some of the cider, and deciding that this was as good a place as any, prepared to spend the night where he was. He lay against the hedge and closed his eyes.

But tired though he was, and though comforted a little by the food he had taken, he could not sleep. After the brightness of the day the early night seemed to grow unduly dark, and the coldness increased to a degree which made sleep impossible. Moreover, the thought of the Somme so much nearer than it had been a few hours before made it a temptation to push on. So, despite his leg which was beginning to hurt him again, he gathered his scanty belongings together and set out once more.

But the curfew was down, and therefore the roads were impractical. He must hazard the far more arduous task of again making a passage across country by night. He plodded on over the wide undulating land with its fields and crops sleeping under the starlight.

An hour later, drenched through with dew and his wound very painful, and with a mist enveloping all sides of the country and obliterating the stars, he realized that he was completely lost.

He sat down in the middle of a meadow and cursed himself for the fool he was to follow this will-o'-the-wisp of the promised river. He should have spent the night, cold as it might have proved, in the neighbourhood of Tollent, where at least he knew his correct position. As he was still deciding where to go for cover for the night, he heard the woman whistling.

He knew it was a woman, and French, because after the whistling she called for her dog by name. With the memory of Paul so fresh in his mind he started immediately to his feet and made his way to the sound. He reached the edge of the field bounded with a wire fence, and found that the bank sloped down to a narrow road. He climbed down and saw before him a high hedge and beyond it, a large house.

The hedge was of holly and high; he judged it to be at least seven feet in height and proportionately wide. He made his way round it, searching for a possible opening. The whistling in the garden beyond continued. He found the gate. It was a white, wooden, solid affair, as high as the hedge and very definitely bolted. He considered calling out for one moment, for whoever was in the garden could only be a few paces away, but on second thoughts he resisted the temptation. He was, he felt, learning discretion by his former mistakes. Then he noticed the wall by the hedge. The wall ran along the length of the hedge, reaching about halfway up. He climbed upon it and found that he could see quite clearly over the top and that the hedge as he had surmised was several feet in thickness. He leant over, gazing ahead, and the holly prickles made him draw his hand away.

He could see the house quite distinctly, a darker shape against the darkness. There was no sign of any movement on the lawn which lay between the hedge and the house or now any sound. He waited for several minutes listening intently, then, clutching his stick and satchel, drew himself on to the top of the hedge and dropped on to the grass below.

The house was distant, some fifty yards away. From this lower level it loomed large and mysterious. He wondered why he had not heard the sound of a closing door if the woman had gone inside. He leant on his stick, resting, while he examined the outline of the building. It rose high to a stack of chimneys on the left, but sloped away to the right. To the right, therefore, must be the back of the house, and it was to the back he would go, remembering that he was for the purpose of all first appearances a tramp and tramps have to keep their place. He began to move stealthily across the lawn.

It was when he was halfway across that he saw the light, a small speck of yellow that gleamed and ebbed. It moved upwards, paused, and glowed. It fell a couple of feet and faded. Someone was outside the back of the house, smoking a cigarette. He dropped down on the grass.

He lay there listening and watching. The silence was uncanny. With his eye intent on the one spot, he saw at length other small specks of light. There was clearly a group of people ahead of him. He began to crawl forward with the utmost caution, on his hands and knees.

He was trembling with excitement, because so near at hand might lie sanctuary and succour. He wondered which would be the best way to approach the woman and her friends. He had no desire to startle them. Perhaps he would get within close earshot, and as she had herself done, whistle. When she called out who was there, he could reply guardedly. If he scared her she might run into the house, taking the others with her, and slam and bolt the door in his face. That would never do. His groping hands encountered leaf and twig.

A low ragged hedge was before him. It seemed to run from the back of the house and away to the left. He peered over, still on his hands and knees, and saw, not four yards away, the gleaming cigarette ends. He thought he could distinguish the forms of the smokers, but the dark background of the house obscured their outlines. He pursed his lips to give the first low warning whistle, then a voice spoke.

He had no idea what the voice said, nor what was the reply that at once followed. He only knew one thing. The voice was a German's, speaking German!

The sudden discovery was like a blow in the face. If he had stepped over the hedge he would have been immediately in their midst. For the moment, as the realization of his predicament dawned on him, he found it impossible to move. Expecting every second to hear a shout, to be followed by a blaze of lights and hurrying figures, he began to crawl back to the holly hedge.

He reached the hedge. He was in a trap with a seven-foot barrier round it. He was locked in. He was shut in with his enemies. At the best they would take him at first encounter as an intruder, a marauder. But he could be a spy, and if they had the merest sense they would open fire at sight. They were armed men. They were soldiers.

He tore at the hedge for a foothold, a handhold. The holly ripped his face and hands. He fought the hedge as if it were a living opponent. The prickles went into his flesh and ripped the skin away. And then he was sprawled, he knew not how, across the top of the hedge and a second later he dropped into the road. He ran across the road and fled to the middle of the field.

He waited, listening. There was no sound from the house. His hands and face were tingling. He realized, with a dreadful sinking of his heart, that in his panic, he had left his stick and satchel by the ragged hedge at the back of the house. And in his satchel was that most precious possession—his map of France!

CHAPTER EIGHT

THE map was gone, but he still had his compass and though his leg was very painful it behoved him to keep going. It was just possible that his belongings might be discovered by the back of the house or that someone had heard his violent passage through the holly hedge and would raise a hue and cry. So with the aid of his compass he set off across country in the general direction of the Somme. At two o'clock in the morning, with his progress becoming painfully slow, he saw a farm.

He saw the buildings on the far side of a field of beet. It was the first sign of any habitation for some considerable time, but remembering only too vividly the frenzied moments of his last halt, he waited irresolute before approaching it.

It was, he thought bitterly, an astonishing thing to view such a commonplace thing as a house with an element of suspicion and fear. All over that other world of yesterday people were comfortably snoring their heads off in bed, and now he himself would have welcomed even the stable floor, with its stench of ammonia, of his first night in captivity. But, half hidden through the wheat he approached the building.

There was a drive leading off from a lane with seemingly a small barn just inside. He pictured the warm darkness within and the scent of hay and how truly wonderful it would be to lie and relax in sleep and let the world go hang. It seemed such a very little to ask. And on the moment he heard Germans singing.

They were singing softly, melodiously and the sound

came from the barn. On any other occasion it would have been romantic to stand alone in the still night and hear so sweet a singing. It was the sort of thing a tourist returned from a trip abroad would relate with an air of spurious poetics. Now it filled him with cold fury.

So that was the way they felt, this picket of the invading armies. They could afford to pass the hours of their watch card-playing or eating or singing. But the cards they used and the food they ate were stolen. The house that sheltered them was a house taken by force of arms and occupied by robbers. He thought of the villages he had passed through and all the men in field-grey, steel-helmeted, who had lounged in the doorways or strutted the narrow streets. They were despoilers, invaders, wreckers. He thought of the boastful words of the officer MacLean, and the two troopers who had accosted him at Cherienne. And though as a professional fighting man he could recognize in an opponent qualities of courage and chivalry, yet he knew as never before he'd known, now in his pitiable plight, how deep was his hatred for this race of bullies and braggarts. So that, despite his wound and exhaustion, despite the shock his nerves had taken, when he had lain so recently so few feet from capture, his fighting spirit rose in him and he knew that whatever might come he must meet it with the most complete determination, and that nothing except death itself should prevent him from once more climbing into an aeroplane to carry his bomb-load to its target.

He made his way back through the corn and, finding a small wood bordering the far corner of the field, climbed over the fence and took what little cover the trees afforded for the remainder of the night.

He left the wood on the furthest side away from the wheatfield at dawn, and remembering the general direction from his lost map, set off by road for Domart by way of Auxi-le-Château.

The villages he passed were nameless as far as he was concerned, but the reaction of each one upon him was uncomfortably similar. Packed as they were with Germans, every passer-by seemed to stare at him. It was no good telling himself that his imagination was playing him tricks, and that his experience of last night was telling on him.

As he approached each village, as the houses on the outskirts first came into view his apprehensions increased. Argue as he might with himself, that his fears were illogical, he could bring no conviction to bear. He doubted very much if he were again accosted whether he could keep up the farce any longer, and he thought to himself how merciful it would have been if Fate had allowed Tom Whiting or Treacy to have escaped with him, because it seemed as if such loneliness in the midst of jeopardy could be soul-destroying.

In the last village he passed through, an incident, imagined or real, occurred which determined him to leave the road and go again across country.

He found in the press of soldiery in the street that his way was temporarily blocked by the stolid figure of a German *unter-offizier*. The man stood before him, truculent, over-bearing. For the moment, Embry could not press past. The other's top tunic button was on a level with his nose. As soon as the crowd of soldiers in the gutter moved, Embry managed to slip amongst them. For several seconds he had expected a heavy hand to fall upon his shoulder and grip him. But he dodged amongst the throng undetected. It was only when he glanced back that he was shocked to see the tall non-commissioned officer staring in his direction. He dodged up a side street, quickening his pace. But the incident, trivial enough, was sufficient to tilt the balance. He left the road again. Within half a mile he was in trouble.

The River L'Authie was the trouble. It was some fifty

feet broad and slow-flowing, but though the bridge of the nearby village of Vitz was in view, he determined to swim across rather than risk the road again. He could see the village clearly half a mile or so downstream on his side of the river, but in the adjoining fields were Germans.

He undressed, wrapping his clothes up in his scarecrow jacket. With the coat sleeves tied round his neck he swam across and reached the other side.

The sun was already warm on his skin as he dressed and rested for a little while in the bushes. He was filled with condemnation of himself for the swimming of the L'Authie. If he had been seen it would have attracted far more attention than by crossing by the ordinary method. But he felt that he couldn't for all the world face up to further personal encounters for the time being.

The heat of the sun increased with the hours and by noon it might have been that of a midsummer day. It was painful, tedious work, going overland, and he had had nothing to eat or drink since the evening before. Sometime about half past four in the afternoon he saw a Frenchman milking a cow in an open field. He crossed the meadow and asked for a drink of milk.

The Frenchman eyed him curiously. He was a big stout man, dressed in blue dungarees, middle aged, with a large moustache.

"You are a British soldier," he said.

There was no implication of interrogation. It was a plain statement.

"Yes," said Embry.

It seemed that only a candid admission could deal with such a frontal attack. There was a pause, then the other lifted the pail from under the cow's udder and without a word passed the pail across to Embry. It was a quarter full of milk.

The milk was warm and sweet. It was like nectar. He

108

gulped at it greedily, and knew that he was taking food as well as drink. He handed the pail back. It was empty.

"I'm sorry," said Embry.

"You are welcome."

"I am very grateful to you," said Embry.

"*Du tout.* I could not see a man starve when I have the means to help him at hand."

He patted the flank of the cow.

"There were two of your men—soldiers—who passed this way two hours ago. They were going in the same direction as you. Have you been in a battle?"

"More or less," said Embry. "I was shot down in an aeroplane."

"That is terrible. War is terrible. I think the end of the world is coming."

"Not yet," said Embry.

"I'm not so sure. Italy has come into the war."

"How do you know?"

"I have a wireless set and I listen in. It is forbidden, of course. These dirty Germans!"

"That's bad news."

"France is in the pincers. In the north are the Germans, down the south are the Italians. I think France will fall."

"I hope not," said Embry. The prospect of walking the whole of France completely infested with Germans was not exhilarating.

"Goodbye," said Embry. "I must be going."

"Good luck. And may there be better times ahead for both of us."

The milk had put new spirit into him and he went on his way more happily resolute. But the news of Italy's entry was disconcerting. Unless a miracle happened, France must surely capitulate, and thereafter even if defeat had not already disintegrated the British Army, it would be forced to evacuate. What purpose then this pilgrimage to the Somme? On the other hand it would take some weeks for pressure from the south to make itself felt and there could still be time for him to catch up with the retreating armies, only it meant a still greater effort. There must be no lagging at all. He pressed steadily on.

Two hours later he was reluctantly forced to rest. He sat in the hedge of a hayfield watching the one solitary labourer working his scythe in the high long grass. It was a peaceful scene with the late sunlight slanting through the trees of a neighbouring wood, the sheer green sheen of the grass and the worker's rhythmic regular movement. It seemed hardly possible that war's dark shadow had fallen across these fields and copses, passed and left them so undisturbed and at peace. He bent and eased the bandage on his leg. When he looked up again, the labourer, leaning on his scythe, was at his side.

"Good evening," said Embry.

"*Bon soir, monsieur.* I suppose you are a soldier."

"That's right," said Embry and wondered why two Frenchmen within two hours had immediately seen through his disguise. Even though Germans at close quarters in the villages had rubbed shoulders with him without any sign of suspicion he thought that maybe after all he hadn't been such a fool to swim the L'Authie, and it wasn't just a touch of wind-up that had forced him to turn his back on travelling by road.

"If you are a soldier you must take care. There are Germans everywhere."

"It seems peaceful enough."

"That is because the civilian population are all gone." He held up his hand. "*Ecoutez!*"

It was there again, the distant mumbling of the guns.

"The battle is beginning again, monsieur."

"Where are they fighting?"

"On the Somme, monsieur."

"Ah! The Somme." And then, eagerly: "How far to the Somme?"

"Fifteen kilometres."

"Not farther than that!"

"No farther. *Alors, bon voyage, monsieur. Bonne nuit.*"

"*Bonne nuit,*" said Embry.

Fifteen kilometres to the Somme! No more than that. And the fighting was there, the British Army was there. The shadows lengthened across the darkling grass and the sun went down behind the wood fringing it with gold. The light began to go out of the sky and a star or two came out. And all the time from his seat in the hedge, nursing and resting his leg, Embry could hear now more distinctly than ever, the far-off thundering of artillery. Because it might be even tonight that at last he would reach the Somme and cross it, that ominous rumbling of distant cannonade was, to his ears, sweet music.

He moved on again soon after eleven o'clock of the same night. It was starlight; the weather was clear and he made good progress by compass and stars across the meadows and through half-grown crops. He knew precisely where he wanted to cross the Somme; west of Abbeville, because as a focal point in communications it would be filled with the enemy, and not too far east because of the junction of the Somme and its tributary the Nievre.

He made his way steadily across the open country, now almost devoid of woods and trees, gaining with every step renewed confidence and now with his goal so close, tuned to so high a pitch of excitement that he reminded himself that he must be doubly cautious. Ahead of him the battle continued. Besides gun-fire he could now distinguish star-shells in the sky and once he saw a flashing beacon winking its signal and he wondered which aerodrome it indicated and if it might be the British at an advanced base. At once he realized they could hardly be such fools as to disclose a position so wantonly. The surmise, he assured himself, was an example of wishful thinking and that he must not let himself be betrayed into over-eagerness.

For the first phase of this last leg to the river the countryside was deserted. Imperceptibly but quite suddenly he found himself in the company of the enemy once more. As usual he heard, first of all, their shouting. He halted in his tracks at once and went forward slowly on his hands and knees. There was no knowing in the darkness what he might unexpectedly encounter. One chance German, a tussle under the stars, a shout, and the journey would be over.

He crawled on, a slow and exasperating form of progress, not to be relieved by the constant necessity of stopping altogether and lying flat as a patrol betrayed their presence nearby or a body of men passed down one of the tracks running at right-angles to the course which he had to cross. In many of the shallow gullies he found parties of men resting their backs against the bank and once a working party servicing a vehicle at a bend in a minor road. A little later, still moving with the utmost caution, he encountered a small gang of engineers bridging a culvert. Some time before he reached them, he could hear the ringing of hammers on iron.

The Germans were everywhere. If they had been round Contes and the road to Tollent in their hundreds, now they swarmed round the sloping ground around the Somme like ants. The sound of the battle was louder now, more insistent in its bursts of gun-fire. The resemblance to the rumbling of distant thunder had given way to the wicked whip-like crack and echoing hollow clang that only artillery could give. More than once he thought he heard the rattle of machine-gun fire. He was, he knew, in the immediate back area of the battle line.

He had caught up with the armies. Though he was tired and hungry the recognition of that tremendous fact was a further spur to his determination. Somewhere nearby the rival enemies were locked together. One step more and he would be through the lines.

He was making his way more quickly now—though from time to time he had to halt and listen—with the ground sloping gradually down before him. Still ahead of him the sky flickered with shell bursts and the star shells danced beneath the stars. He wondered how the position lay and if, as he hoped, the British were still north of the river. If his luck held as it was going now, he might even be, by this time tomorrow night, in English hands. At last he saw the first hint of dawn breaking over the sky and, taking out his watch, saw it was three fifteen in the morning, with another three miles to go to reach his objective. He remembered inconsequently that the coming morning would be 4th June.

But the first light was rapidly approaching and he must find cover. He would hide for the day, and make his final venture the following night. He looked about him.

The land on the north slope of the shallow valley was bare beneath the already greying sky. Though it was to a degree cultivated, it had a bleak inhospitable look, with never a sheltering wood in sight. He grew anxious, wondering if he had pressed on in his eagerness too impetuously, overrunning that part of the terrain where he could have hidden with comparative safety. But it was too late to retrace his steps; daylight would be upon him soon. He moved forward to a cornfield just on his right. The corn was half-grown, scarcely three feet high. It would make a very indifferent hiding-place, but he had no other option other than to lie down where it was thickest and hope for the best.

Dawn approached rapidly. In a very short time the sky was bright. The sound of battle was very close. He could see shells bursting in the sky and could now distinctly hear machine-gun fire. Peering through the thinly planted corn he could see the line of the river before him, the folds in the ground and the general demarcation of its course. It was a heartening sight. He relaxed, lying on his face, the increasing heat of the rising sun warming his back.

No doubt he had been drowsing after the strain of the night's long passage, with its constant halts and alarms, for the crash of the first salvo of shells nearly brought him to his feet. The earth trembled beneath him and clods of earth fell nearby. He gasped with surprise, because although he knew he was near to the battle-ground, he had not imagined he was actually in it. He was soon to know.

He lay pressed close to the earth, wondering why anyone should trouble to shell an empty cornfield, when there was the roar of a battery's guns from behind him and he heard the whistle of the missiles over his head. He peered round cautiously and saw smoke eddying from a small copse five hundred yards in his rear. There were several minutes' silence and then the Allied battery from over the Somme opened up again and a second salvo fell less than two hundred yards away. Within seconds the German artillery concealed in the copse returned the fire. Embry was in the middle of an artillery duel.

The exchange of fire lasted for nearly an hour. He lay where he was, realizing that it was impossible for him to move under the very eyes of the Germans in broad daylight, but gradually both sides abandoned the duel, so that after a while all he could hear was the undertone of the general engagement. At seven o'clock of the morning German Stukas flew over and bombed the far side of the river. He could see the bomb bursts clearly and he made a mental note of where the Allied lines must be.

The tumult and the movement of the battle was all around and above him. He thought of the congested road through the Forest of Hesdin and the traffic flowing through Contes and the other villages and marvelled that he had travelled all the way to the very spearhead of the attack. He wondered, too, who were holding the positions which the Stukas had bombed, if they were French or British. He had for some reason unknown, always assumed from the start that it would be his own countrymen whom he'd finally overtake. He wondered how the battle was going and longed desperately for his aeroplane again, so that he might have his share of it. He hoped that the chaps were out with Stokes leading them. They'd probably be bombing far back, attempting to disorganize the enemy communications.

The excitement of battle was in the vibrant air and it affected him so that he said to himself over and over again with an intensity which was almost like a prayer: "I *must* get back . . . I *must* get back." It was almost an anguish to be inert and skulking in a field of corn when all this tremendous business of life and death was going on around him.

The rhythm of the fighting rose and fell, a crescendo of gunfire that made the air shudder, sinking again to the distant chattering of machine-gun fire. The battery behind opened up again, salvo after salvo, and he found himself waiting intently for the answer from the Allied guns, but the replies were infrequent. He tried to assure himself that the inadequacy of the counter battery work from across the river was probably due to a deflection of target, decided upon for some very good reason. It was infuriating to imagine that even this small section of the enemy in his rear were having things its own way.

Then with a thrill he saw two squadrons of the French air force, which he recognized at once by their roundels, sweep over and bomb enemy positions some two and a half miles ahead. He could have jumped to his feet and shouted them on. The enemy "flak" was bursting all around them. Instead he lay in the corn and cursed his luck.

But he knew where he was. He was somewhere between

the German artillery and their advance infantry. And he must keep alert. Whichever way the battle swung, so he must take advantage of it. He thought what a moment in a lifetime it would be to see British tanks suddenly climb up the slope towards him. The German battery behind him thundered again. He took out his watch and saw that it was nine o'clock.

The corn in which he lay, now in the broader daylight, seemed more sparse and thin than ever. It was very poor cover, but some distance away it seemed to grow higher. He wondered if it might be merely a rise in the ground or if indeed the seed had fallen on a richer patch of soil. He decided to take the chance and crawl towards it.

He made slow progress, because every few yards he must pause and wait and glance around to see if his movements had attracted attention from the wood. He was vaguely aware that such precautions were useless because if he were seen he had no preconceived plan of action. There was nowhere else to which to retreat. But this kind of progress—crawl, halt, and check up—was becoming a routine.

Halfway across the intervening space, as he parted the corn-stalks gently before him, he came across a field-telephone wire stretching from one side of the field to the other. There was nothing extraordinary in such circumstances in finding so commonplace an item of war equipment. But encountering it so suddenly, completely unsuspecting of its possible presence seemed to emphasize the proximity of his enemies even more than the tumult of battle that enveloped him. He was greatly relieved to reach the higher corn at last.

The sun was growing hot. His lips were dry and he moistened them with his tongue but they dried again immediately and felt sore. The sound of battle had sunk to a grumbling of the guns and only now and again came the chattering of small-arms fire. He wondered if thirst were going to prove his bitterest enemy through the day, which he must face till the blessed night fell, and he could take the last step of this long and perilous journey. But whatever was to come could be endured with the end so near at hand, with so much in the past endured. And the thought was a great comfort, to begin to understand fully something of what the creature called man could contend with in certain grave circumstances. It was as if in the greater moments of life there was a hidden source of strength which could be drawn upon, an unexpected power whose steadfast presence only peril could reveal. Almost at once he heard the sound of the approaching motor-bicycle.

He peered fearfully through the blades of the corn and to his amazement and dismay, saw a German cyclist, his machine plunging and swaying, coming across the corn-field, directly towards him.

CHAPTER NINE

THE motor-bicycle was in low gear, the engine just ticking over, while the rider straddled his seat with his feet trailing the ground to keep his balance. The machine rocked and jolted and it seemed to be as much as the rider could do to keep the handle-bars aligned, but he came steadily on, his head thrown back a little, as if to enlarge his field of vision beneath the rim of his steel helmet or as if he were casting his gaze well ahead, searching.

Embry said to himself: "This is it! I've had it!" There seemed to be no doubt about it. The trooper's course was absolutely directly towards him. He'd been seen. Someone in the wood had spotted him as he'd crept across the field. Maybe, long before that, they'd suspected his presence and had only waited for him to betray himself. And they could afford to wait. At any time should he have broken cover he would have been completely in the open. A single well-aimed shot could close the account. He could see now how the front wheel of the bicycle jumped several inches at each irregularity of the ground.

But there was just a chance. If this man had been detailed to search for him and bring him in, it was very poor tactics to send him on his own. At least two men should have been detailed. It was not like the Germans to make elementary errors of that nature. He might be a signaller bent on tracing a breakdown in his wiring. There was a wire across the field. He might be an ordinary despatch rider, taking what he imagined was a short cut. Such speculations, though they passed through his mind in the flash of a second, led nowhere. Embry only knew one thing that he himself might be, and that was to be a casualty. The bicycle was only thirty yards away when he decided to pretend to be dead.

He lay on his face, his cheek resting on one hand, the other hand at the end of his outstretched arm he turned palm upwards. He spread his legs a little, turning his right foot in. He hoped that he sprawled in the ugly, ungainly attitude of a corpse taken by shrapnel.

The sound of the bicycle came nearer. It seemed the only sound in all the world, despite the clatter and rumble of the surrounding battle. It came closer and closer, till Embry was certain that he was the object of the search. He thought swiftly. He would lie doggo—"playing possum," wasn't that what the Americans called it? As the cyclist drew level he would hold his breath lest the rising and falling of his back ribs through the thinness of his scarecrow's jacket should betray him. If the bicycle stopped it would mean that the rider was getting off or at least was straddled practically over him. If he were challenged he would make no answer. If he received a kick in the ribs he would take no notice. Only when the fellow rolled him over would he act. Then as he was turned, he'd grapple with his enemy and tear his throat out. That would teach these Huns to belittle him by only sending one solitary trooper to bring him in. The sound of the approaching machine sounded as loud as a tank.

The sound increased. It became so loud that it was almost deafening. It was almost on top of him. He drew in his breath and held it. He could hear a voice now, guttural, gasping. The rider was swearing as he rode. Voice and engine tumult mingled together sounded again immediately above him. Almost he thought he could hear the swish of the corn as it was brushed aside. The voice fell silent and the noise of the engine receded.

It grew less. It seemed too good to be true but the sound

was fainter. He breathed again. Then he raised his head a very little and saw scarcely twenty yards from him the German trooper's back. He'd passed him by.

Only when the man was out of sight and beyond the corn could Embry dare move. When at last he shifted his position he saw the tracks of the bicycle and the markings of its passage by the narrow path of crushed corn. The trail passed within three yards of where he lay. He thought again: "This must be a sign. I *shall* get through."

He lay all day in his cornfield, while the sun beat down on him. The ground grew hot and there was no shade anywhere. The heat was excruciating and his thirst was agonizing. By the afternoon his lips were beginning to crack and his tongue was swollen. But the excitement of the battle and his thought of the imminent climax to his journey helped to turn torture to discomfort.

The rhythm of the battle had taken a certain measure. It gathered its sound, continuous and insistent, within itself as it were, one overtone embracing all the minor themes. At an interval, almost to be marked, it would release from within itself this concentrated mingling, so that one terrible and overwhelming blast thundered and belched over the ground and through the skies. In the ensuing lull the lesser tones of the lighter arms could again make themselves heard, until it was time for the avalanche of discord to rise and fall once more.

So it went on through all the afternoon and evening, but Embry, during the dragging hours, planned just where he would cross the Somme that night. He could see clearly from his position the cleft in the bank far below in the shallow valley where the tributary ran in from the north-east. Some way downstream a few desultory trees leaned over what must be the river itself. By the third tree he would make his attempt. It would, he knew, take some reaching. The Germans, he was convinced, were still on his side of the Somme.

But the crossing successfully accomplished, there still remained one outstanding danger. How should he effect immediate recognition by his own folk in the darkness? As a reward for all his endeavour he had no ambition to invite a British bullet. He though the matter over with care. As soon as he was certain he was in the British lines he would walk boldly forward, dropping all pretence and disclose himself as openly as possible. Were he challenged by a British officer he would state who he was in exact detail: "I am 09254 Wing Commander B. E. Embry of 107 Squadron, Number Two Group, Bomber Command, Royal Air Force."

That would suffice for an opening gambit to commissioned ranks, but he doubted if the other ranks would understand the significance of so much detail and might indeed become unduly suspicious and trigger-happy. Therefore he decided that the better introduction to the British Tommy might be more in the nature of the vernacular:

"God sink the —— crows, but I've —— well walked all the —— way from —— Contes."

He was quite certain that would be the better means of approach. But though the thought that by this time tomorrow he might be in British hands and talking his own tongue once more was stimulating and kept his spirits high, nevertheless he had had nothing to eat for fifty-two hours and it was eighteen hours since he had drained the Frenchman's pail of milk. So that the long wait through the evening till last light was irksome in the extreme. But at eleven o'clock night had fallen. He left his hiding-place in the corn.

He crawled through the corn, because his enemies were packed tight close around him. No doubt there would be a small gap between the gun batteries and the infantry lines, where the chances of stumbling on to a patrol or an entrenched company would be less but the nearer he drew to the river, the more dense would be the massing of troops. But again it was possible that the Germans themselves would be pressing forward under cover of darkness and might be congregating wherever their pontoon bridges might have been laid. There might be spaces along the river almost devoid of troops. He could only trust to his luck.

He reached the boundary fence of the cornfield and began to climb over. He had heard for the last few minutes the sound of aircraft overhead and could have sworn they were British. Now he was sure as bombs began to fall ahead of him and he was caught in the glare of dropping flares.

He was caught astride the top bar of the fence but dived at once into the ditch beyond where he lay utterly still. The countryside was brightly illuminated and he could see in the far distance the line of trees on the river bank, which he had noticed at noon. They stood out clearly with the flares falling behind them. Beyond again came the flashes of exploding bombs, while the sky was picked out with the pyrotechnics of light flares and star shells. He waited for some minutes after the flares had burnt out lest he should have been seen.

The battle on the ground was dying down. Only occasionally would the guns speak and only at intervals was there a flashing in the sky. Nevertheless there was at all times a faint and far-off murmurous rumble of armour and vehicles, a low undertone as of the outraged earth protesting, so that it seemed to Embry that every hillock and tuft of grass could be concealing a man and that a myriad eyes were searching for him in the darkness.

He made his way on his hands and knees, halting every few yards and listening, then groping on again. Another wave of British bombers came over and he had to drop flat once more but he could see that now the land without any intervening obstacles ran smoothly and gently down before him and that the slopes were uncultivated, the grass being rough and sere. Once again the darkness swept over everything.

He crawled for a mile, progressing with the constant halts but slowly till he decided that the night was sufficiently advanced to afford cover in itself, so he rose to his feet and walked carefully in the chosen direction. He knew immediately with a sudden conviction that he was in the vicinity of the river.

He could smell it. He could smell the air tainted with the musty odour of river-mud and slime. It was the unmistakable smell that every countryman would at once recognize. And his pulse quickened because this was the portal to his journey's end. He saw the trees looming up before him. He had found his mark.

He dropped on his hands and knees again because this was the place where the Germans would be thickest. It was not improbable that they were dug in along the bank. At least, there might be machine-gun foxholes at regular intervals to cover a possible crossing. So he crawled on again, with still greater caution, through the trees and the low bushes around them till in an instant of sheer joy, he saw the river. He pushed his way through a clump of briar and was on the bank.

The Somme flowed past, black and glistening under the stars. Its surface was as smooth as glass as it glided by. He sat on the bank, watching it, fascinated. This was the river of his dreaming and the dream had come true. It was almost unbelievable. He peered over the bank. It fell sheer, seven feet down to the glistening inky water. It would be impossible to get down and into the river without making a considerable splash. The sound of a man leaping down could probably be heard several hundred yards, upstream and downstream. But somehow he must get into the river.

He sat on the bank and took off his clothes. He could

see now the other side and judged the far bank to be some ninety feet away. Beyond, the ground appeared flat and featureless till it met what appeared to be a causeway, a quarter of a mile further on. But it was no good anticipating what awaited him, until at least he was on the other side. He had still to decide on a way down the bank.

He made a bundle of his clothes, with Paul's precious hat secured safely in the middle, and wrapped them up in his scarecrow jacket as he had done when crossing the L'Authie. He knotted the arms of the jacket round his neck and immediately saw the overhanging limb of the riverside tree.

The stout branch jutted out over the water, parallel to its surface for some feet finally dwindling to foliage which drooped within inches of the stream. He paused for a moment listening as always before making a move. He could still hear the sound of the battle but it seemed very far away, a faint half-hearted echo of the noontide fighting. Nor, for some time now, had there been any further sorties of Bomber Command, so that only the starlight lit the scene. He made his way to the tree and climbed upon the branch.

The bark was rough to his bare thighs and the bundle round his neck was a hindrance. It occurred to him, struggling through a maze of smaller branches, how disastrous the loss of his clothes might be. The loss of one shoe could be a tragedy. The thought worried him so much that he wasted several minutes making sure he had secured the bundle to the best of his ability, then he crawled forward till the branch beneath him began to sag.

The thought that it might snap and precipitate him headlong into the water below decided him at once to continue his progress hand over hand from beneath the branch. He lowered himself gently over and went forward again. Within seconds his toes touched water. He passed further on hand over hand, his weight bending the branch still lower till gradually he was lowered into the river. He let go of the branch and it flew back into place, its leaves a canopy over his head.

He stood in the river with the water up to his armpits. The touch of the water on his bare flesh was a benediction. He stood quite still not only as a precaution but revelling in the physical joy of the cool and cleansing stream. He rubbed his chest and midriff with his hands, raised one foot and then another, washing away all the ingrained sweaty dust of the broiling day. Behind and above him the tall bank towered and the stretch of water to the other side, now that he was on a level with it, seemed alarmingly far away. But he knew he could make the distance. He thrust his arms gently forward and raised his body in the first strokes.

He swam slowly, using the breast stroke so as not to break water and to prevent any splashing. The current was sluggish but at what particular point he landed on the far bank was immaterial because now at long last he was crossing the Somme to safety.

He paused midstream, treading water, while he drank sparingly, remembering his early training in Field Service Hygiene which directed the student that water in the middle of a stream was cleaner than that at the edge and that a man parched with thirst should only quench it with sips. He swam on.

He reached the opposite bank without difficulty. It was, as he had thought, very much lower than the other. He drew himself out of the river and lay for a moment in the straggling rushes. He was breathing deeply, not only through exertion but through genuine excitement. He had achieved his purpose. He was over the Somme!

But for the familiar, still more distant intermittent rumbling of the battle, all was silence. The trees on the northern bank were now dark shadows, with the open starlit ground behind them rising to the low horizon. He gazed across the river to the slopes which he had traversed on hands and knees and it seemed to him that the river divided one life from another; behind were the doubts and trials; ahead the promise and the fulfilment. The water lapped at the foot of the bank before him and the starlight was reflected on the glissade of the main stream. Nowhere was there a sign of human activity; no hoarse and guttural shouts, nor the clicking of a rifle bolt or the rattle of a tommy-gun magazine. Only this gentle silence of the soft darkness with even war itself only a far-off slumbrous murmur. Suddenly for a few brief moments came the only interruption of the night.

It was a mere enough incident but it seemed to set a seal upon his thoughts, to make a fitting ending to this phase of his pilgrimage. Somewhere behind the trees on the north side must have been a track which he had not noticed in crossing. for a car in low gear was passing. The sound increased, died away, passed. And Embry in his confidence and in the glow of his success, said aloud:

"I shan't see you devils again!"

With that he rose to his feet to survey his position.

The ground before him was flat and level. He could see some considerable distance ahead the outline of the causeway. In the foreground were occasional stunted trees and a great many pools. Moss and soaking vegetation, sodden and clammy, were beneath his feet. The water oozed between his toes.

He deliberated whether to dress again but decided that the passage that had to be made to the causeway might quite easily incur the negotiation of several small streams; he was better off as he was. With his precious bundle still secured round his neck, he set off.

He felt refreshed and cleansed and light of heart, for despite his hunger the promise of what lay before him was an incentive to walk well past the dawn if needs be. He strode forward.

He dropped to the level of his waist at the first step. The black and oozing mud gripped him round the middle and drew him down. He clutched at a handful of rough reeds, but the clump came away in his hand. The bog sucked him down, till he was up to his chest. He grabbed again at a tuft of coarse grass, obtained a hold and prevented himself from sinking further. He searched with his bare feet in the slime beneath him for a foothold. He found none. He knew that if he let go of the grass tuft, he was doomed.

The realization of his plight was terrifying. This dreadful deathtrap had awaited him at the end of all these miles, yawning wide for him when he had all but won through. He tried to drag himself clear but the effort made him sink at least another two inches. He realized that it was useless attempting to extricate himself in an upright position. He must take the chance and try to assume the position of a swimmer and raise his body horizontally. He pressed his head and chest forward, bearing down heavily on his handhold.

He thought for the moment he was lost. The bitter evil mud ran over his mouth and as he tried to straighten his back into the swimming position it felt as if a ton of weights was on his ankles dragging him down. Very slowly he continued to raise his buttocks and draw his legs up underneath him. He kicked violently, hauling on the tuft of grass at the same time. He moved a few inches forward. Twenty minutes later he managed to crawl on to the firmer ground by the tuft.

He was black from head to foot. The stench from the bog was so vile that he felt sick. He ran his hands over his body trying to rid himself of the mud, and remembered in a sudden panic the parcel of clothes he carried and which in his distress he had forgotten. They were still there but covered with the black filth. It was two hours later that he reached the causeway and climbed its bank.

There was a road along the causeway and its hard gravel surface was reassuring after the terror of the bog. He could see now on the higher level how the marshes spread left and right limitlessly. It was a miracle he had come out alive. And now again borne on the light late-night breeze he heard the sound of the battle once more so that it seemed he had crept out of a half world of silence and horror into the world of men again. Clothed in nothing but the black slime of the marshes, stark naked beneath the waning starlight, he set off down the road.

He found the stream half an hour later. It ran in one of its meanders practically alongside the causeway. He scrambled down the bank and after testing the bottom, lowered himself into the water. He washed himself clean, ducking his head time and time again till he was sure that no particle of the foul mud remained. He cleaned his clothes to the best of his ability, dressed himself and moved on again.

Dawn was coming up, but he walked on boldly, confident that he must be through the lines, though puzzled at the quietude of his immediate surroundings. Sooner or later, he told himself, he would stumble on a British patrol or hear the voice of an English sentry challenging him. That would be the moment! A hundred yards farther on he saw the village.

It lay to the left of the causeway down one of the numerous tracks that criss-crossed the marshes. Daylight had come and he could clearly see the cluster of buildings, huddled together in the customary casual French fashion. On the outskirts lay what appeared to be a small farm. He decided to make the latter his objective.

He walked openly and easily along the track, though watchful for any movement ahead, but it was still early hours and no doubt the village slept, though it had strangely enough, even at the first distances, a look more of death than of slumber.

128

He reached the farm and found the gate open. It swung idly on its hinges, unpadlocked. Just past the gate was a small barn and some hen houses in a stable yard, while the house stood at the far end of the drive. He passed through the gateway and found himself in the stable yard.

There was no one about. In one corner of the yard was a dog kennel, empty. Its dog chain lay idle on the ground. It seemed to Embry a very significant detail. And those mercurial spirits rose again, for the night was behind him and the sun was climbing up the east, so that when he saw the hens' nesting-boxes ranged along the wall he almost ran to them to pillage them of their contents, should there be any. He went through the boxes with an impish delight and told himself that he was as good a leprechaun as ever came out of old Ireland. He found seven eggs and promptly pocketed them. He turned towards the barn.

It was, as he had hoped, built with an open ground-floor, unhampered by doors. There was a cart without wheels between the two main supporting timbers and a few broken farm tools, a pitch-fork, and a well-worn spade in a corner. But beyond, a ladder tilted up to the open hatch of what must be a loft immediately under the roof. He climbed up the ladder and peered in. The loft was nearly full of straw. It was one of the most inviting sights he'd seen for a very considerable time. He climbed in through the hatch. He knew at once that this was an ideal resting-place. He was exhausted and must sleep, therefore pending further investigation of the whereabouts of the allied armies he would make this a temporary head-quarters. He laid his eggs safely in a corner and climbed down again, intent on exploring the farmhouse itself.

He approached the house cautiously, keeping close to the hedge of the drive, though at heart he was confident he would be, if any one were at home, in friendly company. But the experiences of the last few days had taught him his lesson, though when he was a dozen paces away he saw that the front door was open, and any fears he might have were groundless. He pushed the door open and went in.

He found himself in the customary kitchen living-room. The table was bare and the place was clean. It had the look of a room deserted by a family on holiday with everything neat and tidy swept and garnished against their return. He climbed the stairs and found three small rooms leading off a landing. The rooms were barely furnished and in each instance the bedding had been removed. There were no signs anywhere of a hurried evacuation but the place was clearly deserted. The battle had swept over it and left it unscathed.

He returned to the living-room and explored the cupboards and shelves. He found no food but four bottles of wine. In the kitchen drawers he discovered a pocket knife, a kitchen knife and fork, and in the sideboard drawer, to his great delight, a quarter-inch scale map of the district. In the yard a bucket stood under the pump. He filled the bucket with water and carried it together with the rest of his plunder up into the loft. He was well pleased with himself. He arranged his belongings in such a way as he saw fit, made a hollow in the straw for his couch and once more descended the ladder to search again for food.

He stood in the yard by the barn at a loss for the moment where to search. He had drawn a blank at the house and there seemed no other possibilities nearby. But if one house were deserted in circumstances such as these then in all likelihood the entire village was deserted. It would probably be worth while to investigate. It was only about another half mile along the road.

It was as he was ruminating to this effect that he heard the sound of approaching transport. A car was coming up the lane behind him on the other side of the building. His first impulse was to spring out to greet it but as a wiser man than that of a week ago, he stepped back into the barn, climbed into the loft and pushed the ladder away so that it fell beside the broken cart. He went to the side of the roof which was just above his head and nearest to the drive with its swinging gate. All the time he could hear the sound of the car on the track below growing louder. With the help of the kitchen knife he eased a loose tile free, so that on the moment he had a look out. He gazed through his loophole into the drive. There was a ten-ton lorry in the gateway. **And it was filled with German soldiers.**

CHAPTER TEN

THERE were a dozen of them. Embry counted them as they climbed out of the truck. Eight of them moved towards the house, while the other four turned below in his direction and were lost to view. Seconds later, he heard footsteps and voices below him. They were in the barn. He leapt into the straw and dug his way six feet down, leaving only a little tunnel for air.

He was very glad that he had had the forethought to remove the ladder but the presence of the Germans was a bitter disappointment. He was still behind the German lines. The allies were as yet in retreat.

He could hear the voices beneath him. He imagined the soldiers hanging up their equipment and resting their rifles against improvised racks. He hoped they were not using the barn as a guard house. It would mean a picket constantly on duty, much too close at hand should he determine to make a break for it. But in a little time the voices ceased and there was silence. He emerged from his hiding-place and looked through the loophole again. The lorry was still there. It would be folly to move till it had gone. He returned to his straw.

He was deeply worried. Despite his many vicissitudes, his fortunes had promised fair. He had survived in circumstances fraught with danger and yet this will-o'-the-wisp of the allied lines was still eluding him. It filled him with the fury of frustration. There was, it seemed, no limit to what must be endured and that sacrifice might be out of all proportion to the end achieved. And then as suddenly as these instances would repeatedly occur in this new-found life of concentrated essences of fresh values, he realized that he had discovered another facet of the truth; that the phrase "neck or nothing," though a popular tag, was in reality a great and fundamental principle. If he were to get through—and of that he was determined—he must be prepared to go forward to the very last breath. There could not possibly be at any time any suggestion of half measures. If a scheme failed, whatever the disappointment and resentment, the scheme must be abandoned forthwith. He saw that he must apply to himself the same kind of ruthlessness that higher authority employed towards one of its units engaged in an operation against the enemy. Personalities were forgotten in the face of the task. The objective was all that mattered. So it must be with him.

The straw was warm and the odour of the loft was musty sweet. He dozed off.

He woke at noon from a half day-dream cat-nap to the sound of bombardment. The tiles of the loft rattled to the thud of bursting shells. He struggled out of his straw bed and went to his loop-hole. He could see the village in the distance. It still wore the same forlorn deserted air but now high explosive was bursting over its roofs. The spire of the solitary church rose from a cluster of small houses in the centre of the hamlet and as he watched he saw a ragged tongue of red fire flicker upwards to the weather cock. The red glow spread till a cottage nestling at the base of the church was enveloped at the same time as a small farm beside it was hit and set on fire.

He found the spectacle reassuring. The British couldn't be so far away after all. The battle was still in the vicinity. It was not impossible that the Germans might be driven back and that he himself might be enveloped in an allied advance, but in a little time the cannonade ceased as suddenly as it had begun. He watched the smouldering buildings with the billowing smoke drifting across the forsaken village.

It was a spectacle so pathetically hopeless that he felt again that surge of indignation that providence should at one moment proffer him his heart's desire and the next snatch it away from his outstretched hands. The bombardment of the village had promised the presence of British arms; now that it had ceased it could only indicate the target had been abandoned once again and that no serious advance had ever been intended. And in that he immediately recognized he was yielding to the temptation which only a short time before he had decided must be ignored. In short, there must never be any regrets or self-reproach or remorse. The last thing he must do would be to curse his luck.

With that determination planted firmly in his mind, he returned to his couch and took three eggs from their hiding-place, together with a bottle of wine. He dug in the cork with his penknife and pushed it into the bottle. He drank deeply. The wine was red and sharp. The eggs he broke one by one, swallowing them at a gulp washing each one down with another draught from the bottle. He slept through the afternoon, scarcely disturbed by the occasional sound of voices.

He woke at dusk and looked out again through the hole in the roof but the lorry was still there. Until it was gone he must stay where he was. And that evening, seated on the ground, their backs to the wall of the farm buildings opposite, the German soldiers sang.

They sang in harmony, strange haunting refrains, songs out of that older Germany of their forefathers who had loved its musicians and had never heard the word "Nazi." The sunset died and a merciful darkness fell over the desolated village and the stars came out. In the loft the night was warm in the scented straw. And still they sang below, softly and tenderly and sometimes it seemed with great sadness, longing perhaps like so many others of diverse creeds and nationalities for a remembered fireside and a hearth and a woman's face haloed in the glow of the embers.

At noon of the following day, 7th June, under a brilliant sun and a cloudless sky, the German patrol left. Embry saw them go, climbing into their lorry with much clattering of rifles and equipment. In a short time there was complete silence.

It was a silence, under that bright midday sky, which was almost eerie. The murmurous grumbling of the battle had long ceased. He knew that the allied retreat must be rapid and that it would be hopeless to pursue the armies further.

He had thought it all out during the morning, reviewing the fresh situation neither with dismay nor elation, bringing to bear on it the same impersonal approach which he had decided appropriate in his self-examination of the previous day. He was determined now, at the first opportunity, to proceed no longer further south, but to strike west-north-west to the coast. Once there he would try to find a boat of some kind to carry him across the Channel to England. He had no idea what kind of boat he would need and very little idea of how he'd obtain one.

The first job was to reach the coast. He finished off his eggs, cleaned himself with water from his bucket and, now there were no longer German voices to disturb him, took a short but deeper spell of sleep. At eleven o'clock of the same night he set out on the second phase of his journey to freedom. He had no regrets for so much time lost and for so little achieved. He viewed the whole affair dispassionately.

He lowered himself through the hatch of the loft, crossed the stable yard, passed through the gate and turned right for the village. He reached it within a quarter of an hour.

It was so quiet that it was awe-inspiring. Had the houses lain in ruins and had scattered rubble taken the place of what had once been buildings, he would have been less moved, but most of the houses were standing and scarcely scarred. He could see nearly every detail in the bright starlight; the half-opened windows with the curtains gently swaying; the nodding flowers in the little patches of fenced gardens; the doors swinging ajar; the garden rake propped against a gate-post; all small familiar things of human habitation were there but the human beings themselves. And it seemed to Embry that this was a most ghostly place and he wondered how many more like this he would encounter and because he was affected by this sad and brooding atmosphere of desolation, he hurried through.

He kept to the southerly course for the time being, for though he would eventually swing westwards for the coast, he would be leaving the Somme well behind. He imagined, and rightly, that the area around the river would be more densely populated than the downs and plains which his map told him lay further south. He was still reluctant, because of his former experiences, to travel by day. Some miles further on he changed course for the west. Within minutes his progress was barred by a wood.

It seemed at the outset, in the bright starlight, a very ordinary kind of wood. But the last time he had made this cross-country kind of passage, he had had his compass, now he was forcibly reminded of the nightmare journey through the crops on the first night after his break-away from the Calais column.

The tracks of the wood seemed to take all manner of directions. He kept as steadfastly to his course as he could but the gradual inclining of a track to left or right could be almost imperceptible. He knew from referring to his map that the wood was about a mile wide from where he had entered. He walked steadily on, avoiding the thickets of bramble when possible and picking the tracks which he thought would lead him in the right direction. But the further he walked he was still in the wood.

He had checked by his watch and he should have been at least emerging on the far side by this time. But there were trees everywhere all around him and they seemed to be fantastically conferring together as if they were antagonistic to him and were contriving how best to bar his way. He was not unduly imaginative but the Celt blood could be stirred by the witchery of the starlight and the memory of the deserted village haunted him. The savagery of war, its lusts and violences, its wild extravagances of emotion, its furies and the diapason of its wrath were all things to be expected, but the thought of the lonely village was strangely disturbing. It lay dead and yet the warmth of life was still in it, as might have been in a corpse but a few minutes old. So now the living trees seemed to assume a life other than their own and he thought how closely and intimately he had lived to all common-place things since he'd been shot down and had found in them, each and all, some deeper significance which it was beyond him to explain. It was as if, in this new intimacy, a corner of the veil were lifted now and again, so that he was almost on the point of glimpsing what might lie beyond. But now he was lost.

He swore at the trees because they were in his way and the nightmarish quality of that other night began to return. He wondered if he were lightheaded with lack of food and sleep for though he had rested in the barn no such respite had covered more than three-quarters of an hour at a time, so subconsciously watchful and tense had been his mind. He leant against a tree trunk and consulted his map and attempted to sort out his thoughts. The foliage was dense overhead and it was difficult to see the stars. He wandered on till he found another of the numerous rides and stared starwards but the rift in the trees was insufficient and it was impossible to determine his position. It was fully half an hour later that he stepped out from the relentless trees.

He was only just in time. Again his old adversary the mist was beginning to obscure the stars. The grass on which he stood was wet with dew, which soaked almost at once through the worn leather of his shoes so that when he moved on, his socks, which were already breaking into holes, became saturated and made his feet sore. But he found that he had at least reached the side of the wood which he had intended but how far to the north or south he could not decide. He consulted his map again but when he once more gazed aloft the high mist had spread and the stars were gone. There seemed only one thing to do. He must take a chance on his direction till he found some landmark which he could identify on his map. Leaving the wood on his right, he set off across the broad meadows, feeling that at any rate he was moving somewhere in the direction of the far-off coast.

He came upon the railway siding just before dawn. He followed it down to its junction with the main line. Other sidings ran parallel at the point of junction. The rails were ripped up and twisted like champagne wire, the sleepers were splintered and torn from their beds, trucks sprawled across the broken rails or were heaps of debris. British night bombers had been at work. But the line with its junction gave him some indication of his position. He had done a round-about-turn and instead of moving directly west had approached the Somme again. He turned in his tracks, disgustedly.

But though he kept on as closely to his course as he could, the crops constantly impeded him. The corn was high and dripping wet and there were times when the fields were so large that to have circumvented them would have been to risk a total loss of direction. He struggled on determined to see the night through and make the most of his time but dawn found him very tired. By first light he had picked a hedge for his daytime hiding-place and crept to the centre of it.

It was almost noon when he saw movement not two hundred yards away on his left, and peering out through the bramble and thorn of the hedge saw an enemy anti-aircraft battery in the corner of a field. Later the guns opened up and at the same time he noticed considerable activity on the main road which was visible from where he lay but he heard no sound of the distant fighting and presumed that he was in the back area of the battle-ground. He would, he felt, have to be careful in his movements because the countryside would doubtless be alive with Germans so that it would be safer to travel by night. In fact it was the only reasonable course to adopt, yet on the other hand progress through the crops was slow and difficult. He argued with himself for and against night travelling, and decided to leave the final choice for the next day.

He left the hedge before midnight and moved off in a north-westerly direction. He was at once in trouble with the crops. Like the trees in the wood, the growing corn was becoming an obsession. There seemed no end of it, for field after field was waist high and saturated with dew. He battled his way through, and towards the early hours of the morning he came upon a village.

It lay in a slight hollow of the ground, sleeping quietly beneath the stars. He wondered if indeed it slept or if rather it was like that other he had passed through, silent in death. He took a track running alongside a meadow, crossed a small wooden footbridge with a single-handed rail and found himself in a side street.

The place had the same air of desertion and desolation. The door of a house nearest the culvert, which he had crossed, was open. He walked boldly up the garden path and went in. He made a swift reconnaissance upstairs and downstairs to make certain he was alone and then began a systematic search for food.

He found nothing at all. There was not even a half bag of potatoes or a morsel of mouldy bread, even the ashcan outside the back door was empty. But in a table drawer he discovered half a dozen letters and some postcards and the addresses told him that he was in the village of Sorel. He searched for the place on his map, found it and came to the immediate conclusion that after the tribulations of the night he had moved only three miles.

It seemed impossible to believe but it was true and he supposed progress in such a state as he was, could be in no way proportionate to the effort. He thought bitterly of the struggle with the countryside, which seemed to raise all weapons of its own, dew, trees, briar, and corn-fields against him. He wondered if he exaggerated this battle with the elements through sheer physical fatigue and lack of food and if in other days he would have ploughed his way through and onwards vigorously and contemptuous of his difficulties, then in the half light he caught sight of himself in a scrap of broken mirror hanging on a hook above the kitchen sink.

The bearded vagabond that stared back at him was scarcely recognizable except for the eyes, as glinting bright as ever, set in the dark and swarthy face. The skin over his cheekbones was burnt mahogany brown and shone like the polished wood itself. The gleaming eyes in the dark-hued face looked fierce and hungry. The working-man's cap with its battered peak aslant his forehead gave him a sinister gypsy look and beneath, his beard was thick and bristling. But there was little time left to contemplate this remarkable metamorphosis or to search elsewhere in the surrounding houses for food, for the sky was growing light once more and he must find cover.

He chose again a hedge, a little distance from Sorel and crawled in, hungry, and for all his resolution, dispirited. The going was proving very hard. All the determination in the world could not force on a machine which was perilously near collapse.

He thought bitterly of the paltry progress of three miles. It was elementary mathematics to solve the problem of whether at the rate at which he was progressing in relation to his condition he could reach the English Channel. He knew it to be utterly impossible. Therefore the situation resolved itself into the same wearisome question: night or day—by which should he travel? But he knew that daylight held no charms for him at all and that the dreadful labour of the night seemed little compared with the terrors of the day with the hourly haunting fear of instant discovery. And yet in his innermost thoughts, he dimly realized that maybe in the end, the decision would be taken from him and that exhaustion alone would decide that only the daylight hours with their added speed could serve the fateful purpose. But he spent that day in his hedge.

He left Sorel as soon as darkness fell. He had seen throughout the day troop movement and passing vehicles and an occasional patrol car. He had not dared to venture out but now night had returned once more and he must make the most of it.

The mist was across the sky by midnight and his sense of direction became obscured. He found himself faced inevitably again with the high crops, skirting the fields, dodging as it were the issue ever before him. He imagined that he was in more cultivated country because the hedges were more frequent and more than once he was in trouble with barbed wire, falling over a loose strand and staggering into the actual fence and tearing his clothes and hands. His progress became very slow.

At two o'clock in the morning he came upon a third

village. As in previous instances it was deserted. This time, he told himself, there must be food. His leg was hurting again and he was limping as he entered the first house.

He knew at once that the house would be almost precisely like the others but the windows were shuttered and it was pitch dark inside. He groped his way around, stumbling against a table and an overturned chair till he found the mantelpiece. He felt along with his hands and found a box of matches. He struck a light.

The living-room was in utter disorder. The chairs were on their side, the check tablecloth was half off the table, the fender had been dragged away from the grate and the fire-irons lay scattered beside it, even the pictures on the wall were awry.

He searched the ground floor, opening every cupboard and peering along every shelf. He found in the scullery a bottle of cider but of food there was no sign whatsoever. Still striking matches, he went upstairs.

The bedrooms were in worse disorder than the rooms below. Bed clothes were crumpled upon the floor and in the front room the china washing-jug was broken. He wondered what sudden alarm had startled this family into such obvious consternation. Here the war must have come upon them suddenly, like a thief in the night. And there by the foot of the bed he saw the socks.

They were woollen and grey with a hole in the heel of one and a hole in the toe of the other. When he picked them up they exhaled a very terrible odour but he knew they were as pearls beyond price. He took off his shoes and there was very little need to take off his own socks, because they almost came to pieces in his hands. He made his exchange. He passed into the next room. He found the nightdress!

It was an affair of flannelette and though the flickering light of a match was scarcely adequate for the closest examination it was he felt sure none too clean but very certainly cleaner than his own shirt. He stripped off his jacket, flung his shirt into a corner and donned the night-dress. With a little adjustment he felt it did very well. He put on his jacket again and went downstairs.

He discovered as he was practically certain he would, letters in the drawer of a little bureau and that he was in the village of Dreuil Hamel. He checked at once with his map. He had gone four miles completely in the wrong direction.

He sat down on the floor, his back to the wall, near the front door. He had to sit down because he was of a sudden so tired that he could stand no more. His leg was throbbing, a rhythmic repetition of pain jabbing down into the bone. He rested his head in his hands, his elbows on his knees. Four miles in the wrong direction!

Only he would wait for a little time, just resting, forbidding thought, only remembering what he had resolved to do when failure faced him; to go on again, never looking back, never regretful, only determined to reach England once again. But for the moment while his disappointment and chagrin were so bitter, he would rest just for the moment . . . just for a little while. . . .

CHAPTER ELEVEN

HE LEFT Dreuil Hamel before dawn. The country in which he found himself was open; fine rolling downs, billowing away to the far horizon. Here and there, but several miles apart, were small copses and more frequently in a sheltered coll of the downs, haystacks. It was one of the latter, perched just under the lip of a ridge, that he chose for his first resting-place as day broke.

He climbed up the side of the stack and dug out a couch where the hay had already been cut away. He took off all his clothes.

He laid them out beside him. They were wet through with the early dew for he had had to traverse two fields of corn before he reached the downs. He felt, moreover, they could do with an airing, especially the nightdress, to say nothing of the socks.

The sun came up warm and bright, as it did day after day in the summer of that terrible year and he felt the warmth on his naked flesh and the gentle loving touch of the light morning breeze on his back and flanks and he knew that if only he had had food, he would not have been all that discomforted, because always the promise was in sight, always the promise in his heart. He was bound to get through.

The downs fell away before him, wide and serene. He watched the cloud-shadows sweep over the ridges and crawl down the far valley sides. There was no sound even slightly resembling that of battle. Like the villages he had passed through, the downs seemed desolated, here was no message of death muttered by the wind down a moonlit silent street, but rather under the fair morning sky the earth stretched itself sensuously basking, fragrant with warm life.

Yet the beauties of Nature were not foremost in his mind. He knew that very soon he would have to decide quite definitely on a course of action. He must watch the countryside intently, observing what activity took place. He studied his map in relation to what lay before him and came to the conclusion that, should he choose to travel by day, this would be the area, with its wide open spaces and scarcity of roads, in which to start. No sooner had the thought passed through his mind than he knew that he had already subconsciously come to that decision. He would travel by day.

Now that his mind was made up he felt more at home with himself. It was, being wise as it were after the event, so clearly the thing to do. His leg was threatening to become a very real hindrance. He had little doubt but it was going septic; he was exhausted and one or two more nights like the last would bring him completely to the end of his tether; moreover, it should be easier to find food by day.

He watched the outspread land before him and nothing moved upon it. He told himself that likely enough, once he set out, he would chance upon some farm, hidden from him now in a fold of the ground. Nor was there any reason why another such a one as his good friend Paul might not appear at the gate and help him on again. One thing was certain—he was glad he'd made up his mind at least to do the right thing.

He was convinced that he was adopting the proper course. He had seen no sign of anyone from dawn till now. He had only got to have confidence and he would face up to anything. And he thought to himself that that point summed up the whole matter, this question of confidence.

So it had been before, as it would be again. He stepped out briskly.

He made good progress. It was highly satisfactory to think one hour by day could do the work of a whole night. He was going in the right direction as well. The certainty of that was completely reassuring. There was no wasted effort now and soon he'd find food.

It was clearly ludicrous to imagine anyone could walk for ever and not find food somewhere. Meanwhile, for the sun was growing hotter, he'd have a drink. He finished the last of the cider, threw the bottle away, and walked on.

At a quarter to twelve he was crossing a clover field. The ground was undulating so that only when he reached the crest of one of the small ridges was his field of vision sufficient to see any distance ahead. Far off, the line of the downs rimmed the sky and it seemed to him that nothing lay in between him and that far-distant horizon but mile upon mile of grassland.

It was while he was traversing one of the shallow inclines and wondering how long it would be before he saw the farm which he had promised himself to see, that he heard the unmistakable sound of an approaching lorry. He was so astonished that he halted in his tracks, amazed.

The sound grew louder. So still was the air that the vehicle might have been some miles away, but when he started on his way again and reached the higher ground he saw the truck about a mile off, driving directly at right-angles to the line of his set course. That there was a road beneath him was now obvious, though hidden in a fold in the ground. What was just as obvious was that the occupants of the lorry might have had him under observation for the last five minutes. And he was sure that they were Germans, for he could, he thought, just discern a steel helmet on the driver's head. He was caught in the open and their paths would cross.

146

His first impulse was to drop flat but he realized at once that the very action would be suspicious. He thought then of changing his course so that they should have passed by well before he reached the road. That again could arouse suspicion. The third course would be to bluff it out—to tramp on unconscious of anything so commonplace as a lorry on a road. He knew at once the latter was the only thing to do.

It was quite impossible to regulate his own walking speed in relation to that of the lorry so that he could be certain of their not meeting together at the point of crossing. The contours of the ground hid the vehicle momentarily and it was clear the road took sudden turns. He decided to cross if possible ahead of the truck. But the lorry was carrying on fast with an open road ahead.

He crossed the road without looking to either side. He could hear the lorry roaring and clattering along on his left as he reached the grass verge and made his way resolutely up the slope that led to the next ridge. At every pace he expected to hear a challenge but the sound of the lorry's progress continued and he was already a good thirty yards on the western side of the road, when of a sudden the sound stopped.

It stopped to the accompaniment of screeching brakes and a bellowing voice. Embry turned in his tracks and stood stock still.

There were five of them. One steel-helmeted, the others in forage caps; four German troopers with an *unteroffizier* in charge. The latter carried a tommy gun, the others had unslung rifles.

They came up the slope at a brisk pace, their weapons at the ready and still shouting. Embry walked towards them. If there were a part to be played it must be played in earnest and with precision. This was the moment he had dreaded. Now it was upon him and his wits were with him. He attempted a smile.

"Who are you?" The *unter-offizier's* French was only just adequate.

The German was on a level with him now. He was a tall young man, weedy rather than thin and like his companions burnt deeply brown with the sun. The rest of the party were all of a kidney, lean, aggressive and very truculent. Embry could almost see the unmistakable aura of the hooligan about them. These were not the young soldiers of Guderian's Panzer divisions nor the men who had stood beneath the trees of the wood near St. Omer. These were the spawn of the Nazi Youth Movement, the little Hitlerites, the bullies and tormentors.

"Who are you?"

"*Je suis Belge*," said Embry.

"That is a lie. You are a soldier."

"No. A Belgian. A refugee."

"You lie. You are an English soldier."

He was not expecting to be kicked. The *unter-offizier's* toecap caught him on the thigh. The blow was too low for his groin but it sent him staggering. One of the Germans gave a sudden laugh. A strange sound, beginning and ending on the instant, bestial, maniacal. A blow from a rifle butt across his shoulders sent him spinning towards his interrogators once more. The *unter-offizier* seized him by the lapel of his ragged coat.

"You are an English soldier in disguise." His breath smelt of garlic.

"No," said Embry. "I am a Belgian."

He thought to himself: "I must keep my temper. Whatever they do, unless they intend to finish me right off, I must put up with it. I've got to play the part I've chosen."

"Where are your identification papers?"

"I lost them on the way."

The *unter-offizier* threw his head back. His teeth were large and yellow but very even. "He lost his papers," he said in German. "He says he lost his papers on the way."

They shouted with laughter at that and one of them brought the heel of a rifle butt smartly into Embry's ribs. For several seconds he could scarcely see for the nausea from the pain. Then he knew they were searching his pockets. They tore the neck of his flannelette night shirt and tugged at the belt of his trousers. They found the pocket-knife and the spoon and fork which he had taken from the French farm and threw them away, though, for a reason never to be known, they left his watch. As they searched and pulled him this way and pommelled him that way, as if he were a rag doll torn by puppies, they gabbled in excited German like little mad dogs yapping.

The *unter-offizier* ordered his men aside and completed the search in an official manner, now that the lads had had their fun.

"No papers. Nothing to identify yourself with. And you still say you are a Belgian?"

"Yes," said Embry stoutly.

"We'll soon find that out. But if you are English . . ." He drew his hand across his throat.

"Now you come with us."

A kick on the flank helped Embry on his way. They reached the truck and he climbed in while they mounted guard over him, then they in turn clambered in and ranged themselves on either side of him while the driver took his seat. They drove off.

His back was sore and his ribs were aching, so that it was painful to breathe freely. He felt stunned and baffled by this preposterous turn of his luck. It wasn't as if he'd walked into a trap. His captors could claim no credit for their prize. The merest mischance had thrown him into their clutches. A few hundred yards one way or the other across the downs or along the road and he would still have been tramping over the grass and not crouched, bruised and beaten, on a wooden seat in a jolting truck filled with vicious young enemies.

149

They had turned from the main road by now and taken a secondary road leading to a small bridge hitherto concealed by a high shoulder of the downlands. Embry could see, as they ran down the incline, the slate-grey roofs of the houses amongst the shrill green of the trees in their early summer foliage. Within minutes they were driving through a gateway opening into a farmyard.

There was a hayrick in the far corner and a large manure heap in the centre of the stable yard. There were farm buildings on either side and the farmhouse stood on the right. It was a bleak, drab little place with the paint of the front door peeling and blistered. They all leapt out and Embry followed them.

He got down slowly because his ribs and back were sore from his thrashing, so that the *unter-offizier* shouted at him again, while a trooper flung open the front door. Someone struck him as he went in and he stumbled but they pushed him down a corridor on the ground floor. There was a room at the far end on the left and they thrust him in, slamming the door on him, but only after the *unter-offizier* had said:

"If you do prove to be an Englishman, we shall shoot you."

He sat down in the far corner opposite the door, with his back to the wall in just the same way he had sat in the cottage in Dreuil Hamel an hour before dawn of this self-same day. There, dispirited and disillusioned, he had communed with himself, fighting down all weakness of the flesh, commanding himself to step forward once again. But now all his resolutions and efforts had been in vain.

The long night marches through the crops, the rivers he had swum, the swamps he had plunged into and struggled through, the starvation and the thirst, all had led but to this.

There was, of course, a limit to all things. There was no sense in pretending there was not. There was so much that could be demanded of a human soul and no more. Now he could only wait for the end.

An hour passed. Now and again he heard German voices and footsteps outside. He made no attempt to try the door or to unfasten the sash of the one window. Any attempt to escape by that means would be not only too obvious but would prove the falsity of any story he might contrive. He must carry through the farce. He must bluff his way through. But what use now to keep the sorry half-hearted act alive?

He was as certain it was the end as he had ever been about anything. They didn't believe his story. He had no means of supporting it. They had only to get an interpreter to interrogate him and his deception was revealed. They wouldn't keep him here after dark because the room was insufficiently secure. Even if he continued to convince them he was a Belgian, they still would have to deal with him. Therefore before dark they'd have to make up their minds what to do. He had no illusions on that point.

They were going to shoot him. This was to be the dirty, disgraceful end, bullied and beaten and shot to death by little German corner-boys.

In the instant the wrath rose in him. It rose from the humiliation of his shameful treatment. It rose in a flame of indignation. He said, "By God!"—and he meant "By God"—"If they're going to do this to me, then someone's going to pay for it!" As always, although the fury seethed within him, his brain became icy clear and he knew what he would do. And this was the time to do it, because between two and three of an afternoon was a bad hour with Germans who were accustomed to overeat and drink at their midday meal.

He went across the room and kicked the door. He kicked it three times, savagely, viciously. The sound of kicking went down the corridor, filled the house. Then he shouted and ran back to his corner opposite the door and crouched down. He heard approaching footsteps and let his head sag forward as in assumed exhaustion and let his arm lie limp at his side. The door opened.

He saw that the young German who entered was much of a height with himself but probably a stone lighter, a clean-shaven pimply-faced young man of about twenty-two, unsavoury, unremarkable. His rifle was slung over his shoulder and his lower lip protruded moistly. He advanced to the middle of the room, his hand ready on the rifle sling. Embry touched his own lips with his left hand, gestured as if raising a cup with his right.

"Thirsty," he said in French.

The German shrugged his shoulders and strode out of the room. Embry rose to his feet. He leant against the corner, half-huddled there, in all appearance a broken figure, lamed and suffering. He could hear the faint sound of a pump being used in the yard outside. The room was stiflingly hot with the heat of the afternoon sun but it was not only the heat that made the perspiration run down Embry's face and trickle to the corner of his mouth. The door opened again and the young German soldier re-appeared. He held a cup half full of water in one hand, the other was still on the sling of his rifle. He advanced casually, a look of curiosity on his face as if he were inspecting some caged animal. He held out the cup.

Embry hit him. He hit him with all his strength and skill and the timing was perfect. His knuckles met the German's jaw with a click and the German's head went back and his legs gave way. Embry kicked him in the stomach before he reached the floor and when he was down he kicked him again. He could have torn the fellow's throat out even if he were dead because he was berserk mad. He snatched up the man's rifle from the floor where it had fallen and made for the door.

Embry ran out into the corridor and at the far end he saw a second German on guard just inside the threshold

152

of the front door. He was wearing his forage cap and had his back to Embry and leant upon his rifle and Embry was down the passage before he could turn. Embry lifted the rifle he had seized, swiftly reversed it and brought the shodden heel of the butt down with a terrible blow on the crown of the sentry's head. The man went slithering to the door-step till he collapsed in a heap with his head at a ludicrous angle on his shoulder. Embry leapt over him and sprang into the yard. He heard the clanking of buckets and the sound of somebody whistling a musical comedy sort of air. The sound came from his left. A third German in shirt sleeves, carrying a bucket of water in each hand, rounded the corner of the house. Embry leapt at him.

The whistle faded from the German's parted lips and, even as he struck, Embry could have laughed at the look of astonishment and pained bewilderment on the other's face. But the brass-plated rifle butt, swung at arm's length, took the German on his left temple and he and the buckets went asprawl. And Embry said: "Crikey! But I'm building up a score!"

He looked around him wildly, frenziedly. No one was watching from any of the windows. There was no one, it seemed, in the small barn and outbuildings. No one came running and shouting. No one fired a shot. But he couldn't stay here in the broad daylight of a June afternoon in the bloodstained stable yard of a French farm with victims, such as these, for company. He made up his mind at once. He would hide on the spot.

He looked round desperately. Somewhere not very far away he thought he heard the sound of a car. He flung the rifle away, ran four paces and dived head first into the manure heap which was in the middle of the yard.

CHAPTER TWELVE

IT WAS a large manure heap, some forty feet across. The weeks of fine warm weather had dried the dung and straw so that he managed to burrow his way down easily, clawing out the manure in great handfuls till he lay at the bottom of the heap. As he had burrowed down, so the straw had fallen into the cavity he had made, covering and concealing him. He felt that, provided no one had seen him make the initial plunge, he would be completely safe till nightfall.

He lay listening but there was no sound of human movement from the yard beyond. It was hot and steaming at the bottom of the dung pit but he lay utterly still, not daring to shift his position. So the long afternoon and evening passed, the hours dragging slowly by. Once or twice he thought he heard the rumbling of transport along the adjacent road, but the sound died as quickly as it had come and all that remained was the buzzing and murmuring of innumerable insects busy amongst the ordure over his head.

It was just after eleven o'clock that night that he crept out of his hiding-place. He extricated himself with the utmost caution, moving only a foot at a time until his head and shoulders were clear.

The stars were out in a clear sky. He could see the unlit farm buildings across the yard and peered anxiously through the darkness to see if the body of the third German whom he had attacked had been removed, but he could distinguish nothing in the lower-level darkness of the yard.

154

He was clear of the heap within minutes and crawled on all fours as close to the ground as he could in a direction away from the buildings. His progress was slow, even slower perhaps than his passage across the lawn on the night he had fought and climbed the holly hedge, but at last he found a taut length of wire barring his passage and he knew he had met a boundary fence. He pressed his way through, only once pausing as a strand of wire beneath him flew back into the position from which it had been forced with a reverberating twang that sounded to him like the booming of a 'cello. But the silence flowed round again as he waited and he knew he was as yet undetected. He crawled on.

He continued his passage on all fours for two hundred yards, and with every yard forward his spirits rose. In this crazy "through-the-looking-glass" world into which he'd been projected a mood could change within minutes. He should by all the laws of chance have been dead by now, but he was alive and he had taken toll of his enemy.

He rose to his feet and looked about him. He appeared to be in open country, a continuation of the downland he had crossed in the morning, though here and there he could discern small patches of woodland on the long slopes of a hillside or a clump of trees on the hillock of a ridge. The stars were still bright and clearly visible. He picked out his old and faithful ally the North Star, took his bearings and strode away to the west.

He reached the village of Huppy well before dawn. He could tell almost at once by its air of quiet solitude that it was deserted. In common with so many other of the senses that his present predicament had quickened he was coming to recognize the emptiness of a place instinctively as soon as he reached it. He walked boldly forward, well satisfied with the ten miles of downland he had left behind him and desperate for food.

He tried two houses without any success. He would, he

knew, have to deal with this question of hunger very shortly, else all the good fortune which had now swung in his favour would be lost. Also he must rest. He tried a larger house, further down the street, and entered it.

In the living-room he found, as he had expected, letters and cards giving him his position; and in the kitchen, in the corner, a large earthenware crock. He raised the lid, peeped in, sniffed.

His nose indicated a possible find. The smell was very faintly rancid but not over-pungent. He put his hand in and extracted a cold and greasy lump. He took it to the doorway and under the starlight saw that it was a piece of very fat pork. He nibbled at it and though it was very salt and unpalatable, his stomach cried out for more. He took another mouthful, laid the precious remains on the table and went in search of what further he might find. His luck was holding.

There was cider in an outhouse adjoining the scullery. There were three great tuns on their wooden jigs and each was broached and tapped. He sampled a mouthful or two, catching the liquor in a cupped hand. It was strong and clean to the palate. He looked round for a bottle and to his delight discovered two on a window ledge behind him. It was still quite astonishing how the acquiring of the simplest articles in existence could become priceless and miraculous. He filled the two bottles, collected his piece of pork from the kitchen and left by the back door as dawn was preparing to break.

There was a meadow behind the house with an un-thatched haystack in the far corner. He walked blithely and light-heartedly towards it. A happier hour was upon him. He had in his hands food and drink and ahead a resting-place which he badly needed; and although it was a struggle to reach the top of the rick and though he must needs delay his meal till he had removed all traces of his footholds on its sides, nevertheless in a little while he was securely esconced in the couch in the hay which he had made for himself; and a bottle of cider and a piece of half-rancid fat were alternately at his lips. Things were certainly on the mend.

He left Huppy on the following night, having decided, in the light of his recent experience, not to walk, for the time being at any rate, by day.

He left at the usual time, striking off again westerly, finding to his infinite satisfaction that the country was still open. Obstructed no longer by high crops and woods he made, with the short grass of the downlands beneath him, the excellent progress of twelve miles, and just before dawn of 11th June he entered the outskirts of Dargnies.

He took an immediate fancy to the farm with the corrugated Dutch barn which confronted him. Though he knew by instinct the place was uninhabited, it possessed a more ample, prosperous appearance. The straw and hay were stacked high beneath their shelters and two cows roamed in the yard. Moreover, judging by their lowing and the tension of their strained udders, they were un-milked. He felt he must bear that in mind. Then he saw the nesting-boxes ranged round one side of the spacious yard.

Several of the nests contained eggs and he collected over half a dozen of them, which he carried into a dairy adjoining the farmhouse. The grey slate shelves were clean and unstained and the many vessels of polished tin and earthenware hanging on their hooks were as bright and shining as they might have been in any Devon farm. Between a separator and a churn in the centre of the room stood several buckets, scoured and bright. He picked up two of them and returned to the yard. This was an occasion to do things in a big way.

He had no difficulty in milking the cows. He used one bucket for a seat and the other one soon sang to the rhythm of the squirting milk. Indeed from the experiences of country boyhood he appreciated the pain unmilked cattle could endure. It was, he felt, eminently satisfying to do both himself and the cows a good turn. In a little while he had nearly half a bucket full. He returned to the dairy.

He chose an enamel dipper from the row of vessels, broke six eggs into it and poured in a pint of milk, still warm and frothy. It was a drink fit for a giant. He went into the house.

The sun was now well up but so greatly was his confidence renewed that he felt he could afford to be bold and take his leisure. The style of the place was quite definitely superior to those of his previous visitations. If there were a certain homeliness about it, there was at the same time the suggestion of some solid worth. The living-room approached more to the level of a dining-room than a kitchen; the small sitting-room rejoiced in mahogany and brass; and in the hall, with its black-and-white tiles, a noble grandfather clock still ticked.

He opened the front panel of the clock and saw the weights were about half-way down. The owners of the place could not have left long. That, no doubt, was why the buildings and their surroundings still carried the air of cheerfulness and warmth which he had first noticed.

It was while he was by the clock that he experienced that first spasm of giddiness which was to re-occur so often. At the same time he felt a constriction in his groin, hitherto unnoticed. It was as if already at the first signs of relaxation, the physical aspects of his predicament must assert themselves. His leg was beginning to hurt abominably but he continued his search through the rest of the house.

He found all necessities of the table and filled his pockets with spoons and knives and forks. He discovered, moreover, much to his relief, another map, and what was to prove more useful, a penknife. Then he went into the garden and picked some strawberries and lettuce and, satisfied that nothing more could be done for the moment, chose a ladder from several propped up against the stanchions of the Dutch barn and climbed aloft.

It was excellent accommodation. The hay was dry and sweet and there were several sacks to be found, piled in the centre. The roof immediately above was corrugated iron as opposed to murky and cobwebbed rafters and there was, therefore, less chance of spiders and earwigs dropping down between the collar of his scarecrow jacket and the flannelette nightdress. He made his couch and laid out his provisions. There was the pork—a trifle more greasily repulsive in the daylight perhaps, if that were possible—some eggs—impeccable dish, even if taken raw —strawberries, no need to be over-critical of their greenness—and lastly the lettuce, and if the outer leaves were full of grit then the centre was clean and juicy, and what was a caterpillar or two amongst friends? Add to all this, fork and spoon as befits a gentleman, and a bottle of sharp, sour, good country cider to wash it all down. What more could any man desire?

After he had eaten he took down his trousers and examined his leg. Maman Paul's bandage was now a thing of the past. His leg was very swollen and all around the small wound the flesh was purplish and inflamed, the skin tight stretched and glistening over a swelling. He examined his groin, and found that the glands in the crutch were swollen and extremely painful to the touch. He realized that the limb, if left untreated, might develop septicaemia or gangrene. He knew no more of practical first aid or elementary medicine than any other man brought up and trained in his particular Service, but common sense told him that a mere flesh wound would not produce a state as serious as this. Either through the vicissitudes of his enforced journey through marsh, slime and mud, infection had entered, or in the first place the wound contained some foreign body driven in by the explosion of the shell that had blown in the window of his aeroplane. He took out the penknife from his pocket and opened it.

It appeared to be a comparatively new knife, its blade bright and clean, its edge and point sharp. He tried it with his thumb. It seemed adequate for the occasion. He held it firmly between two fingers, cut firmly and deliberately a quarter-inch incision over the swelling.

The pus spurted out, yellow and noisome, and the glistening tight lump of the swelling became flaccid. He waited several seconds as blood trickled down to his knee and then he squeezed the wound gently till it was rid of its purulence, washing it clean with water from the bucket which he had carried into the loft. He saw the cause of the trouble.

There were two specks of perspex embedded in the flesh. He could see them clearly as he trickled water over the place; he recognized them for what they were at once, remembering the near-miss that had smashed in his side window. It was two small fragments of the splintered window which were causing the festering. He marvelled that two such morsels could make such trouble, poisoning the whole thigh. The matter, however, must receive attention. With finger and thumb he pressed the side of the wound and the two fragments came away.

He stayed in his bunk of hay for twenty-four hours, scarcely moving but to take a drink or break an egg and eat it. His leg still hurt very badly but the swelling in his groin seemed to have subsided a little and the thought that the origin of the trouble had been removed was a rare consolation. At one of the periods between the familiar snatches of sleep he studied his newly found map and came to the conclusion that he was certainly not less than ten miles from the coast. He could, he felt, now that his

Where Embry swam across the River Somme : in the background
is the bog in which he nearly lost his life.

On the left is shown the château near Neufchâtel. When Embry reached it on 15th June, 1940, it was deserted but recently had been a German headquarters. Here he found food, drink, and fresh underclothing. In the Dutch barn (*below*) at Dargnies near Eu, he operated on his leg and extracted fragments of his aircraft.

goal was in sight afford to rest awhile and conserve his strength, for the task ahead might even necessitate rowing across the Channel and the perils of the sea were even greater, he supposed, than those of the land. Therefore, he consoled himself with conceiving various plans, though very little, he realized, could be decided upon before he was actually on the coast and could assess the facilities available. He would, though, collect all the food possible within the next day or two, carrying it with him against the prospect of a prolonged voyage at sea. Thus, with the pain of his wound gradually abating, he sank with quietude and some measure of contentment to sleep.

In accordance with his plan, after he had descended from his couch the next morning and milked the two cows, he set about collecting what food might remain, to furnish the reserve which he had decided was essential. He made a tour of the nesting-boxes and collected no less than thirty eggs. He carried them cautiously to the dairy and placed them on a shelf taking a pride which he knew was laughable in ranging them in straight rows. When the pattern was complete they looked very well. He was quite delighted with it and now that he felt so much better in health, delighted also with himself.

He returned to the house with the idea of discovering something in which to carry his possessions, a bag or a cloth or a pillow-slip. He found nothing suitable downstairs so went above, choosing a room overlooking the main street. While he stood by the window, staring down, interested in viewing the village by daylight, two men came striding down the street.

They were tall and young with sticks across their shoulders, carrying bundles of their belongings. They walked erect and with a swinging gait; two carefree, well set-up youngsters, whom he was sure were British soldiers in disguise as French peasants. They were past him before he could hail them, swinging by the front of the house and down the main street at a fair steady pace.

He ran downstairs and out of the house at once, determined to overtake them, if only to warn them of that soldierly way of walking of theirs, which was bound to betray them. Even so, in his eagerness to meet with them, he himself nearly forgot to assume his customary shuffling gait.

But to his surprise he found after several minutes of walking that they were not alone in the street. Other people were beginning to appear. There was a small group further along by what appeared to be a church, and a woman with a child in her arms was trying the lock of a cottage opposite with a key. The villagers were beginning to filter back, so that it seemed to Embry that the Germans must have advanced even further than he had imagined and that, although he was so near the coast, the area would be well in the rear of their armies and therefore practically unmolested. Therefore, he quickened his pace, more anxious than ever to overtake those two, who, combined with him, might make a useful crew in a sizable boat, to say nothing of their companionship. He was almost on the point of breaking into a run, being not more than twenty-five yards behind them, when the German patrol appeared out of a side turning.

Indeed so swiftly was he moving, so intent on his purpose, that he practically stumbled into the two young men with their sticks and bundles. The German patrol— an *unter-offizier* and three men—had halted the young men and on the instant Embry could thank his stars he had not been able to catch up with them. He had no taste for interrogation with what lay in the yard of a farm some few miles away near a manure heap. So, at once, he sidestepped as if to move past the group, wondering even at a moment so tense as this how the devil he was going to get back to his precious collection of eggs without hindrance; but even as he was passing them by there came the well-known guttural shout for him to halt. He turned and faced them.

The two young men were already moving off under an escort of two Germans. The *unter-offizier* and one trooper stood before Embry and the former looked him up and down before he said: "We want you, too. Come along."

Embry wondered, for one desperate moment, if he could succeed in dashing up the side street and dodge amongst the lanes till he reached open country again; but the *unter-offizier's* hand was on his belt where his holster was strapped, so Embry shrugged his shoulders and without another word they led him away. He wondered what they knew of him and what they might have heard. There was an empty feeling in the pit of his stomach.

Fifty yards further down the street they turned into a house on the right. There was a notice-board in the passage and printed papers hanging in a clip from a nail. Here, clearly, was German local headquarters. He passed through a door on the left and was at once before the German Intelligence Officer.

The room was bare with a table only along one wall and another running across the window overlooking the street. The Intelligence Officer with an *unter-offizier* sat at the first table, a clerk sat at the other. The escort stamped, saluted, turned about, and left the room.

"Your identification papers, please."

The Intelligence Officer's French was perfect. The two young men searched in their pockets, produced their identity forms and handed them across. Embry stood aside and knew that he had only a few brief seconds to evolve a plan before his own turn came.

It would have to be a very good plan. It would have to show a little more forethought than he had revealed in the last twenty-four hours. He was face to face with the enemy once more.

There could now be no dash down a corridor with a swinging rifle butt and Germans going down like ninepins all around. There could be no leaping to safety as he had leapt from the ranks of the Calais column under the very muzzles of the machine-guns; here was to be no battle with fists and broken heads, but a cold duel of wits. And all the time the coast was only ten miles away.

The Intelligence Officer was talking, snapping out his questions and in French, as good as his own, the two young men were answering back confidently and accurately. And Embry thought: "The seconds are passing and I haven't got a plan. For God's sake let me have a plan." He thought again: "I can't be a Frenchman now for my tongue will betray me at once. I can't be a Belgian, because in a nearby town there is a Belgian with a beard and a ragged coat who is wanted for assault if not murder. What the hell, then, can I be?"

The seconds passed and the Intelligence Officer handed their identity cards back to the two young Frenchmen. Embry thought: "I've got it now. They spoke the truth. So will I. I'll be myself. I'll be an Irishman."

"Very well. You may go."

The two Frenchmen went out.

The Intelligence Officer raised his head in Embry's direction. He was a thin, handsome fellow of some twenty-five years; a cool cultured young man, correct in his manner.

"Your identity papers, please," he said in French.

CHAPTER THIRTEEN

"Les cartes d'identité, s'il vous plaît."

Embry shook his head. The Intelligence Officer rapped on his desk.

"Tout de suite, les cartes."

"Cartes—non," said Embry.

"Mais, ce n'est pas possible. . . ."

He broke into a rapid torrent of French, making his points with a darting emphatic finger. Even if he had been a fair French scholar the speed of the other's delivery would have baffled Embry. He allowed the flood to envelop him for several seconds, then he waved the German to silence.

"Too fast," said Embry in his own particular French.

The Intelligence Officer attacked from a fresh angle.

"Who are you?" he asked in English. He spoke with a strong accent but with copy-book clarity.

"Non," said Embry unconcernedly.

"Who are you? Where do you come from?"

"Non savvy."

"Can . . . you . . . speak . . . English?"

"Engleesh," Embry grinned. "A leetle . . . yes-no?"

He thought to himself: "It's all in the balance. He's watching every move. This man knows his job." It was blade to blade and riposte to the parry.

"Sprechen sie Deutsch?"

Embry shrugged helplessly.

The Intelligence Officer leant back in his chair, turning to his *unter-offizier*. They spoke rapidly together, throw-

165

ing a gesture from time to time to the clerk at the far table. The Intelligence Officer took up the interrogation again. His attitude was full of suspicion, his look intent, his eyes fast on Embry's face; the spider in the centre of the web, ready to scuttle across its net and seize its fly; the cat crouched ready to spring on the mouse.

"What is your country?" he asked in French.

"Non savvy," said Embry.

"Le pays . . . Oh, mon Dieu . . . what a fool is this fellow! *Le pays . . . quel pays? . . ."*

"No good," said Embry.

The Intelligence Officer broke into English again.

"What country do you come from?"

Embry shook his head. He thought to himself: "I can't go on playing dumb much longer. If I tax their patience too far, they'll have to find some way of getting rid of me and that will probably be the local gaol pending inquiries. I don't like the idea of inquiries. There's probably a description of me already being circulated to all head-quarters within fifty miles of the farm where I bumped those Jerries off."

The Intelligence Officer muttered, swearing in German:

"Donnerwetter—Mein Gott in Himmel."

He snatched a sheet of paper from his blotter and wrote the same question in capitals: "What is your country?"

"Ah," said Embry. "Give me."

He took the pencil from the German's hands and drew the sheet of paper towards him. He made the rough sketch swiftly, the cross he added last.

The cross was practically correct for Galway. It was a point to be maintained. The *unter-offizier* took the paper from Embry, studied it and then held it triumphantly beneath his superior's nose.

"So," he said to Embry, "you are English after all?"

"Non," said Embry.

166

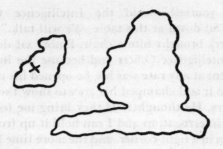

"But you see," said the Intelligence Officer. "This cross shows it."

"Not English," cried Embry, "Irish!" he shouted. He struck the table before him with a clenched fist. "Irish . . . me! English . . . *merdes! Bah! L'Angleterre—fineesh!* To bloody hell with England!"

He leant across the table till his face was only inches from that of his interrogator.

"You call me Engleeshman, I spit on you! England—no damn good. Engleesh . . . salous! Me—Irish. Sinn Fein. I.R.A. Republican. You tell *me*—me—English! . . ."

He shook his fist in the Intelligence Officer's face. The German laughed; he threw back his head and laughed like a boy, showing his teeth and half-heartedly fending Embry off. Embry was nearly across the table and the ink bottle was on its side and the ink was running over the papers on the blotter and still he shouted, till the clerk from the other table sprang from his chair and seized him by the arm. The *unter-offizier* joined them and he, too, was laughing. He patted Embry on the back and dragged him forcibly to the centre of the room. There he calmed him down, explaining that no insult had been intended, that it was merely a question of establishing identity and nationality came first. Still Embry protested, sulking, muttering to himself. To be taken for an Englishman! To be mistaken for one of those swine!

"Calm yourself," said the Intelligence Officer in English. "Sit down at this table. We will talk."

The clerk brought him a chair. Embry sat down opposite the Intelligence Officer and because the initiative of the moment at any rate was his, he opened his mouth and pointed to it and champed his jaws to show them that he was hungry. He thought: "If they bring me food, it will delay the interrogation and I can hold it up from time to time if I'm in a tight corner, and the more time I have, the better will my story be." Moreover, his hunger was real and to order food was a sign of his own ability to control a situation where a single false move would mean the walk to the roped stake and the firing squad.

The clerk fetched a loaf of bread and a tin of jam from an adjoining room and Embry tore at the loaf with his teeth like a wolf and dug out the jam with his dirt-ingrained fingers so that his beard became dusty with crumbs and clotted with the droppings of the jam. The young German officer looked away with distaste. It seemed to Embry that the act was going very well indeed but somewhere, sometime there would be a trap laid. He must go very warily indeed.

"Now," said the Intelligence Officer. "Let us continue."

They went about the task with the help of pencil and paper and by making themselves understandable to one another in pidgin English and broken French.

He was an Irishman, Embry told them, one time member of the Republican Army that had fought against the English. He had carried out a great deal of sabotage, indeed, in England itself; he had been one of the most active members of the I.R.A., putting acid in letter-boxes amongst other things. He was particularly proud of the work done actively in England. It had been carrying the fight to the hated enemy's own front door. At this there was an opportunity for a little more fist-shaking.

He was then put in gaol, he continued, for his activities,

but he'd escaped, beating up one of the English warders on the way out. Just before the war he had gone to Belgium.

"Whereabouts in Belgium?"

"Brussels," said Embry promptly.

"Your occupation?"

"Washing up in a café."

He felt he had navigated that passage reasonably well; but, he told himself, there still could be a trap. He must keep alert.

"Continue with your story."

"Story's the right word for it," thought Embry, and readily continued. Yes, he'd worked hard in the café because he'd wanted to save enough to return to Ireland, to his wife and family. So he had a wife, had he? Indeed, he had. And her name? Maureen, begorra. But he hadn't seen her for months now. The war had overtaken him, the café was no more and he'd been driven south with all the rest of the refugees. And that was that.

They took it all in. The *unter-offizier* nodded his head from time to time in intelligent sympathy, but the Intelligence Officer tapped his notes with the tip of his pencil. Then he asked quietly:

"What language did you speak in Ireland?"

"Erse," said Embry, who had not spoken one word of Erse in his life.

"You don't speak my language, or French, or English at all well. But I expect you speak your own."

"Of course," said Embry and knew at once that he was in a corner.

"Speak to me in your own language, then."

"Burra-pag jeldi karo," said Embry without a moment's hesitation, speaking Urdu. *"Dawazer bund karo!"* (Hindustani for "Bring me a large whisky and soda" . . . "Shut the window.")

The Intelligence Officer grunted. He raised his eyebrows to the *unter-offizier*, who nodded. They seemed well satisfied.

"Who is in charge of the Irish Army?" said the *unter-offizier*.

"Michael O'Leary," said Embry, making up the first name that came to mind. "Surely you know that?" he added. "A very famous soldier was Michael O'Leary," said Embry. He added that he thought everyone would have known that. Of course they knew it, the Intelligence Officer replied testily. Certainly they themselves knew all about O'Leary, they'd wanted to know whether Embry did, that was all. Was this O'Leary married?

"Twice," said Embry, quite confident in creating a family background for a personality who only existed in his own imagination.

"There was a divorce?"

"No. A motoring accident. Like the Queen of the Belgians. Very sad."

They agreed. Very sad indeed. "And this," said Embry to himself, "is where I take these silly clots for a ride."

"When will you win the war?" he asked.

"We've already won it," said the Intelligence Officer.

"That's good," said Embry. "Now I can go back to my wife Maureen and my children in Ireland."

The Intelligence Officer shook his head. "No. We shall send you into Germany."

"I don't want to go to Germany," said Embry, speaking the truth for a change. "I don't want to go to Germany at all. Why do you want to send me? You have won the war, you tell me, and I tell you I have fought the British, so we are comrades—friends."

"You would only be there for a short time."

"But why send me at all?" There was nothing like pressing home the attack when the initiative was his. "Why not put me on a German ship," he said boldly, "and send me to Ireland? That's the thing to do."

The Intelligence Officer considered the proposal. His attitude was one of official but sympathetic interest.

"In time we will find some way to send you back."

"But I don't want to wait," said Embry. "I have wasted weeks as it is."

"We will see."

"Let me find my own way then. Let me get to Spain and there I'll find a ship."

"How did you get here?"

"From Brussels. I walked by night and laid up by day."

"How did you get over the Somme? All the bridges that were not down were watched."

"I swam it."

The two Germans conferred together. Embry sat at the table and waited their verdict and felt like a schoolboy in the headmaster's study.

"We must refer the matter to higher authority," said the Intelligence Officer. He laid his pencil on his blotter and picked up a sheet of paper.

"But why must I wait?" said Embry.

"Take him away," said the Intelligence Officer in German.

The *unter-offizier* took Embry by the arm. He led him across the room and across the passage to another very similar room beyond. There was a mattress on the floor, the German indicated it with a jerk of his head and went out, slamming the door.

Embry lay on the mattress and attempted to sort his thoughts out. One thing seemed palpably clear. There could be no half measures on this matter. Either he had succeeded or he had failed. Either he would live to continue on his way or he would die almost at once. It was as simple as that.

What was not so simple was to determine the next move. He was not to all appearances closely guarded and it might just be possible to make a dash for it. But this house was without doubt a headquarters and there were bound to be Germans in plenty in the immediate vicinity. If a break-away succeeded, well enough; but if it failed, it would be utterly fatal. The bottom would be knocked out of his story. They'd start to work on him again, possibly check back on facts and in the end he might break down. No, better the present anxiety and suspense than to take as great a risk as that. In the vernacular, that was his story and he was sticking to it.

But the map was still in his pocket and it occurred to him that an Irish dish-washer would scarcely have even the elementary skill to read a map, far less set a course by it. He took the map from his pocket and ate it.

That is to say he ate half of it, but finding it extremely unpalatable, pulped the other half only and pushed it into the mattress. Thereafter he stretched himself out and tried to rest.

But it was difficult to relax. The shock of this second recapture had come so rapidly upon the other. He wondered with what sources the German Intelligence Officer and his staff were getting in touch; no doubt they would check up with similar local administrative establishments throughout the whole neighbourhood. It was going to be a near thing. The door opened and a German sentry came in.

The German was young with a pimply, spotted face, like that first of Embry's victims, but white where the others had been sun-burnt brown. His shoulders sloped, even the rifle on its sling looked too heavy for him. A sallow, pallid, undergrown young man, who with Embry's fingers round his throat would have snapped like a reed. But Embry refrained, because he had resolved on a course of action and, come what might, he must keep faith with himself.

"Come with me," said the sentry and turned his back and went out, so that for one wild moment Embry must struggle with himself to prevent the leap forward and the flailing arms but he followed the young German down the passage and out into the yard at the back. He thought: "So this is it! This is where they do their shooting." Then the German pointed to the pump.

He was watching Embry curiously, an uncertain uneasy look of the half-scared and Embry, not understanding in any way but with the certainty that death was not very far off, could only spread his hands and mutter: *"Ne savez pas."* The German picked up an enamelled mug from the foot of the pump, filled it and handed it to his prisoner.

Embry drank and handed back the cup. He asked: "What are they going to do with me?"

For reply, a shrug and a shaking of the head and then the German's thumb inclined towards the gates of the yard. They went out side by side and turning right met the main road of the village. They walked briskly with Embry shuffling along as well as he could. As they progressed the certainty of his own approaching end increased. It was as he had surmised; they had been on the telephone and got the description of the wild-eyed tramp who'd done the job down the road. And it fitted. That was how he put it to himself. This was definitely the end. They wouldn't have shot him in the yard of the headquarters anyway. It was too much in the middle of the town and the German tactics were clearly to handle the civil population as gently as possible. Therefore he was being taken to a nearby wood, some sheltered glade, probably even now littered with corpses, the recognized shooting gallery of the local German administration. On the other hand, why the friendly gesture of a cup of water, and why only one man to escort him to the firing squad? Or was it to be a one-man job, a short order and a shot in the back? Whatever answer there might be to this confused problem, one point was apparent. He was quite equal to dealing with the youngster at his side, armed though he might be. Very well then. He would fix him.

Sooner or later, he told himself, they would have to leave the main street and branch off down a side turning. That would be the moment to tackle his man. There were too many people about in the main road. Then he realized how many more people there were than there had been an hour before.

They turned from the street and took another, narrow and twisting a way through the ill-assorted buildings. Here, at any moment would be the place for his attack but there were still people about. They were gathered at the doors of the cottages and at their garden gates; they were lounging against walls and the women chatting together, while the children tugged at their skirts. The village was returning to life.

This was deplorable. In all other circumstances he could have rejoiced but now he could never have raised a hand but he would have been seen and the alarm raised. He must walk like a sheep to the slaughter-house. Then they were through the outskirts of the village before he realized it and had halted in the middle of the road. On all sides the open country rolled away in bare downland.

They stood face to face. The German's rifle was slung on his shoulder. He looked very frail and irresolute. There was nobody in sight now.

"Go," said the German, and he pointed where the road curled away to the north-east "Go," he said again.

Then, despite himself, Embry grinned, because this was too good to be true. But "Go" the little German sentry said again and turned away. Then the hand that a few seconds before would have been at the escort's thin throat was upon his sloping shoulder.

"Germans very good people," said Embry.

"Au revoir," said the little German soldier and turned about and marched back along the road towards the village.

CHAPTER FOURTEEN

Too good to be true. He walked along the road in the direction the little German had indicated. He walked alone and unmolested. A few minutes ago he had been preparing to kill a man and they had parted in a most ludicrously friendly fashion. And here he was, free once more and on his way.

He was in high spirits. The downs rose gracefully on either side and the later afternoon sun was warm. His leg was better and he had eaten. He was glad he hadn't killed the little German, not necessarily from any question of sentiment but from the practical point of bad tactics. It would have been a gross error of judgment. He supposed that maybe the devil did look after his own. Anyway, that was the way it had gone, and it was too good to be true.

The repetition of the tag brought him up with a jolt. Things indeed could be too good to be true. His present elation could betray him even now. He had no business to be congratulating himself but should rather be examining the present situation and its possibilities from every angle.

He told himself that he was being far from clever; he was in the first instance following his late escort's instructions which was folly; there was nothing to prevent his former interrogators from still following up their inquiries or for that matter from belated news of his three assaults reaching them. There was, in short, nothing to prevent their changing their minds and following after him. He was allowing his feelings to run away with him instead of taking action. He was now over half a mile from where the German had left him. He looked back. Smoke was rising lazily from the distant village, basking in the late sunlight. There was nobody on the road. He left the road, and changing his direction to the north-west made his way across country.

Two miles further on he found suitable cover in a thick hedge.

He left his hedge at the usual time of eleven o'clock. The night was bright with stars and the open country offered no difficulties to his progress. As once the Somme had urged him on with its promise of the British lines, so now the thought of the English Channel speeded his steps. By dawn he reached an isolated farm on the last high slopes of the downs.

He lay just under the lip of the low ridge and beyond the land seemed to fall gradually and gently to a horizon unmarked by any loftier range of hills, so that the conformation of the ground seemed to indicate a decline towards the very sea itself. His goal, he felt, was in view.

He lay in a field of beet, some hundred yards from the farm buildings. He would not allow his eagerness to override his caution. It was not until two hours later, with the sun already mounting into the morning, that he saw any movement, then the figure of a man emerged from the house and crossed the yard to a barn. A minute later he reappeared, bucket in hand, and approached a sty at the end of the yard. Embry rose to his feet and openly crossing the beet field, entered the yard and approached the Frenchman.

He said in his best French: "*Bon jour.*" He was quite settled in his mind how to approach the situation. The direct method should succeed. The man who by now had taken a fork and was raking out the muck of the sty, turned and stared at him solemnly. He was an elderly man, mild-eyed and quietly self-possessed. He revealed no surprise at Embry's sudden appearance from his field. He leant on his fork and after a pause and studying his visitor from his beard to his ragged trouser bottoms, returned the greeting.

"Can you give me some food?" said Embry.

"Who are you?"

"*Anglais*," said Embry. "English Colonel of the Air Force. I am escaping from the Germans."

"*Alors.*" The farmer propped his fork against the wall of the sty. "Come with me."

There were a man and a woman seated at the kitchen table as they came in. Embry's escort spoke swiftly and the man answered in his patois. Both man and woman regarded Embry indifferently, uninterestedly. It was as if they were more than accustomed to wild-looking strangers and were resigned to many curious things; but the woman rose and, crossing to the stove, pushed the coffee can over the charcoal bed and, returning to the table, began to carve the long loaf.

"*Merci*," said Embry and started his breakfast.

"Where are you going to?"

"I am making for the coast. Am I near it?"

"You are four miles from Cayeux-sur-Mer," his new friend told him. "It is a town by the sea."

"Can I find a boat there?"

"I don't know. None of us roams far afield these days. We keep near our homes. I've not been in Cayeux for weeks. There are too many Germans about."

"Do you know anyone in Cayeux—a fisherman from whom I could hire a boat?"

"A little boat, is it?"

"One I can row."

"You're not going to row across the Channel?"

"I can try," said Embry.

"*Ma foi!*"

"I don't see why not. Sixty miles—without a sail?"

"They say the English are mad, of course."

177

He consulted with his companion. They spoke too rapidly in their patois for Embry to follow them at all closely but it was apparent the farmer's friend shared the farmer's views. The woman, now busy washing up at the sink, threw a name at them over her shoulder. Thereafter she continued at her work, oblivious to what might be contrived.

"That would do." The farmer felt in his waistcoat pocket and found a scrap of paper and the stub of a pencil. He wrote a name laboriously, licking the pencil point at the forming of almost every block capital. Then he handed the paper to Embry.

"That's the name of a fisherman. In days past he had plenty of boats. A big one with sails and another with an engine. And little ones such as you desire."

"If he's got a big boat he could sail me across. That would be marvellous."

"Maybe he has. I don't know. But you can inquire in Cayeux. Anyone who works near the shore would know. He was a big man in business."

"I am very grateful to you."

"It is nothing. We must help one another these days. It was through trying to help us that you are in trouble now. We ought to be grateful when we are allowed to be."

"I had another good friend like you," said Embry. "He sheltered me and put me on my way. He would have been shot with me if we'd been discovered."

"So shall I be, if you are found here. So I will show you where you can hide. It is no good going into Cayeux before four o'clock. My friend the fisherman is not generally back from sea before then, and you don't want to loiter too much in those parts. There are too many suspicious people. Now follow me."

He led Embry across the yard to the barn. Straw was piled high and the place smelt sweet and clean. Embry climbed into the straw and lay down.

178

"*Au revoir*," said his friend. "*Bon voyage, monsieur.*"

He closed the barn door and went out. The early morning sunlight warmed the roof above the heap of straw, and sunbeams glanced through the chinks of the planking of the door and the silvery dust glittered with slender shafts of light.

He lay back in the straw, drowsy and rested. He wondered what news of him had been signalled to his family. But it was only four miles to Cayeux by the sea. And the sea that lay between him and England was only just sixty or more miles across. It was as if he were nearly home already. He was going home, he told himself. There was only the sea between them. Glory be to God, but he was going home. He rolled over on his side and slept for a while.

He reached Cayeux-sur-Mer after an hour's walking about four o'clock in the afternoon.

It was a typical seaside town, but with no harbour and with many of the shops shut and boarded up. He made his way swiftly through the outskirts and found himself in a short time on the water-front.

There were several fishermen seated on a bench and others standing nearby, while some half-dozen upturned boats had been hauled above the high-water mark. He noticed that one of them had been stove in. Two German soldiers came out of the café across the *place* and disappeared up a side street.

Embry turned to look again at the sea. It was low tide. Across a French river a British army might have been ready to welcome him, but therein had lain a great disappointment; now only across this stretch of water lay England. He only needed a boat.

There seemed to be plenty of boats scattered along the beach, some lying at the end of their cable-road, others with their painters made fast to an out-haul block or a windlass.

It shouldn't, he felt, be difficult to strike a bargain of some kind. He held two trump cards; the justice of his cause and his precious slip of paper with the magic name on it. He approached the group of fishermen.

They eyed him with curiosity; not in any unfriendly fashion but in contrast to the indifference of the man and woman at the farm, with a sort of knowing interest, as if to say: "Here is another one up to his larks." Embry bade them good day, and they returned the compliment.

"If you can help me," said Embry, "I would be very grateful."

They nodded and laughed, and one old man with gold ear-rings and bright-blue eyes chuckled and patted Embry on the arm.

"The name on this paper. He lives here? Where can I find him?" asked Embry.

They took the paper from him and handed it round amongst themselves, peering over each other's shoulders, snatching it from one another, turning it this way, that way, holding it at arm's length till they all began to talk together, contradicting one another, arguing, gesticulating till the old man with the ear-rings hissed them to silence. He handed the slip of paper back to Embry.

"He is not here."

"But I was told he lived here, that all you fisher folk would know him."

"Mais oui! He did live here. But when he heard that the Germans were coming, he ran away."

"I see," said Embry.

But this setback should not defeat him. After all the name had acted as an introduction. He was at least on speaking terms with the local people and these were fishermen who must own boats.

"What did you want him for—this man whose name you had?"

"I wanted a boat off him."

"A boat?"

"Any kind of boat." He pointed towards the beach. "Any of those."

"You want to go to—where?"

Embry paused for the moment. But the facts would have to be stated. He must trust these men.

"England," he said.

There was another pause. The Frenchmen glanced from one to the other, raised their eyebrows and gestured a little with their hands in the way Paul had taught Embry to do.

"Your country?"

"Yes," said Embry.

"But you were fighting over here?"

"Yes," said Embry.

"We understand."

The old man nodded and smiled and Embry's heart warmed towards him and his friends because it was obvious they were on his side and would do what they could to help him; and though the perils of the sea lay before him and he had no doubt they were great, nevertheless he was taking one more reach nearer home and perhaps the last reach of all.

"I must cross the Channel," said Embry. "That's why I want a boat. Unless there is someone willing to take me over. In a trawler, perhaps. A big boat, yes? Or if not that, in a little one which I can row and sail myself. Please help me. I will see that you are paid."

They all began to shake their heads and murmur but the old man held up his hand to silence them.

"There are no vessels of any kind making a passage to England from any French ports or coastal towns in German hands. It is the first thing they stopped when they occupied this our town of Cayeux."

"Then I shall have to sail myself across," said Embry.

"There is nothing you can sail."

"Well, who owns all that lot?" And Embry pointed towards the beach again.

The old man rose and plucked at Embry's sleeve.

"I will show you," he said and he was smiling no longer.

They went side by side across the *place* and the road to where two dinghies and a coracle were fastened to a bollard. The floorboards lay on the beach beside the boats.

"*Voici*. See for yourself."

Embry looked at the boats in turn. In each instance the planking had been stove in at the bows and in the stern sheets. The immobilizing must have been done with a sledge hammer for the holes in the boats' sides would have taken a man's head.

"That is the second thing they did. They smashed our boats. All of them. The big one, the little ones. The ones on our beaches and the ones in our sheds. There is not a whole boat in Cayeux. There will not be any boats on the coast where there are Germans. How do they expect us to live? As for you, my young friend—you have come a long way?"

"Yes," said Embry shortly.

"And you expected the sea would solve your problem?"

"Yes," said Embry.

"I am very sorry for you. It must be very hard to bear. Disappointment is more than just sorrow when your life is at stake. I understand. I am an old man and I know. God be with you, that is all I can say."

"Where do you think the British are now?" asked Embry.

"They say they are in Dieppe."

"And the road to Dieppe?"

"Follow along by the way you came and then you will see a fine main road that goes south. You will meet it just outside the town. That is the road you take. But there are many Germans about. *Prenez garde!*"

"Thank you," said Embry. *"Au revoir."*

On the outskirts of the town he encountered a German patrol, crossing his path from one side street to another, but he made no check in his slouching gait and they passed without a look, but he knew at once he must wait till darkness before he set out for Dieppe. But unlike the other villages through which he had passed Cayeux was not deserted and it was only when he was well clear of the town that he came across an isolated and empty cottage.

He knew it was empty because the place was semi-derelict. The door swung on one hinge, its window-frames were broken and the weeds of the garden grew riotously up its cracked walls. He pushed the battered door open and went in.

He stood in a narrow passage, the far end of which was filled with the remains of broken furniture and packing-cases. There was a doorway left and right, in each instance without a door. The walls were in disrepair, in many places with the laths showing where the plaster had crumbled away. The floor was bare and so thick with dust that it had almost turned to dirt; his steps made imprints on it. He looked into the room on his left.

It was dark and small with a sour, stale smell of age-old filth. There was a litter of paper everywhere mounting to a heap in one corner. Black cobwebs festooned the ceiling. Of all the places he had inspected as possible hide-outs this was the most uninviting. He turned to the room opposite.

The moment he passed over the threshold he knew that within those four walls was the source of the unpleasant odour which had assailed him on his first entrance to the house. It was a penetrating acrid stench, with a strangely sweet secondary smell, which was all-pervading and revolting. Like the other room it was in utter disorder, with refuse and rags in a great heap before a fireplace. It was a large heap with a chair with only three legs fallen across it. Beyond that the room—darker than the first one since the panes of its window were almost intact, so that its grimy glass forbade the light—was empty.

There seemed to be a movement on the surface of the rags, and at the same time he heard a faint but regular buzzing and recognized it at once as originating from the swarm of flies crawling and hovering over the heap. He surveyed the scene with disgust, realizing that he would have to endure these unpleasant surroundings for some hours to come. Then, with his eyes growing accustomed to the dim light, he saw at the far end of the heap, the outline of a boot, toe-cap upwards, heel to the floor. He hurried back into the other room.

He chose a corner remote from the passage, kicked the rubbish aside and sat down. His surroundings were the worst he could have selected as a background to his present mood.

He felt for the moment baffled, because so often, again and again, he had so nearly succeeded in his task, only to be foiled at the last moment. He had reached the sea in the sunlit afternoon, full of hope, now in the dingy evening light that filtered into the hovel, he was tempted to indulge his depression.

But the mood passed, as it always did, and passed all the more quickly when he called to mind how he had resolved never to repine, however great the temptation might be. As soon as one plan failed, then another must be immediately made. He wished there were a door to the room to keep the stench out.

He left at the first sign of darkness and found without difficulty the main road to Dieppe. The night was fine and starlit and he made good progress. After some twelve miles, he found a signpost and confirmed that he was taking the right direction, though the town of Eu stood in his path. He was loath to pass through any town of size because of the curfew, and determined to evade it by a detour across country. Half an hour later he was confronted by the river of the same name.

But the crossing of a river was by now but a mere bagatelle. He undressed, made his clothes into the usual bundle, fastened it in the usual way with the sleeves of his jacket tied round his neck and swam across.

He came out on the other side into parkland. The wide meadow had a lawn-like appearance and the trees planted with an ordered regularity convinced him that it was a park. He saw the house, a high château, standing secure amongst its flower beds and terraces, asleep under the stars. He skirted the house and walked on for another three miles.

It was beginning to grow light and in another hour it would be day. He felt he had done well and the thought that Dieppe was so much the nearer was reassuring and his spirits rose again. Nevertheless he was tired. The strain of the last few days had been considerable, and though his leg had benefited by his treatment, it still pained him. He decided to rest and when he came upon a large farm he felt, whether the place were inhabited or not, that this was his opportunity.

He found on the far side of the group of buildings a barn, filled with corn and sacks. It was a fine, dry, lofty place, fresh and sweet in marked contrast to his last hide-out. He made a couch for himself of sacks and lay down. Within seconds he was asleep.

He awoke to the sound of voices. He was suddenly awake and knew that it was broad daylight and the voices which sounded from outside the barn were certainly not speaking French. He rose and stole stealthily to the door and peered out.

CHAPTER FIFTEEN

THERE were five men and four women and half a dozen children in the farm yard busily searching in every likely cranny for hens' eggs. The nesting-boxes had already been rifled. A fifth woman was at the open back door of the farm scouring a frying-pan with grit from the path.

They were a tattered, tousled crew, the men unshaven and bearded, the women swarthy and with tangled hair. They chatted together in an unknown tongue like jackdaws, the women squealing with delight every time they found an egg and the children cried out and crowded round to have a first look. Embry stepped out of the barn and said *"Bon jour"* in a loud voice.

The effect was immediate. Everybody stood stock still. Then as the tallest of the five slowly approached Embry, they straightened themselves, but all eyes were on him.

The man who stood before him was broad and strong, dark-eyed and high cheek-boned. He carried a stick, or rather to Embry's way of thinking something more in the nature of a cudgel. He was scowling. Then he rapped out a question in some unintelligible gibberish. It was obvious what the question must be.

"Belge," said Embry, tapping his chest. *"Belge."*

"Ach!" The fellow faced about and rattled off a sentence or two. Everybody relaxed and smiled. One woman made a strange little attempt to curtsy. The man turned to Embry again. He indicated himself.

"Pole," he said and then with a comprehending sweep of his arm including all the company present, *"Poles."*

"Good show," said Embry, wondering how on earth Poles had got involved so far from their own country, but then anything could happen with several million refugees on the run. The Pole pointed to his mouth, produced an egg from his pocket and made to eat it. Then he pointed towards the house. Embry thought they were getting on famously. A quarter of an hour later they were all sitting down to breakfast in the farmhouse kitchen.

It was a magnificent meal. The women with their instinctive knowledge had ransacked the deserted house expertly. They had found bread and butter and bacon, moreover there were knives, forks, cups, and saucers. Embry sat down to a cooked meal of eggs and bacon such as would have done credit to the Wattisham Mess. As the meal progressed conversation, as it was so often to prove, with the use of a few mutually understood words, became possible.

He asked how the war was going and if they had any definite news. They replied that Rouen had fallen. This was vital information and he repeated his question to make sure that there was no misconception of the facts but they reiterated the point vehemently. Rouen had fallen.

He wondered if there ever would be a time again when it would be possible to conceive a plan and keep to it for more than twenty-four hours.

So Rouen had fallen and therefore Le Havre would most certainly have gone as well; and with Le Havre gone, the scheme to pick up the British lines at Dieppe was clearly impracticable.

What then should be the next move? The French would never let Paris fall unless they were utterly overwhelmed, therefore there would be a determined counterstroke made before Paris, possibly round about Beauvais. So change direction Dieppe to direction Paris and there was a new plan evolved as rapidly as eating a dish of eggs and bacon.

He left his friends waving him farewell from the steps of the farm as if the place was theirs and they had been his hosts. He found a secondary road running past the farmhouse gates and finding it led approximately in the right direction went on his way.

It was not long before he came upon a cottage. He had passed no one on the road nor had there been any sign of other habitation.

The little house was trim and fresh. The paint was clean and its garden filled with flowers. In this back-lane were no signs of war and its frenzies. There was a hive in the garden and a dove-cot and one old lady with a little net cap on her white hair was tying up a rambler to the porch and another little old lady trowelling away at a flower bed.

"*Bon jour,*" said Embry with considerable gusto. "*Bon jour, mesdames.* Can you tell me the way to Paris?"

The old lady by the porch laid her scissors on the bench inside and stared at Embry over her spectacles. The second old lady pattered down to the gate and looked over it, her lips pursed, her head cocked on one side like a small bird.

"*Paris,*" said Embry again.

The first old lady joined her sister at the gate. She explained carefully that she did not know the way to Paris. Papa had never considered great towns of any kind suitable for young girls, but Neufchâtel was on the way to Paris, so maybe that would do?

"Neufchâtel?"

Both old ladies pointed down the lane in the direction he had been taking.

"*Merci,*" said Embry. "*Merci bien.*" He doffed his unbelievable hat and went on his way.

When he met the main road with the signpost "Londinières—Neufchâtel" he knew he was travelling the proper course, and now as the former occupants seemed to be reoccupying the countryside, it would, he considered, be relatively safe to walk by day. He would then, he decided, walk four hours and rest two, regularly through the twenty-four hours of the day and night and in so doing, walking for sixteen hours a day, he could cover forty miles in that period. He had to the best of his knowledge just over a hundred miles to do.

The plan was excellent but like all other plans had to be implemented and half way between Londinières and Neufchâtel—a matter of some twenty miles—he found himself very tired. It was then that he decided to make the rest of the way on bicycle.

It was an idea following naturally upon the resolution to travel in daylight, and with the knowledge that the main roads would be in fair condition and also that now with the signposts still standing he could easily find his way. But at the time the idea struck him as so novel that he was delighted with himself. The business of thinking swiftly and thoroughly, of making plans promptly, and as promptly scrapping them without undue regret if necessity demanded, was certainly showing dividends. There was a farm, standing a little way back from the road. He went blithely up to the front door and rapped on it with his knuckles.

The man who opened the door never ceased scowling from the moment Embry opened his mouth. Good morning, and had the man a bicycle? The man had. Would he be prepared to lend it, please? No, he wouldn't. Did he not realize this was a very deserving case? No, he didn't. If he would be good enough to listen. . . . No, he wouldn't. Very well then, perhaps he would care to sell a bicycle at a very fine price to be paid, on credit, after the war? . . . The door was slammed in Embry's face.

He walked on, determined more than ever to get what he wanted. A mile further on, he reached a cottage, very similar to that of the old ladies who had directed him to

Neufchâtel. There were flowers in its garden and bees but there was nobody about and there was a bicycle propped against the window sill by the side of the front door.

It was a woman's bicycle in excellent condition. He decided to steal it. He had no scruples about the matter whatever.

He opened the gate very carefully, inch by inch, raising the latch very gently and lowering it without a sound. The flowers nodded under the high noon sun and the bees sang drowsily. It was just the right sort of hour to steal a bicycle. He went up the short pathway, step by cautious step, almost on tiptoe. His prize-to-be, glittered delectably in the strong light; she was ravishing. He stretched out an arm and laid a hand on the saddle. There was a sudden shout. His hand fell to his side. He turned about.

There was a large woman at his side. Her hair was sleek and plastered flat on her head and as black as her bright angry eyes.

"What are you doing, rascal? *Va-t-en!*"

"*Pardon*," said Embry.

"You were going to steal that bicycle."

"Never," said Embry. "Not me. Never."

"You had your hand on it. I saw you as I came from behind the bean sticks."

"I thought it was going to fall."

"So! You are very considerate about other people's property."

"It's too good a bicycle to let it get damaged."

"Well, what are you doing in this garden, anyway?"

"I was going to ask for a drink. I'm on the road."

"Well, wait here, then."

She returned in a minute with a glass of milk.

"Thank you very much," said Embry and drained the glass.

"Now be on your way. Keep your fingers to yourself. Keep out of mischief. *Au revoir.*"

"*Au revoir,*" said Embry.

Within a score of paces from the cottage he told himself that he'd lost his chance. When she had gone inside to get his drink he should have seized the bicycle, dashed through the gateway and leapt upon it. By now he'd have been a quarter of a mile away.

That's what he ought to have done. He should have assessed the chances for and against in an instant and made a decision. He hadn't done anything of the sort. He'd talked a lot of flannel to get out of the accusation and then just lapped up the milk and said goodbye. He was losing his grip.

Or was it that, despite a resolution to seize ruthlessly every opportunity that arose, there were occasions when it was impossible to take advantage of a kindness? She had never questioned his need for a drink. Damn the woman!

He looked back over his shoulder. She was still at the gate. She waved to him. Embry waved back.

He reached Neufchâtel in the late afternoon. All the time *en route* he had encountered Germans, sometimes singly, sometimes in large patrols but he had attracted nobody's attention and he was feeling very confident in his disguise. It was, he supposed, a matter of familiarity with the pose and, of course, practice. He was quite certain that with reasonable luck he would reach Paris.

But the war of that early summer of 1940 was moving far more quickly and decisively than many had considered possible. While Embry trudged his way through France during those sun-bright days of June, armies were being scattered and broken, crowns were toppling and the vast grey hordes of the enemy were sweeping on and wherever a gap showed, Guderian's panzers poured through in full flood.

At a street corner on the outskirts of Neufchâtel he

encountered a group of French refugees. He knew they were refugees because of the barrow they pushed before them, filled with the usual sad collection of household goods and bundles of clothing. A parcel fell as they passed Embry and, picking it up, he made the incident the excuse for an exchange of news. It was the only means he had of keeping anywhere on the track of events.

They told him in as many words that Paris had fallen.

He was as much shocked by the news as by the dislocation again of his plans. Paris had fallen. It seemed incredible. Where could the British Army be then? Had the Germans then been victorious all down the line?

He made a detour round the town, travelling slowly, being footsore and distressed with his thoughts. It seemed to him now a very friendless world, a world emptied of those comrades who had made his life the very pleasant thing it had been. The distances he had travelled and the troubles with which he had contended seemed very small in comparison with what might come. It was like taking on all the world single-handed.

But he made a new plan. It seemed to him so excellent that he grew lighthearted again. He would still make for Paris, even if the city were in enemy hands and occupied by the Germans. He had changed his nationality to suit the immediate purpose several times before, so now he'd change it again. He'd be an American this time. He would go to Paris. He would be an American citizen in distress and he would go to the American embassy and the Americans would get him out of France. Just like that; and all under the Germans' very noses.

But he must still have a bicycle as well.

Some miles from Neufchâtel, he saw the château. It stood back from the main road in its own grounds, a tall, commanding, and elegant building. He pushed open the wrought-iron gates and now, since he was an American

In Paris, seeking the American Consulate (*shown on the right*), Embry entered the Hôtel de Ville, then in use as German headquarters. He left hurriedly. At the Consulate his bluff failed, but at a Salvation Army Hostel (*below*), he secured a bicycle on which he set out for Orleans.

Issued to Embry by the French, these two passes tell their own stories.

TRANSLATIONS

Above. The English airman, Colonel Embry, dressed in civilian clothing (escaped prisoner), is authorized to proceed to England and to use all means of transport in France, including goods trains. The colonel does not possess any proof of identity. General Commanding the Twelfth Region, Limoges. 24th June, 1940.

Left. Examined on departure from Sete, 3rd July, 1940, is going to Perpignan to get instructions from the English Consul. Colonel Embry is accompanied by Private Albert Edward Bird. Military Commandant, Gare de Sete.

and therefore unassailable, he marched boldly up the drive to see what he could find.

He was still looking for a bicycle and nothing this side of Paradise was going to stop him from getting one.

He saw that the house was deserted even before he reached the great flight of steps that led up to its Gothic-arch doorway. The blinds were drawn down in the tall windows and the windows of the upper floors had been boarded up. In the gold and rose of the June evening, the huge grey house had the air of some ancient *grande dame* of a remoter age, dozing, her hands folded in her lap, benign and yet imposing.

On the grass verge by the foot of the steps he found, to his great delight, a loaf of bread and a slab of chocolate. The bread was mouldy but the chocolate was fresh. He hoped that, taken together, the one would counteract the other. With both in his pocket, he went round to the back of the house to inspect any garages or outhouses that might be there.

There were smaller buildings in plenty: sheds, lock-ups, stables, greenhouses, and garages. But there was no sign of a bicycle. He returned to the front of the house.

The main door was locked. He descended the steps and passing to the side of the house so that he should be out of sight from the gate, opened his penknife and carefully cut out a pane of glass from a lower window by removing the putty. He climbed in.

He was in a library; a long gracious room with shelves of books almost up to the ceiling. The highest shelf was topped with a row of marble and alabaster busts. The fine mahogany table that reached half over the centre of the room was still brilliantly polished without a speck of dust on its shining surface. He crossed the room, opened the door and found himself in the hall.

It was very impressive. The grand staircase, marble and bronze, swept up to a gallery beneath the domed and painted roof. The floor was black-and-white check in marble and the rugs were exquisite. The light fell through stained-glass windows and there was a fine oil painting of a Venus with attendant Cupids, while a great glittering chandelier hung overhead. But perhaps the most interesting point of all was the notices on the several doors that led off from the hall. The cards neatly printed on each centre panel gave the rank, name and office of a German officer from a Colonel-General down to a mere *unter-offizier*. Here, indeed, had been until only very recently, a German Headquarters at a high level. He went upstairs.

The rooms above were on a par with those of the ground floor, high airy bedrooms and dressing-rooms, in an excellent state of decoration and repair and left spotlessly clean. He wandered from one to the other fascinated by the familiar aspects of a civilization which for so long seemed to have belonged to another and almost forgotten world. He touched the silk counterpane and felt the texture of the Rose du Barry curtains. Then he found the bathroom.

The bath was marble and let into the chequered floor. The taps and the fittings of the adjustable shower were of gleaming chromium. There was a double-tiered glass shelf laden with cut-glass bowls and flasks of bath salts and powders. He sniffed at the salts and found them to be verbena. There were dishes with cakes of soap, yellow, cerise, white. There were brushes and combs in ivory. Then he turned to the huge mirror which flanked nearly the length of one wall.

He laughed. It was the most ludicrous thing to compare the gaunt, bearded, unkempt dirty rascal with his tattered coat and cock-eyed hat, his broken shoes and ragged trousers with the magical Midas background of silver and stone behind him. So that he moved at once towards the bath and turned on the taps. There was no water.

German thoroughness, he thought, to leave the property in perfect condition even to taking the precaution of cutting off the water at the main. But surroundings such as this with the opportunity they offered, must not be rejected. There was, he remembered, a greenhouse at the back and every greenhouse had its own water supply and every water tap its own bucket. He ran downstairs and returned with a bucket of water.

He put the bucket in the bath and stripped off his clothes. He took stock of himself again in the glass. Despite the occasions when he had swum across rivers, the perspiration and dust of the day had stained his waist and shoulders. There was ingrained grime around his ankles and he told himself that it was high time he had a bath, ere other companions began to seek the shelter of his trousers. He noticed that his shoulders and what he could see of his back were blue and brown from bruises from the beating he had received from the German rifle butts. Then he washed.

He splashed the water down and over himself and he chose a splendid cake of soap and lathered it all over his body. It was such sheer sensuous pleasure that he soaped himself from head to foot three times. He sluiced himself clean and dried himself on a fleecy towel, revelling in the marvellous pleasure of cleanliness. It was the first time he had used soap and a towel for the seventeen days that he'd left Wattisham. Then with his toilet completed he set about a more complete inspection of the premises where he had already promised himself to spend the night.

He fetched another bucket of water from the greenhouse and on the way back collected a pocketful of cherries and some lettuce. These he carried back to the dining-room where he had already deposited his mouldy loaf and slab of chocolate. After all, if the thing were to be done, it should be done properly, so he went through the sideboard and found the silver and knives and laid himself a place at the head where the German Colonel-General would have sat. As he put a goblet glass in place it seemed to him that it would be better filled. He wandered into the kitchens and pantries till he found the cellar stairs.

There were pipes and pipes of wine in the cellar. The bottles, of every shape and kind, lay in their bins, row after row. He spent a little time enjoying a bottle of champagne and returned upstairs.

He dined excellently. Even the bread, washed down with good wine, seemed palatable. Later, as twilight began to set in, he went upstairs again, intent on a final exploration before he went to bed for the night.

He chose a room in the front of the house overlooking the drive so that, should anyone return, he would stand a chance of hearing them and have fair warning. Moreover, on the landing outside stood a tallboy of considerable proportions, a noble piece of furniture with a false top. If, then, he was disturbed, it would be comparatively easy to climb on top and take cover there. It was not a prospect which he relished but it served to settle his mind against the night's rest. He went in to make a search of the dressing-rooms.

He found in the wardrobes and chests of drawers innumerable garments: suits, single and double breasted, which were of no use to him, since he must still play the role of refugee-tramp; overcoats, riding breeches, but above all underclothes; silk vests and silk shirts and silk pants. And socks. He stripped off his stained and matted garments and the next minute felt the delicious sensation of pure silk against his skin. He returned to his bedroom, very well pleased.

It gave him considerable satisfaction to read the name on the notice on the door. He was going to sleep in the absent General's bed. Moments later he pulled the fine linen sheets about him. He was asleep almost at once.

196

He left the château with the sun well up in the sky. He had washed, trimmed his beard with a pair of scissors found in a dressing-room drawer and put on his brand-new silk underclothes. He was rested and full of confidence. He felt that at last his luck was in. Then, some eight miles from Neufchâtel, and making for Beauvais, his surmise became fact.

The little wayside garage and bicycle shop just off the main road stood by itself. It had a corrugated-iron roof and a single petrol pump; a broken-down, pathetic little place where war had shattered, with scarcely a stroke, someone's enterprise and hopes. He tried the double doors in the front but they were locked from the inside. He went round to the back and stared through a dingy window. The first thing he saw among the shadows was the outline of a bicycle!

He broke into the workshop at the back. There was a mechanic's bench on his right with a tool kit left open by a small lathe. Propped on the opposite wall was the bicycle and there were others beside it. Then he saw that no single machine was complete and intact. They were a collection of crocks.

There was one with handle-bars and without pedals or a back wheel; there was one consisting of a frame and a front wheel; there was one with two wheels and no seat or handle-bars. There was, moreover, a heap of discarded wheels, buckled and with their spokes gone, in company with a litter of broken driving chains, pumps, and lamps.

But there were tools on the bench and time was his own. He selected a frame, a saddle, and all the other components. Laboriously but skilfully he began to assemble them, a pedal from here, a set of handle-bars from there. He found one fair wheel, but the only other one with sufficient spokes to bear any weight was buckled. Therefore with infinite patience he widened the front fork of the frame to allow for the play of the buckled wheel, made

197

a new axle from a piece of iron piping and finished the job with a series of metal bushes to keep the contraption in place. Contraption, he thought, was a very fair name for the job. It had taken him two and a half hours to build.

He took it outside into the sunshine and it looked even more uncouth than it had in the shed. It seemed shy of the daylight with its twisted front wheel, its seat a litle awry, its rusted handle-bars. But he mounted it and rode off. It had an action peculiarly its own, but it worked.

He rode it triumphantly for fifteen miles on the road to Paris.

He was riding his bicycle with nonchalance and assurance when he met with the German column. They were advancing towards him down the long dusty road, marching infantry and patrols of cyclists. He had no intention of avoiding them even if had been possible. For was he not now an American citizen, making for Paris and hadn't he the means of transport beneath him and would he not soon be there?

It was all over so quickly that he was on his feet and trudging along before he scarcely realized it. Half-way down the column, as he steered his erratic course, a German trooper broke ranks, sprang towards him and seized the handle-bars of his machine. Embry came to a dead stop.

"Donnez-moi," said the German. "Give it to me." He wrenched the bicycle from Embry's hands. Embry had no option but to let it go. Here was no place or time for argument.

There was nothing for it but to continue his passage to Paris on foot.

CHAPTER SIXTEEN

ON 15th June he had made his bicycle. It was taken from him on the morning of the same day. He reached the outskirts of Paris on the evening of 18th June.

Despite his wounded leg and his bruised back and shoulders; despite privation and exposure, despite the strain of being constantly alert and ever watchful; despite disappointment, humiliation and fear of discovery, with possibly three men's deaths to be accounted for should he be re-taken, he made the passage to Paris on foot and alone. He covered eighty miles in three days.

He reached the suburb of St. Denis at sunset of 18th June. He was no longer a solitary traveller tramping the long straight lanes or crossing the rolling downs with only the sky and the earth around him, those two had proved friends when acquaintance had ripened, but who could be as fickle as the wind that moved between them. He was in the company of men again.

Here on the fringe of the great city, outside its many gates, where the buildings had been assembled in their haphazard way, he felt that he had already entered on another phase of the long road home and that from now on, far from avoiding his enemies, he would be rubbing shoulders with them at all hours of the day and that he must increase his cunning, for only that and a bold front could carry him through.

He broke into a deserted villa and slept on a bare bed, ready for what the day might bring.

He left St. Denis after five in the morning, when the

curfew was lifted. He walked down the long straight streets looking for a café. He still had a few of the francs Paul had given him and he was hungry.

Though the hour was as yet early there was considerable traffic on the road, lorries and carts filled with country produce, cyclists on the way to work, and, as always, Germans in vehicles. He reached the city of Paris about seven thirty and found a small café which was open. He took a seat at a small round marble-topped table under the striped awning outside and ordered coffee and rolls.

It was a strange feeling to experience the movement of a great city again around him. The artisan-cyclists trundled past, their knapsacks on their backs or the day's food in a cloth tied to their handle-bars. He thought of his bicycle, which he had enjoyed for so short a time and then he wondered what all these passers-by, the natives of this famous city, were thinking over the loss of their freedom and the blow to their pride. All the time and in all places were Germans. It was as if Paris had been prepared for an occasion.

"I will join you, monsieur, if I may. One's coffee drinks better in company."

He looked up and saw at his side and already seating himself, a little Frenchman. He was an elderly man, with a drooping grey moustache and brown eyes, as mournful as a spaniel's. He wore a high starched collar and front, with a black tie scarcely wider than a piece of tape. A gold ring of a cable pattern served the purpose of a knot. His hands were gnarled and wrinkled, and the nails were those of a man who had laboured in fields.

"To think I should have lived to have seen this day. I have heard my grandfather speak about 1870 and what happened after Sedan and I myself was on the Marne when we held them in the last war." He spoke excellent English. "But now they have just marched in."

"Say, did nobody make a stand?" said Embry, practising his American accent.

"No. We were broken. Split in two. They declared Paris an open city. Nobody fired a shot in her defence. *Et maintenant—ces merdes!*"

"That's just too bad."

"Where do you come from, *monsieur?*"

"Noo York," said Embry.

"I thought so. You can usually tell. I was coachman to a great family whose château was in Fontainebleau and often the guests were Americans. You could tell the difference between the English by the voice."

"Well, maybe, maybe," said Embry. "But I reckon ours is the purer tongue."

"I'm no judge of that, *monsieur,* but I am afraid it will be a long time before we see many of your countrymen or the British again. They say they started the quarrel."

"Say, I've heard that before," said Embry. He felt he was getting well into the part and he was exhilarated with the prospects of the vital occasion which must soon come at the American Consulate.

"For myself," continued his acquaintance, "I do not believe that. The English have had a terrible beating. They would not have been so beaten had they been prepared for war. Nobody goes to war and starts a quarrel unprepared. No. It is the Germans again and I am very afraid for France. I know Germans. My family whom I served used to travel a great deal. These German soldiers are not like the ones who destroyed Louvain in 1914 and raped the Belgian women and cut off their breasts. These have been instructed not to insult or upset us. I can see it in their manners and their ways. They are too polite. And there are some among my countrymen who will say as time goes on: 'These Germans are not such bad fellows after all. We made a mistake about them.' And they will be won over and the Germans will do what they like with them, make them work for them, build for them, slave for them. And some of our women—bah!"

"Well, I sure think you've got something there," said Embry.

"*Alors*—I have seen a lot of the world and these Germans are very clever. They can see everyone else's weaknesses and use them for their own purposes. They themselves have only one weakness."

"And what might that be?" asked Embry.

"They can't see their own."

The little Frenchman rose to his feet, brushed the crumbs from his waistcoat and buttoned his jacket.

"Well, *monsieur,* thank you for your company. I will bid you good day."

"*Au revoir,*" said Embry. "And before you go, tell me, please, how I find the American Consulate."

"The American Consulate? Now let me see. It is not so far from here but I doubt if it is officially open till after half past eight or nine. You take—now—one, two, yes the third street on your left and then the second on your right, across the *place* by the Hôtel de Ville, where the German authorities have set up their headquarters, and the Consulate is nearby. You intend to call there, I take it?"

"I'm a refugee," said Embry. "Say, don't these garments tell that story?"

"I thought perhaps you might be. I hope your Consul will be able to help one of his own. Good fortune to you."

"Well, feller, that's mighty fine of you," said Embry.

They shook hands.

"So long!"

"*Au revoir, monsieur.*"

He ordered another cup of coffee when the Frenchman had departed, because his watch told him he had time to spare. He had no wish to find the Consulate not yet open

202

and to be found lingering in its vicinity and attract unnecessary attention. It was not beyond probability that
the German special police had already been authorized to
stop and cross-question any foreign characters whom they
might consider suspicious. It was growing warm, too, as
the sun rose higher and the coffee was good.

He was well pleased with himself. Of all the objectives
which he had attempted, this of Paris had, on the whole,
been the most easily achieved. He had succeeded in his
task. He was within the capital city of France, not half a
dozen streets away from an authoritative organization
which at a mere stroke of the pen could speed him from
Europe to freedom—and to fight again.

He was full of confidence in being able to carry off the
part of an American. His late acquaintance had been fully
convinced to such a degree that he had recognized his
assumed nationality. Well, it was going to be a very exciting morning. If his luck held he might even be crossing
the Channel by this time tomorrow.

He paid his bill, left the café, and made his way without difficulty in the direction in which he'd been
instructed.

The building in which he found himself was very
imposing for a consulate but there was no one in the hall
of whom he could ask which floor the section dealing with
cases such as his occupied, nor any door marked "Inquiries," so he made his way to the imposing staircase,
quite confident that he was on the right track. As he
mounted the stairs several civilians passed him with
papers and files in their hands. He was on the point of
stopping one of them but thought better of it. He looked
around him eagerly. His hopes ran high. Then on the
moment he was left without any doubt where he might be.

Two high-ranking German officers, bareheaded and
arguing with each other, emerged from a room at the end
of the corridor opposite and rapidly crossed the landing.

Within a second at least half a dozen other uniformed Germans emerged from various doors and clattered past. He realized at once what he had done. He was in the Hôtel de Ville, the German Headquarters in Paris. He made for the head of the stairs.

He descended rapidly, expecting to hear at any moment the alarm being raised behind him but no one challenged him and he reached the street again to mingle with the crowd. But the incident had startled him so much that he had allowed himself to be taken off his guard. His eagerness in his new environment had betrayed him. Now doubly cautious, he moved swiftly away from the Town Hall and waited several minutes before he inquired of a passer-by where the American Consulate might be. It was in the Avenue Gabrielle. The American flag fluttered over the portal. He walked into the Consulate.

This time there was a civilian doorkeeper on duty. He looked Embry over with curiosity.

"Good morning," said Embry and he hoped his American twang sounded as well as it had a little time ago.

"Good morning," said the doorkeeper, still staring.

"Say," said Embry, "you'd look a bit rough if you'd done all the walking that I've done."

"Can I help you then?"

"Sure you can," said Embry. "I'm an American citizen and I've come right down from the north of France. I got mixed up in this goddam war and lost all my property."

"If you will come with me, then. . . ."

He led Embry upstairs to a room with a long reception counter. There were several girls on duty interviewing various applicants. It all seemed very efficient and business-like. Embry waited for some time for his turn to come.

It was useless, he felt, to prepare too involved a story at this stage of the proceedings since he had no idea of what manner of questions he might be asked. The more flexible the tale, the more readily he could adapt it to any emergency.

"If you please . . ." said a woman's voice.

"My name," said Embry, "is Harry J. Walker. I'm an American and I've lost my papers. This goddam war."

"I'm so sorry."

She was a mild little woman with mouse-coloured hair and pale eyes. He liked her smile.

"Say," he said, "it was like this. I was up north, Dieppe way, spending a holiday and then these durned Europeans have to start fighting and I get mixed up in it. And it wasn't no fun, ma'am, it sure wasn't."

"Didn't you get any warning of what might happen? Many of our people have got away, you know."

"Warning! Shucks! They were on me before I knew where I was. And that's when I lost all my papers."

"How did you get here then?"

"Walked, ma'am. On my flat feet. Every darn foot of the way."

"Good gracious me."

She drew a paper towards her, picked up her pen.

"Your name again?"

"Walker. Henry J. J. for John."

"Your home?"

"New York, ma'am."

"When did you leave there?"

"Just prior to the outbreak of war."

"The date?"

"Well, I just can't remember off hand. . . ."

"Never mind. How did you come?"

"By sea."

"Direct from New York or via England?"

"Via England, ma'am." And to himself: "Thank God, I'm on safer ground."

"You know England?"

"Oh, sure, ma'am. Sure. Sure."

"What parts?"

"Lots of parts. London, Dover, Land's End."

"You travel a good deal?"

"Well, I should say so,"

"You have private means, I take it?"

"When I can get my hands on 'em, ma'am. But I've lost my papers."

She laid down her pen on the desk.

"Were these the clothes you came over in?"

"Why no. I lost all of them. The Germans took them."

"But you must have had something on at the time."

"They came at night, ma'am."

She raised her eyebrows a little and a smile twitched upon her lips. And Embry thought: "I've given her the works. She's fallen for it. I'll get a free passage out of here to England or I'll eat my hat."

"Why do you come here?" she asked.

"Well! As an American citizen. . . ."

She glanced swiftly to either side of her. Her colleagues were busy with inquirers. Then she leant a little over the interviewing counter towards Embry.

"Do you know what I should do if I were you?" she said.

"I'd be sure grateful for your advice, ma'am."

"Well, I should go away and clean myself up and then I'd come back and speak the truth!"

She smiled again. He knew that if it were not for betraying him, she would have been openly laughing. Her eyes met his for a moment and they stared at one another and maybe being a woman, she saw something which was not fitting for laughter; for she became of an instant serious, quizzical. And still Embry's eyes held her.

206

"I'll tell you the truth *now*!" he said.

There was a room nearby and without another word she lifted the flap of the counter and beckoned Embry to follow. She closed the door of the room behind. They were alone.

"What is it you have to say?"

"My name is not Walker. It is Embry. Basil Edward Embry. I am a Wing Commander in the Royal Air Force. I am a British subject. I was shot down operating over St. Omer and taken prisoner. I broke away from the Calais column of the prisoners of war. I have been on the run night and day ever since the last week of May. I've had a hell of a time. Do I go on?"

"Yes," she said. "Please go on. And please sit down. You can trust me, you know."

"I know that," said Embry.

"You're a much better Britisher than an American."

"I thought I was rather good."

"I thought you sounded like something out of a phoney film. I thought it was awful. Now—go on, tell it all to me, please."

He drew his chair up beside her and he told her of all the things that had happened from the time he baled out till the present moment. He left nothing out. She made no comment till he reached the end. She sat very quietly, very attentive. Then she said! "I think I can help you. But we must be careful."

"I've learnt something of caution lately," said Embry.

"There's an Englishwoman downstairs who we believe is looking after British interests. She goes by the name of Mrs. Roberts. I don't think it's her real name, because she's married to a Russian, who works in the Consulate. Well, Wing Commander, we think she's been put there for a purpose. I'll take you to her."

"I'm very grateful to you," said Embry.

"It's a pleasure," said the little American. It was obvious she meant what she said.

He had repeated his story to Mrs. Roberts. He had again omitted nothing, only wondering all the time what impression he was making on this grey-headed, middle-aged English gentlewoman. It must, he felt, to her be a fantastic tale. Much depended on her reaction.

"Where would you have gone if you hadn't been brought down to me?" she asked at the conclusion.

"I don't know," said Embry. "I hadn't thought beyond the American Consulate. I had an idea that I'd make a good American. Apparently I'd be a dead loss on the other side of the Atlantic."

"Where would you have slept?"

"I hadn't given that a thought either."

"If you'd been found on the streets—well, you know what would have happened?"

"I could make a pretty fair guess," said Embry.

She rose and went to the window and looked down into the crowded street below. Somewhere a clock struck ten. She waited there several minutes and Embry thought: "She believes the story all right, but she's making up her mind what to do. I thought it would be all in the clear once I got here but it doesn't seem to be. Damn!"

She turned at length and her eyes were troubled.

"So many of them," she said, "Germans in the city in the streets below. You wouldn't stand a chance."

She returned to her desk.

"My husband," she said, "was in the Intelligence during the last war. He's the one to have the ideas how to get you out of France. He knows everybody."

"You are very kind," said Embry.

"But you've got to stay somewhere till we decide what to do with you. You had better stay with us—at our flat."

"Stay with you!" said Embry. "That's terrific. But you don't know who and what I am."

"I've heard your story. Yes."

"I'm an escaped prisoner of war with a rather disreputable record from the German point of view."

"I realize all that."

"Do you know what the penalty would be for you and your husband if you're caught harbouring an escaped prisoner? Do you remember Nurse Cavell?"

"I do," she said.

"Well?"

"I leave here at twelve sharp," she said. "You must be near the entrance to the Consulate. When I come out, follow me. On no account, of course, must you recognize me. I shall go to the Metro. Follow me and take a ticket to Montparnasse. When I get out of the train, you get out. I think that will work."

"It's got to," said Embry. "I shall be there. God bless you."

He left her then, marvelling as once before he'd marvelled at Paul's magnanimity, learning that in the most commonplace people there was a greatness of spirit which only peril to others seemed to call forth. Then, as he had two hours to spare, he decided that another meal of some kind would help pass the time.

As he reached the Champs Élysées he heard the sound of the band. It was a stirring, martial air that reached him over the head of a large crowd which was gathered on the boulevards. He crossed over, pushing his way to the front. It amused him to observe the open glances of disfavour if not disgust which his stained rags gave rise to from several members of the throng pressed about him. But he saw the parade.

They were coming down the length of the Champs Élysées from the Arc de Triomphe. A magnificent brass band led them and behind column after column of German infantry followed in full marching order with their bayonets fixed. They came steadily on, with a sombre reverberating rhythmic tramp of ironclad boots, their officers at the head of their companies. It was the official German entry into Paris.

The band blared out and the drums rattled and thudded and Embry thought what a spectacle would this have been with the British Brigade of Guards sweeping down this open road. He thought how the crowd again and again would have yelled and cheered. But, now, the close-packed press about him were silent and sullen, stupefied by their conquerors' trampling feet, stunned by defeat.

He was outside the Consulate just before twelve. There were a considerable number of people passing in and out and he wondered if noon were the hour fixed for a change of shifts. He had to keep a close watch on the door without drawing attention to himself. It would be a tragic anticlimax should he miss Mrs. Roberts. But when, at length, she came out, she paused for a moment on the threshold as if to give him the opportunity of recognizing her and then set off swiftly down the street.

He followed her, keeping some thirty yards behind her. He had already taken the precaution of buying a ticket on his way back from parade, so that there should be no chance of his losing her if he were held up in the ticket queue.

He sat on the opposite side of the train to her, several seats further down. Once their eyes met and it seemed to him that she quite openly started as if an unsuspected hand had fallen on her shoulder, so that he told himself that despite her outward appearance of calm, she was inwardly agitated and on edge. He could well understand it.

They were a quarter of an hour in the train and when she left he had no difficulty in following her but now he felt more conspicuous without the crowds about, so he allowed the distance between them to increase, which led to a moment of dismay when she disappeared into a small block of flats.

He quickened his pace, disconcerted momentarily with her so suddenly out of view but he found the main entrance without difficulty and started to mount the stairs. Now that he was out of sight of the street the impulse upon him was to rush the last steps to his new hiding-place, but he still kept up his slouching gait. It was not until he reached the fourth floor that he met her.

She was standing by the door of her flat, which she was holding open with one hand. The moment he came level with her, she clutched him by the arm and hustled him inside. Then she bolted the door. He noticed as she took off her hat that her hands were trembling.

CHAPTER SEVENTEEN

THE next time he saw her frightened was when he inadvertently moved near the window of her sitting-room. She cried out at once.

"Don't go near the windows, please."

"I am so sorry," he said. "I should have thought of that."

"It's not your fault," she said, "but the Germans have been very suspicious in the last few days and they have been searching a lot of houses in Paris. Now you'd better have a bath and then I'll have a look at that bad leg of yours which you told me about."

He had his bath and she dressed his leg. It had broken out in boils and was becoming a serious nuisance once more but she cleansed the septic places with iodine and then bandaged them. They lunched together. It was the first conventionally served meal he had had since his lunch at Wattisham on 27th May.

He went to bed in the afternoon and slept, eased in mind and body, so that when he awoke to the sound of a man's voice in the hall, he was confident that it could be none other than the master of the house.

He found his host, who was a telephonist at the Consulate, to be a small grey-haired man of some sixty years; quiet, cultured, and with very little trace of his Russian origin. They discussed the situation over supper.

"If I could only get a boat," said Embry.

"No chance at all. Every port is closely watched and there are patrols along the shore at all key points to say nothing of the Germans either confiscating or destroying all sea-worthy vessels as a matter of course. I think you should make for Bordeaux."

"Are the British still there?"

"Yes, to the best of my knowledge. But you should get away as soon as you can. There are tens of thousands of refugees on the road to Orleans. You should try to get mixed up with them and carried along with them but the Germans are already beginning to sort them out to return them to their homes. You don't want to delay."

"Could I get a train?" said Embry.

"No. There are no trains running out of Paris."

"Then I'll have to resort to my first love," said Embry, "and get a bicycle. Can you get me a bike?"

"I'll try," said Mr. Roberts.

He woke the following morning to find his hostess at his bedside with a cup of tea. Later, there were eggs for breakfast and English marmalade. She explained that she liked to keep up the tradition of the English breakfast, had always done so since her marriage but now with the war she doubted if they'd be able to do so. It was only when he had finished his meal, that he realized that it was a very terrified woman who had been talking to him.

He immediately blamed himself for her state of mind. She was frail and very nervous. He was convinced of the fact when she explained that she would not be going out to her job that day. He was more convinced, when about the middle of the morning there come a knocking at the front door of the flat.

He was in the sitting-room at the time reading a novel which he'd picked off the shelf, Mrs. Roberts was dusting the room and at the sound, the cloth she was using fell from her hand. Embry picked it up and handed it to her as the knocking continued. She thanked him with a nervous nodding of the head.

"There's someone at the door," said Embry, thinking on the instant that it was a ridiculous statement to make. As she left the room and went out into the hall, he realized he must leave.

It was impossible to stay any longer. If his stay were extended any longer he had no doubt that she would break down altogether. Then as he heard the front door shut he heard Mr. Roberts' voice: "Left my key behind . . . and I couldn't do any good." The little man came into the room with his wife.

"I've had no luck," he said at once. He crossed to the window and standing by the curtain, looked down into the street.

"No, it's all right," he added. "I thought I might have been followed."

"You weren't, were you?" His wife's voice was urgent.

"No—only . . ." He broke off. Then to Embry: "I couldn't get you a bicycle."

"That's quite all right," said Embry. "It was only too good of you to try, but I'm on my way, anyway."

"You're leaving?"

"Yes."

"What will you do?"

"I'm going back to the Consulate to see if I can raise some money. And then I'll make for Bordeaux as you suggested."

"I'm sorry I couldn't do more, but I have found out that there is a Colonel Shaw at the Consulate who is looking after British interests and I've talked with him."

"And then you said you hadn't done anything for me!"

"It's the bike I meant. Isn't it extraordinary how important quite trivial things become when there's a war on?"

"Precisely what I've found out of late," said Embry.

"And now goodbye, and I cannot thank you enough—goodbye."

He found Colonel Shaw at the Consulate without any difficulty. It was quite apparent to Embry that he was expected and that his story had already been told. The Colonel appeared to know his business and his views were concise.

"Here are three hundred francs, Wing Commander, to help you on your way. I suggest to you that you do not leave Paris as you've been advised to do. Instead, you should report to the Salvation Army Hostel in the Rue Cantagrel. Here is the address." He scribbled on a slip of paper and handed it to Embry. "You will find the Salvationist in charge an excellent fellow. The position is this. The War Cemetery gardeners—I speak of the fourteen-eighteen war—are coming in from the outlying districts and are being collected at the hostel in order to be returned home. They are all British, of course. Mix in with them and pass yourself off as one of them and get back to England as a repatriated gardener."

"Thank you," said Embry. He pocketed the address and the money and left.

The scheme didn't appeal. It seemed to Embry too haphazard and half-hearted. It was far from foolproof. The gardeners assembled at the hostel and employed as they had been for many years by a British organization, would have identification papers. He had none. He might be able to hoodwink a few Germans but he was not likely to succeed with his own countrymen. Nevertheless, he would take a look at the place.

It was a very different district from the one he had just left. He could tell at once, as soon as he left the station. There was a squalor and drabness about the streets that spoke of poverty. On the instant came the inspiration. It's the poor, he told himself, that help the poor. He had got to leave Paris. He had only got three hundred francs.

He'd got to have some more money. Very good, then, he'd beg for it. He chose an *épicerie* on the opposite side of the road.

There was nobody in the shop but the proprietor, who was slicing liver sausage on a piece of grease-proof paper.

"Refugee," said Embry.

"*Comment?*"

"Refugee . . . American . . . very hungry."

The shopkeeper threw a slice of sausage across the counter.

"*Non, merci,*" said Embry. "*Money . . . argent!*"

"*Va-t-en,*" said the shopkeeper and retrieved his piece of sausage.

On the pavement outside Embry considered the problem. Clearly enough that hadn't been the right line of approach. He tried the shop next door, a milliner's.

"*Malade,*" said Embry, to the woman at the counter. "Refugee . . . American *malade*. No money. *Très pauvre.*"

She fumbled beneath her apron and produced a five-franc note.

"*Merci, madame, merci,*" said Embry.

His next attempt was at a café on the corner. He was rebuffed by a man seated at the table outside but was given ten francs by the manageress who leant over her desk, her big bare arms folded. It was apparent that the women would prove more tractable. In this instance, she questioned him closely on his experience. Who was he? Where did he come from? Was his home destroyed? He made up a story as he went along but several customers also gathered round and made a small collection for him. He thanked them and left with fifty francs to the good.

He took in turn a stall in the next street, a cobbler's shop, and, as one of the best bets, a laundry which he found with the door open and the steam swirling out. Most of the girls gave him a coin or two. He went gaily on his way.

He toured that particular spot of the district for another hour amused at the latest rôle which had been forced upon him. He found considerable zest in approaching all manner of people in different circumstances and positions. The most unexpected could happen. A pompous little man who looked like an alderman and sported a very solid gold chain across his waistcoat was only worth two ten-centime pieces but a shrivelled little woman with a black shawl round her head and shoulders came up with twenty francs.

He plied his new trade till half-past five of the afternoon and then, availing himself of the privacy of a deserted builder's yard, counted up his takings. He had collected just over five hundred francs. He was highly elated.

But he was in two minds as to whether he would go to the Salvation Army Hostel or not. It would provide an anchorage for the time being but he was more than ever averse to awaiting events in contrast to forcing the pace on his own. He wondered if he could steal a bicycle and ride out of Paris before the curfew.

He wandered the streets, occasionally lounging about at corners, watching all bicycles and their owners, particularly with reference as to where a rider would leave his machine. There were plenty of bicycles about, propped up by the kerb, leaning against a wall, or resting by a shop window but they were all reasonably accessible to the persons concerned and there was none he dared risk taking. It would be fatal if he fell foul of the French police.

The more he thought over the latter possibility the more he became convinced that he was wasting his time. Even if he should succeed in seizing a machine, the least hue and cry would lead to disaster. He determined to go to the hostel.

He reached the hostel at six o'clock and found a young

French Salvationist in charge, who spoke good English. He seemed to Embry to be an excellent fellow. He asked Embry the usual questions.

"I'm an American," said Embry reverting to his former part. "I got involved with the war up north and lost everything. I'm trying to make for Orleans."

"I myself spent two or three years in America," said the Salvationist. "I hope you'll manage to get out of France all right. But things are in a terrible state."

"I could get out if I had a bike."

"Have you got any money?"

"Eight hundred francs."

"I think I can get you a bicycle. I'll try."

"Can I get a meal here?"

"Yes. In there, through the swing door."

"Then I'll keep fifty francs for a meal and give the rest to you. I'm very grateful to you."

"That's all right. I'm only too glad to help. I'll see you later."

Embry made a good supper. The food was served on the cafeteria principle. He chose a table well apart from the rest. The attendance was poor and he supposed that not many of the inmates, judging by the looks of them, had the price of a meal in their pockets.

Some forty minutes later the Salvationist returned. He carried a small wad of notes in his hand. At the sight Embry's spirits fell.

"No luck?" he asked.

"Oh yes! But I've put your bike in my office and locked the door. Things have a habit of disappearing round here. You can have it in the morning. You'll have to spend the night here. It's too late to get anywhere before curfew. Here's your change."

"Change!" said Embry.

"I only paid seventy francs for it."

"You're a marvel," said Embry.

218

"Now I'll show you where you sleep. We lock you in at night. Curfew is not raised till five in the mornings so you want to wake up about half past four so that you can get as early a start as possible. This way, up the stairs."

The dormitory led off a landing at the top of a flight of stairs. An interlocking grille was folded at the side of the stair head, so that even before they reached the sleeping quarters Embry had the impression of a prison.

There were over a hundred beds in the ward, each with its rough pillow and two blankets. The lavatories and ablution benches were at the far end. The floor was bare boards.

"Not exactly a palace," said the Salvationist, "but it is a roof over your head."

"It'll do me all right," said Embry. "I've slept in stranger places than this of late."

He went to bed at eight o'clock but only to sleep at intervals. At nine o'clock the grille was slung across the main entrance. It was like being in jail. In the dim light of two blued electric bulbs the shapes and shadows of his companions became monstrous and fantastic. He lay between beds occupied on his right by a French soldier and on his left by a tramp. The former muttered and whimpered in his nightmarish sleep, the latter snored like a saw mill, and above all was the foetid stench of unwashed bodies and foul linen. It was indeed another such night as he had endured as a prisoner at Hucqueliers in the church with young Treacy, and again it seemed interminable till at last on the stroke of five the grille clattered back and the stairway was again open. He went down to the Salvationist's office and found his bicycle.

"My very best thanks," said Embry.

"*Au revoir*. God bless you."

His objective was Orleans. He took his direction from the Salvationist, and then, remembering how Germans

219

purloined any bicycle that looked serviceable, he half deflated his tyres and rode out of Paris. After covering about fifty miles of his journey he found that a blister was forming on his right buttock. As he passed a cottage with its open door he saw a rocking-chair and on the chair was a cushion. He sprang from his bicycle, darted up the path and snatched the cushion. Then he remounted and with this new treasure under his arm, pedalled furiously away. Ten minutes later, he dismounted, fastened the cushion on to the seat with string from a parcel of food he had bought the evening before in Paris and rode away once more.

The acquisition of a bicycle after all the previous disappointments was very encouraging. He passed through Arpajon and later with Etampes behind him he encountered a horse-drawn German army lorry. There were a half-dozen Germans aboard, singing. He pedalled up alongside and took the opportunity of a tow with his hand on the running-board. The German songs had a lilt to them that went with the morning and with his own good humour. Now and again he beat time with a free hand. The Germans laughed and encouraged him.

He reached Orleans about one o'clock and passed through the town. It was full of German soldiery and vehicles massed together. Two miles further on, as he came upon an enemy-occupied aerodrome, he could see German fighters and Army Co-operation aircraft flying off it and because he considered it his duty to investigate anything that might be of use to his cause, he decided upon a little private spying. He hid his bicycle in a haystack nearby and then sauntered along a side road that led up to the aerodrome. He was interested in their kind of ground defence. He counted sixteen light automatic guns round the perimeter and six heavy guns near a wood. He made a mental note of their positions and rode on again. He would, he told himself, make a special report on this particular lay-out for the Air Ministry, when he reached England. He was more confident than ever that he would get home.

An hour later, having eaten the food he'd bought in Paris, he reached Beaugency, sixteen miles from Orleans. There was very considerable troop movement and the German police were holding up all traffic to enable their own columns to pass through. It was galling to be delayed but he found a market-garden and entered and helped himself to fruit. It was very refreshing; more so because it was free of charge.

As soon as the traffic block broke up, he moved on once more, another twenty miles to Blois. The town had been damaged and some of the roads were obstructed, so he made a detour to reach Veuvray, another thirty miles further on. Then since it was growing dark and he was tired, he went to cover in a barn, climbing aloft and taking the ladder with him, his precious bicycle concealed amongst a litter of impedimenta below.

He had ridden in all one hundred and forty-two miles on the first day out from Paris.

He was away by five o'clock on the following morning. His progress of the previous day had encouraged him and he covered the eight miles to Tours in a very short time. He knew the town of old, having spent part of his honeymoon there.

He would, he knew, have to cross the Loire, but when he reached the river in the centre of the town, the old bridge was down, its arches broken and its road track destroyed. In its place the Germans had built a pontoon.

But the German police, as at Beaugency, were holding up all traffic. One hour passed, then another. On every side of him were refugees, pressing slowly, painfully forward. It was their silence that impressed him. Here was no clamouring for permission to move on or a storming at the authorities, instead only a dull apathetic sullen quietude of a people subdued and already accepting the fate that had overtaken them.

Then to his dismay he saw that there was a German police picket at a check-point at the head of the pontoon bridge. Everyone that was attempting to cross was being examined. Leaning on his bicycle, he could see from where he stood on the crowded track, the police handling identification papers.

CHAPTER EIGHTEEN

HE SAT on the bank above the Loire, his bicycle beside him. This was indeed a predicament, to have ventured so far and now to be confronted with an obstacle such as this. Nevertheless, he considered, he should have expected something of the sort for the Germans would be endeavouring to sort out refugees and return them to the rightful areas as soon as possible, if only for the sake of facilitating their own troop movements.

The traffic across the pontoon bridge was immense. Column after column of troops passed over with their supply lorries and ammunition trucks. Several times he saw light armoured vehicles. Now and again a small group of refugees would collect at the bridge-head in the hopes of crossing but would invariably be held up by the infantry. On more than one occasion he saw a repetition of the trick that had been played on him on the road to Paris; a German soldier would break ranks and seize one of the civilian's bicycles. Embry let the air out of his tyres.

In all, four hours passed before the traffic became anything like normal.

He watched carefully from his position above the bridge. The troops had gone through by now and the last of the lorries had rumbled over the pontoons. The pedestrians below, men with their bundles of belongings on their shoulders, women pushing prams cluttered with what little remained of their worldly belongings, children dragging at their mother's skirts, formed and reformed into small crowds at the check-point, only gradually to disperse as the foremost trickled through after examination.

There was, he decided, only one way to cope with the situation and that would be to deal with it boldly. He would force his way through when the crowd was most congested. He rose, picked up his bicycle, and descended the slope.

He waited, edging his way to the left of the crowd. The police check-point was on the right of the bridge. Within several minutes he was level with it. Then he pushed his way ahead.

It was for several moments something of a struggle, for with the press of bodies about him, the bicycle was an impediment, but though he was loudly cursed and a woman protested in a shrill voice he got through and was on the bridge with far less difficulty than he would have imagined. He pushed his bicycle before him and mingling with the trailing throng reached the middle of the bridge. He progressed slowly till he realized that he was being hemmed in once more. There was a second police check-point at the far end of the bridge.

There was nothing for it but to employ the same tactics. He had for a moment the unpleasant feeling of being completely trapped, but, choosing the right moment, he pushed his way through. No one challenged him.

He reached the south bank of the Loire and five minutes later was bicycling rapidly along the road to Poitiers in the direction of Bordeaux. It was 22nd June.

Some twelve miles out of Tours, pedalling along at a fine rate and jubilant with his successful crossing of the Loire, he encountered a German staff car halted at a crossroads. He recognized it as such long before he reached it and recognized the occupants as officers. He gave them no further thought, as Germans had formed so familiar a part of his background these last weeks, and the old sensation of being watched all the time had disappeared. Therefore, when they hailed him as he passed, he immediately approached them and jumped off his bicycle.

"*Dites-moi* . . ." said the German officer at the wheel. "Tell me the way to Erves, if you please."

Whereupon Embry, caught for once off his guard, said in perfect English: "I beg your pardon?"

"*Comment?*"

"*Non savvy,*" said Embry, breaking into his pidgin French instantly realizing his mistake.

The second officer repeated the inquiry slowly, more deliberately.

"Which . . . is . . . the way . . . to . . . Erves? . . ."

"Ah!" said Embry and pointed vehemently in the opposite direction to that which he himself intended to take.

"*Merci.*"

They drove off. But scarcely before they had turned their car Embry himself was on his bicycle and pedalling furiously away.

He was alarmed at his astonishing indiscretion. He had not broken down under interrogation and had extricated himself with credit from some difficult and dangerous situations; but he had allowed a moment innocent of danger to become one fraught with peril. It was as if, unknown to himself, he were playing tricks with himself. It was extremely disconcerting.

He at once dismounted and took cover in the hedge against their possible return; but no car came back, so that after a while he rode on.

Some six miles from La Celle St. Avant he ran across a company of German soldiers lining the road. There was a small bridge over a stream where the column ended and he was in two minds whether he should get off and slake a thirst that was beginning to trouble him, but on second thoughts, considering it might be foolhardy with so many Germans about, he rode on.

Two minutes later, he could reassure himself, as he so often had done in the past, that there indubitably must be a devil that looked after its own. He heard the shout before the first burst of machine-gun fire drowned it. He rode on with all the speed he could muster. A French aeroplane, its guns blazing, was "beating up" the German troops which he had just passed. It only ceased firing as it passed the little bridge. Embry could see the dust spouting from the road where bullets hit its surface. Beyond, several figures sprawled face downwards. The aeroplane roared over his head and wheeled away.

Half an hour later he reached La Celle St. Avant. Here, he thought, would be an opportunity for a meal. The village appeared peaceful and in the smaller places such as this the fear of being molested by any officious German was considerably less. There was a small café at the very entrance to the village with a score or more of villagers seated round the door. They shouted to him as he passed and though he had no idea of their message he waved back at them, because they seemed friendly; but he rode on unwilling to stop and eat at a place where he had already attracted more attention than he desired. He would look for a café on the other side of the village.

As he rounded the corner a hundred yards further on, he realized the import of the shouted message.

The street was empty. It had all at once, in a most strange fashion, the air of those other deserted villages through which he had passed. It had the same desolate appearance of a place which was no longer used for human habitation and yet there had been quite a little crowd at the café on the outskirts. Then on the instant six German soldiers, appearing from nowhere it seemed, sprang at him, their bayoneted rifles at the ready. He clamped on both brakes and fell from his bicycle.

He was for the second time in the middle of a battle.

He picked himself up as they closed in on him. He could see beyond them another group, half-crouching, pressed close to the wall, their weapons in readiness, advancing down a side street. There was the sudden crash from round the corner of an exploding hand grenade and a burst of rifle fire.

"*Pardon*," said Embry. "*Pardon.*"

The Germans drew back. He picked up his bicycle, leapt on it and pedalled back like a madman the way he had come.

When he reached the café again, the group of villagers crowded round him. They began to explain the situation together in very loud voices and with great vehemence. It was some time before he could understand a word they were talking about. Then, gradually, he got the gist of the matter. They had warned him as he had ridden past. No one could deny that, could they? If a man couldn't take a warning, then no one was to blame, *n'est-ce-pas*? He was very lucky to be still alive. There was a fight going on. The French were on the far side of the village and the Germans were driving them out. It was house to house fighting. *Mon Dieu!* What a life!

And then they all returned to their seats as if nothing had happened and took up their coffee and glasses of wine as if it were a carnival day and the tumult in the distance were merely the sound of a fun-fair.

He ordered a meal of ham and eggs and coffee, and it was excellent. Every now and again there were bursts of firing and the occasional crash of a grenade, but nobody took any notice, so that he decided that it was likely enough only a "mopping-up" operation in progress and that with the result already foregone in favour of the Germans, the villagers knew precisely their margin of safety.

They were a friendly collection of very typical working-class French. He was appalled at the apathy and indifference they showed towards the struggle that was going on beneath their very noses. One of them during the meal asked if he were a Spaniard? He supposed that with his dark beard and sun-blackened face it was quite a reasonable supposition and since he'd been so many characters and played so many parts up to date, he supposed he might just as well take another.

"*Oui,*" said Embry, "*Oui, Espagnol.*"

"I thought so," said the other. "You can usually tell."

Embry was about to make for the door when the German trooper came in. He was a squat, burly little man, with the usual German arrogance when dealing with civilians. He began to make a round of the tables, demanding identification papers. The business appeared to be merely a matter of form for he scarcely examined the documents but turned them over and tossed them instantly back on to a table or chair. Nevertheless Embry suffered some extremely anxious moments awaiting his turn. There was only one way out of the café should he decide to make a dash for it, but even so the Germans were in force outside. But his unkempt and disorderly appearance came to his aid, because the German gave him one look of contempt as Embry muttered "*Espagnol,*" and passed on.

But though through all this crowded day his luck had held, he felt he needed a rest. He approached the proprietor of the café and was shown a barn at the back of the house. Adopting his usual routine he concealed his bicycle and climbed aloft.

There was a chink in the planked-up window of the dormer, and, peering through, he found he had a very fair view of the village and of the fighting which still continued. He could see parties of Germans creeping, their arms at the alert, round the sides of houses and sometimes dashing across the street to gain a point of vantage and then take cover again. Once he saw two German soldiers carrying a third man between them using a rifle as a seat. The wounded man was smothered in blood. Now and again smoke would rise in small puffs and then float away but there was no shell-fire. He watched this minor battle for a little time, then lay in the straw and rested. As darkness fell the fighting died down. He went to sleep.

Shortly after midnight on 23rd June he left the barn in La Celle St. Avant, took his bicycle and rode back the way he had come till he should meet the first side-road and turning off, make a detour of the village and obviate any further incursions into battles which didn't concern him.

But the darkness of the night baffled him and instead of striking the road for Poitiers he found himself in the light of dawn on the road leading to Le Blanc, which he reached at ten in the morning. By his initial mistake he had bicycled over seventy miles for a distance which should have been just on thirty-six!

The church bells were ringing as he entered the town. There were German cars and vehicles about but there was no sign of troop movement and no sign of German soldiery.

In view of the fighting which he had witnessed the day before, the atmosphere of well being, which pervaded the place, the streets no longer cluttered with refugees or marching Germans, the sunny pavements neglected by the crowd, made a very strong impression on him as he rode through. There might never have been a war on at all.

He reached La Trimouille, twelve miles further on, an hour and a half later and went to a restaurant and ordered a meal.

Again the quietness of the town roused his curiosity, so that he asked the waiter, who attended him, the reason for the absence of the enemy.

"It is all over."

"What is all over?" asked Embry.

"The war is over. An armistice has been signed."

An armistice! So the French had finally collapsed and were out of the war. It hadn't taken long. But what would England do now? What was she contemplating? It couldn't mean that England was beaten too? It couldn't, not England. He must get back. At once, at once he must get on his way. He was no use to England here.

Some miles out of La Trimouille he encountered a two-seater sports car driven by a young Frenchman with a girl at his side going in his direction. Once again as he had taken a tow from the Germans in their wagon, so he laid his hand on the side of the car.

"Good morning," said Embry in his best French.

"Go to hell," said the other in the vernacular.

The girl laughed and Embry grinned and the driver scowled and tried to ditch Embry by driving him on to the verge, but he hung on for five miles till the car turned from the main road. The girl waved him goodbye.

Twenty-five miles further on, passing through Le Dorat, he saw the French army for the first time, a company of officerless, dispirited troops, battle worn and haggard. He passed the time of day with them and went on to the town of Bellac.

He was so tired that he could scarcely ride his bicycle. For days he had longed for a bicycle; now he never wanted to see one again. He would try, he decided, to hire a car to take him on to Bordeaux. But first he would eat.

He chose a large restaurant and, leaving his bicycle outside, went in.

He was not surprised that the customers turned and stared at him and whispered amongst themselves. He was quite well aware what his appearance must be; his tattered clothes, white with dust; his face grimed with dirt and perspiration, his beard matted. He was more than surprised that he wasn't ordered to leave at once, but he had as yet to meet his host.

He made his way through the main restaurant to the lavatory and washed himself. The very sensation of soap put new heart in him, but he knew he must cut a sorry figure as he returned and took a seat at a vacant table.

Those at the adjacent tables were talking about him. He was quite certain of that though it was impossible to catch what they said, but he felt their attitude was much the reverse of the young Frenchman who had tried to refuse him a tow with his car.

It was a strange thing to contrast the behaviour of different people under the stress of war.

Now on every side were genial faces and though the women's glances were covert he knew they were secretly beaming on him. How was it, he asked himself, that a gathering such as this, instinctively seemed to recognize what he might be while he hobnobbed with refugees and was scrutinized by his enemies and remained undiscovered? However, the pleasant atmosphere encouraged him to choose a large meal and he ate hugely.

The proprietor crossed to Embry's table and waved the waiter aside.

"You have enjoyed your meal, *monsieur*?"

"Very much, thank you," said Embry gravely, not knowing what might come next.

"There is no charge."

"Pardon?"

"There is nothing to pay."

The proprietor stood by Embry's table, a tall, well-built man, clean shaven and erect. He looked at Embry for the moment very solemnly as if there were much that he would like to say but knew it was forbidden. Then the proprietor smiled very gently, in a friendly way, and said:

"I was once a soldier myself." And then he repeated:

"There is nothing to pay. You will please, allow me that pleasure."

"I am very grateful to you," said Embry. "It is wonderful the way one finds friends."

"You honour me, *monsieur*. Is there anything else in which I can be of service to you?"

"Can I hire a car for Bordeaux from anywhere?"

"You will find that very difficult. So many vehicles have been commandeered. But there are two garages run by friends of mine." He gave the addresses to Embry.

"Thank you," said Embry.

"Au revoir, monsieur. Bon voyage."

"Thank you again," said Embry.

He tried both addresses with no success. A car for hire in Bellac? *Quelle idée!*

He rode on and the country became very hilly, so that his progress with constant dismounting, became very slow. The bicycle became a burden. He struggled on, because the news of the armistice was haunting him in so much that he had no idea how it would affect the British forces. Had they capitulated as yet? Would they evacuate Bordeaux immediately? Would they be gone when at long last he reached the lines they'd held? He must keep going. Press on. That was the thing. Press on.

He had covered another seventeen miles when it began to rain. It fell in torrents, running in rivulets along the dry road, steaming up from its hot surface. It penetrated his clothes. He struggled on till he saw a gateway leading to a farm. He could go on no longer. He was at exhaustion point. He got off his bicycle and stumbled towards the gate. Beyond the gate was a barn.

CHAPTER NINETEEN

HE LAY naked in the straw, his clothes hanging from nails driven into the wall of the loft, where, the night before, he had left them to dry. Just before dawn he rose and dressed again. He was sorry that the farmer, who had let him sleep in the barn, and who had last evening given him half a pint of warm milk, would not be up so that he could say goodbye and thank him. He felt he owed a great debt of gratitude for that milk.

Nevertheless he was so stiff and sore that it was painful to dress. His leg was badly swollen and fresh boils had broken out inside the thigh. He was in a sorry state and knew it. The long march to Paris and the last two days of high-pressure cycling on top of his former privations were taking their toll. He mounted his bicycle with difficulty and rode off slowly and painfully.

It was more painful on the bicycle than off it, for contact with the seat again revealed how badly his skin was chafed. He pedalled on, telling himself that if he persisted he would gradually warm up and the pain would decrease. But the first half hour was agonizing and he was more than once tempted to walk, but he must lose no time if he were to reach Bordeaux.

He was relieved of the decision as to what he should do, when he met the French supply column. He came upon them suddenly round the corner of a wood. The road was solidly packed with horse-drawn vehicles and men. The column moved slowly and laboriously, a congestion of traffic. He was forced to dismount and make his way on foot, attempting to pass the converging vehicles. As he did so, he saw French officers by the roadside.

They were seated on a bank beside their car and one of them was brewing coffee in a billycan over a little spirit stove. A battalion of French infantry was ranged on either side of them. Without any hesitation Embry approached them.

He said in English: "Good morning."

They all turned towards him at once curious, alert. He liked the look of them, all young and well turned out for field-service conditions. The man at the spirit stove sniffed at the contents of the billy-can. Over the rim he returned Embry's greeting in English.

"Good morning," he said. "What can we do for you?"

"I am an English officer, an escaped prisoner of war and I'm on the run."

"The devil you are." He translated the news to his companions. They stared at Embry still more curiously.

"I am a Wing Commander in the Royal Air Force. I was shot down over St. Omer. I've walked and bicycled so far. I'm making for Bordeaux, where I hope to find the British."

"Are you wounded? I saw you limp as you came up to us."

"Only slightly," said Embry. "But it's giving me some trouble."

"Well, let me ask my friends what we can do. It is difficult. There is an armistice, you know, but only between us and the Germans. I don't know how the British stand. We are on the move to lay down our arms."

He conferred with his fellow officers. They came to a decision that appeared to be unanimous.

"We will take you to Limoges. You know of it?"

"Of course," said Embry. "A garrison town. The French Aldershot."

"Precisely. I will drive you there. I have my Captain's permission. Then I can hand you over to the French authorities and they will know what to do and at least dress your leg."

"That's very good of you indeed," said Embry.

"*Pas du tout*. You would do as much for me, Colonel, in similar circumstances."

"Have you any use for this?" said Embry and indicated his bicycle.

"One of my men would be pleased to have it. Thank you."

"I never," said Embry, "want to see another bicycle again in all my life."

"I understand. Now, perhaps, we will start."

"By all means," said Embry.

They reached Limoges in twenty minutes' time and drove directly to the Fortress. Seated in a staff car again with a uniformed officer beside him brought back to Embry's mind the last time he had driven in such circumstances with the German General's coat around him. Then he was being driven into captivity, now to freedom.

He lay in the bed of a single-bed ward of Limoges military hospital where they had dressed his leg, lying midway between sleep and wakening and thought back on all that had happened since he had been led to the Chief of Staff's office. He had been introduced to the General in command of the garrison and had told him his story and his plan to reach Bordeaux. The General had given him papers of identification and a pass to travel free on all French railways. They were safe in the pocket of the high-necked jacket they had presented to him together with a new pair of trousers from their clothing store. There had been great piles of second-hand civilian clothing alongside the military equipment. Then the escorting officer had given him a razor. Now, with his leg treated, he felt at ease.

He wondered how long they would keep him in hospital. He hoped it wouldn't be long. He was still so tired that he felt he could lie there for weeks and let the world go hang while he slept round the night and day but he knew he must still press on with all speed to his objective. It was extraordinary how a few hours could alter the entire situation. No longer need he trudge the roads as a tramp or pedal his way under the blazing sun or torrential rain; when the time came he was going by train, and he would have papers to help him along.

They had been very good to him, sympathetic, responsive, and kind, these French allies. Then he realized that they were allies no longer. The little General was no more a commander except on paper and in so far as it suited his opponents in the field. Embry lay on his warm bed and wondered how he himself would have felt as a member of a defeated army. The very word defeat was horrifying. He turned over on his side, the easier to sleep.

He responded at once to the knock on the door, raising himself on an elbow and calling out, "Come in!"

The French officer who had escorted him and whose razor he was going to use came in and shut the door behind him.

"The General's compliments, Colonel. I have a message for you. The Germans are in the vicinity of Bordeaux, it is not safe for you to try to get there. We are also expecting the Germans to occupy Limoges, possibly tonight. You must go further south at once. The General suggests Toulouse. It is two hundred and ninety miles further on and probably beyond the Germans' advance. We will put you on your way. I am afraid this is a great disappointment for you, but things move very fast these days."

An hour later Embry was being driven in a French staff car to Brive-la-Gaillarde for entrainment to Toulouse.

He spent the night in the requisitioned French barracks at Brive-la-Gaillarde. He was given quarters to himself and before he went down for a meal, he shaved. The vagabond receded from the mirror and a more familiar reflection replaced it. It was like greeting an old friend.

He dined with the French officers of the garrison and there was only one moment amidst all their hospitality which embarrassed him, in so much as he was touched by the gesture which was as practical as it was friendly. A senior company officer approached him.

"You will forgive me," he said, "if I seem presumptuous, but we all know the position that you are in and how precarious it can become any moment. And you have some way to go as yet."

"You have been extremely good to me," said Embry.

"That's as it may be. It would have been the same if the tables had turned the other way. But my friends here realize that when you leave you will need money. We have collected this amongst ourselves. Please to accept it."

He pressed into Embry's hand a roll of five hundred francs.

Embry left Brive-la-Gaillarde at nine o'clock of the following morning. Several of his friends of the previous night saw him off. They drove with him to the station and put him on the train for the French Army Headquarters of Toulouse. *"Bon voyage,"* "Take care of yourself," "Good luck," they cried and waved their hands. Their hands were still aloft as the train steamed out. With the knowledge of the disaster that had befallen them, they seemed to Embry, although they were smiling their farewells, a forlorn, sad party of already forgotten men.

There were several civilians in the carriage and two French officers. The latter eyed Embry curiously, but made no comment as he sank back in his seat and though it was early in the day he went to sleep. There was much leeway to make up.

He awoke to find the French officers in the seat opposite anxiously regarding him.

"Forgive me," one said. "I heard, of course, what my

countrymen and fellow officers said when they bade you farewell. My name is Captain Le Croix. Is your leg hurting?"

"It needs a dressing," said Embry.

"I will see if I can help you."

He left the carriage and within a minute returned with a French nurse. With grave concern she dressed his leg.

"You must take great care of yourself," she said, as she left the compartment.

"You are English, *monsieur*?" It was the second French officer speaking.

"Yes," said Embry.

"There is an English soldier on the train. Would you like to see him?"

"Certainly I should," said Embry.

"Fetch him, Jean," said Le Croix.

"How far have the Germans advanced?" asked Embry.

"I don't know, *monsieur*. There is an armistice and it is being decided what areas shall be occupied. I think I understand your position. Like the others I wish you luck, and for the time being, my services are yours. You go to Toulouse? To our Army Headquarters? Good. I will show you the way. Ah! Here is Jean and the British soldier. Come in, please. Now this is a British officer. You will have much in common."

"Good morning, sir," said the soldier who was in battle-dress. "Glad to see you, sir."

"Take a seat," said Embry and shook hands. "Let's get the preliminaries over. I'm a Wing Commander, R.A.F., shot down at the end of May over St. Omer. Now let's hear your story."

"Name of Bird, sir. Lance-Bombardier, Royal Artillery. I was wounded in the back—splinters—in the fighting up north. They got me into hospital, sir, and everything seemed to be going along okay when the Jerries overran us. You'd scarcely credit the speed of their advance."

"I would," said Embry. "I've been chasing it for several weeks."

"Well, they took over the hospital, sir, just before I became a walking case. It didn't do some of our sick any good, either, but I got on my feet again and one night I was escorted to the latrine in an air raid and I clocked the escort one with my tin hat. Then I got away. I've been travelling in trains ever since, looking for a way out of France."

"Precisely what I'm doing. We'd better join company."

"Nothing I'd like better," said Lance-Bombardier Bird.

The train was slow, stopping at nearly every station, so that they travelled all day, not reaching Toulouse till seven-thirty of the same evening. Captain Le Croix, true to his word, led them to the French Headquarters. He had been stationed at one time in the town and knew the way. Once arrived there, they were soon before the Garrison Intelligence Officer.

Embry showed his papers of authority and identity from Limoges and stated his case.

"There is a ship leaving Marseilles for England to-morrow and she may be the last one to leave."

"That is wonderful news. Then it's Marseilles we want."

"Good luck."

They returned to the station in high spirits. Here at last seemed some opportunity for definite action as against the heart-breaking pursuit of a will o' the wisp.

"When's the next train to Marseilles?" Le Croix inquired at the station.

"There is no train to Marseilles."

"Well, the first train in the morning, then?"

"There are no trains for Marseilles at all tomorrow."

The French Captain explained the news to his companions.

"That's torn it," said Bird.

"Not yet," said Embry. "There's a French Air Force station here. Where's the telephone?"

He got on the telephone to the Station Duty Officer of the French Air Force of Toulouse and gave his credentials and a brief outline of his story.

French Air Headquarters seemed to be on their toes.

"Certainly. If you will report here with your credentials first thing in the morning, say eight fifteen, we will arrange to have either a car or an aeroplane to take you to Marseilles."

Embry returned triumphant to his friends.

"That is excellent," said Le Croix. "And as there is nothing more I can do, *au revoir, monsieur*. And all good fortune."

They shook hands and parted, and so another friend had come and gone.

"I wonder where he's off to," said Embry. "He was a decent chap."

"Losing himself, I daresay," said Bird. "Lots of them do. I've heard them talking in the train—I can pick up a little of the lingo here and there. There's not much cop in being a French officer now. Best to slip off, unobserved, like, and take off your uniform and get absorbed into civvy street and hope for the best."

"It's as bad as that?"

"I think so, sir. They've no anchorage, sir, of any kind. They've nowhere to report to, no headquarters to give them proper instructions. It's not deserting to my mind. You can't desert from something which ain't there."

And with this philosophic statement Lance-Bombardier Bird stretched himself out on the concrete ramp of the station platform where they were sitting, as the hands of the station clock indicated nine of the evening.

"Curfew may be on," he said. "Look at the clock. We'd better stay put. It's not worth taking a risk at this stage of proceedings. I don't know the rules of this town."

"Very well," said Embry.

If his bed was hard and cold nevertheless he could snatch an hour or so of sleep for the coming morning seemed full of promise.

They reached French Air Headquarters punctually at eight fifteen on the following morning. They'd had breakfast in the town on coffee and rolls and Embry had learnt more of his companion's background, of his years with the Green Line Bus Company and his enthusiasm as an Army reservist. He was to Embry's way of thinking a very excellent fellow and a good soldier. It was a pleasure indeed to have him for company. Now so near to the last reach in the long trek to freedom, he was deeply grateful within himself to the Providence that had guided his footsteps through a France swarming with his enemies. It was, he felt, a sure sign of that selfsame Providence that the duty officer with whom he had made contact last night should have been so much on his job and so very ready to co-operate.

He made himself known at the Guard Room and stated that he had an appointment. With whom? Embry explained that it was arranged last night with the officer on duty. It had surely been passed on? Within a few minutes he was being escorted to the Orderly Officer's office. It wouldn't take long now, he told himself, before they would be aboard a steamer bound for England.

The officer who interviewed him was of junior rank and wore a small black moustache along the edge of his upper lip. There was pomade on his marcelled hair. Embry explained the position and repeated the Duty Officer's promise.

"Quite impossible," said the Orderly Officer. "Oh! Quite impossible, without the General's authority and consent."

"But the ship's leaving today."

"You must see the General. I can't possibly author-
ize transport in a case like this. My rank's not high
enough."

Nor ever will be, thought Embry. He said: "When does
the General arrive?

"Oh! About half past nine."

"All that time wasted! And a ship ready to sail! Can't
you get him by phone?"

"*Mon Dieu*, that would be most irregular. He would be
very vexed."

"Have you been in the fighting up north?"

"No. We have been here all the time in reserve."

"So I thought," said Embry.

"Pardon?"

"I will see the General as soon as he comes in, if you
please," said Embry. "And I'd like that to be clearly
understood. Where do I wait?"

The Frenchman shrugged, indicated a door opposite
with his pen and picked up a file from a tray. The interview was over.

Embry fetched Bird from the corridor outside where
he'd been waiting and together they passed into what had
once apparently served as an orderly room.

At nine forty the General arrived at his headquarters
and ten minutes later sent for Embry. He was a middle-
aged little man with a mournful drooping grey moustache
and pince-nez nipped on to a thin red nose.

"I have heard your story," he said, "I will see what I
can do."

"Thank you, sir," said Embry.

There was a pause.

"Is there anything more you want?" asked the General,
as Embry stood waiting.

"Well, the matter is really rather urgent, sir. There's a
ship waiting. . . ."

"Yes . . . yes. I've heard all that," said the General

242

with some irritation. "I've said I will do what I can."

"Very good, sir," said Embry, and as there seemed nothing more for it, withdrew.

Eleven o'clock struck on the headquarters clock and there was still no news from the General. Bird had stopped cursing by now and sat on the edge of one of the orderly room chairs and gnawed a thumb nail. The Orderly Officer had long since left to make his routine rounds. Twelve o'clock passed and there was still no word.

"Do you think the old —— has forgotten us?" said Bird.

"No. He wouldn't do that," said Embry.

By one o'clock he wasn't so sure that his assurance to Bird hadn't been wishful thinking on his part.

Precisely at one thirty an orderly entered the room and told Embry to report to the General. As the orderly was about to saunter off, Embry called him back.

"You'll escort me to the General," he said sharply.

The orderly withdrew a hand that was about to go into a pocket. He very nearly clicked his heels.

The General began to speak as soon as Embry entered the office. He had removed the pince-nez from the bony ridge of his nose and held them between finger and thumb emphasizing his points.

"I have given your case very careful consideration," he said. "Very careful indeed."

It's taken long enough, thought Embry.

"I have looked at it from all angles. You see Marseilles is nearly a hundred and eighty kilometres from here. It's a long way."

Not as long as the Germans' advance, thought Embry.

"I can do nothing."

"I beg your pardon," said Embry, astonished beyond measure.

"I can do nothing," the General repeated.

"But your officer . . . last night. He promised me a car—an aeroplane. . . ."

"I can't be responsible for what a junior officer thinks himself entitled to promise. And I intend to make an example in this instance. The final decision anyway is not mine and I repeat, I regret without referring further to higher authority, that I cannot spare transport at a moment when we may have to move."

"But, sir," said Embry earnestly, "I don't think it's all been made quite clear to you. I've come right down from the north. I've walked a lot of the way with a wounded leg. I've been nearly bumped off more than once. I'm on the run. I'm a wanted man. There's a charge against me. If I'm caught I shall be shot out of hand. And now that I'm nearly home but for the last lap, you can't refuse me a lift to a ship that's waiting only an hour and a half's flying time away."

"I think, monsieur," said the General, "you forget yourself."

"I do not forget myself, sir," said Embry. "That is one luxury that in my circumstances I cannot permit myself. I wish you good day, sir." And he went out.

Together with Bird he hurried back to French Army Headquarters in the town. Six precious hours had been lost. He found, by good fortune, the same Intelligence Officer on duty. He told him what had occurred.

"It's unspeakable," said the Intelligence Officer. "But these things happen. I warn you transport is difficult, but I will see my commanding officer."

He returned a quarter of an hour later. "If you will report to the guard room you will find a car and a driver to take you and your friend to Marseilles."

"God bless your soul," said Embry and meant it.

They drove steadily all through the afternoon and early evening, only stopping for a hurried meal and to buy a couple of bottles of wine to take with them. When night fell they seemed to increase their speed with the roads comparatively free from traffic. The stars glittered above in a cloudless sky. They reached Marseilles at six thirty on the morning of 27th June.

They drove at once to the docks and found the Harbour Master's office without any difficulty.

"There is a ship," said Embry, "that is sailing for England. . . ."

"There was," said the Harbour Master. "She sailed just over two hours ago, at dawn."

CHAPTER TWENTY

"Now when you've finished swearing," said Embry to Bird, "I will explain a certain attitude of mind which I've come to adopt of late."

They sat with the driver of the French staff car in a café by the Marseilles dock-side.

"Since we have joined up together," he continued, "you'll have to get used to my view-points. From the very hour I broke from the Calais column I've had disappointment after disappointment, despite the terrific kindnesses I've met with from different people. I'm not shooting a line when I tell you I've been down for the count more times than I care to remember, but I resolved on one thing one night when I was alone and hungry and pretty well all in and that was that whatever happened I'd never look back, but always think forward with hope. This isn't a sermon I'm giving you but a protective measure, as it were, which you can adapt to your own use, because there are no two ways about this racket in which we're involved. You're in it up to your neck willy-nilly and it's your neck or nothing! That's all there is to it. When I was operating my Squadron before I was shot down I told them since we'd got to have a war they could damn well enjoy it, and since you and I are escapists, we might just as well have our money's worth and make a bellyful of it. Get it?"

"I do, sir," said Lance-Bombardier Bird slowly.

Embry left them at their meal and went into the town and had a hair cut. He bought a map and had studied it even before he rejoined his companion.

"Port Vendres," he said, pointing out the town on the map to Bird. "It's right on the Franco-Spanish border and is on the coast. It looks as likely a place as any."

The driver rose to his feet.

"*Au revoir, monsieur*. I must return now."

"You'll take us to Port Vendres?"

"My duty was to bring you here. I cannot go out of my way. It is not allowed."

"See here," said Embry and indicated the map, "Narbonne is on your way back to Toulouse. Drop us there and we'll take the train."

" Well, I see no harm in that. . . ."

Embry and Bird arrived at Port Vendres by way of Narbonne in the early morning of 28th June.

It was a typical town of its kind, drenched with the southern sun that shone from its perpetually blue and cloudless sky, while the sea, a deeper blue, tideless and on this particular morning as placid as a lake, reached up to the yellow sands and to the harbour.

They walked round the town and chose a café and went in. The proprietor, who was already about, dusting down his table tops, attended to them at once with an alacrity that revealed an amiable spirit. He was a fat little man with waxed moustache and a habit of rolling his eyes. He stood beside them while they ate.

"You have come far, *messieurs*?"

He spoke quite fair English, learnt no doubt from the tourists of happier days.

"A long way," said Embry.

The proprietor glanced at Bird's battledress.

"You were fighting the Germans, eh?"

"Trying to," said Bird.

"And you too, *monsieur*?"

"Yes," said Embry.

"And you are English, both of you?"

247

"We are."

"I expect you are hoping to get to England?"

"Quite right," said Embry.

"It is very difficult. But I would do anything to help you if I could."

"That is very kind of you."

"No. My son was killed in the retreat. Now, Perpignan is not very far from here and there is an English consul there."

"That might be very useful," said Embry.

"Excuse—there are some customers. They come here each day. They are Belgian. I think it would be safe for you to meet them. They are like you. We know each other by our Christian names, that is all. These days people come and go and all have their stories but you seldom hear them. I suppose even walls have ears and it is not always good to know who is who and what he is up to." And then raising his voice and speaking in French: "*Messieurs*, please to come this way. Here are friends for you."

They crossed towards the proprietor at once, two Belgian officers in uniform and another in mufti. The proprietor introduced them: André, tall and slim with greying hair; Leopold, his son, a young subaltern; Philippe, in civilian clothes. They all had a smattering of English.

"Are you trying to get out of France as well?" asked Embry.

"Certainly we are. That is why we have come down to the coast. We have a motor van which we have left concealed outside the town."

"There are no boats sailing anywhere," said the proprietor, "as the port is coming under Italian control. That will be nice, will it not, to have Italians here who have done nothing for themselves, but have stabbed us in the back. Bah!"

"When are they coming in?"

248

"Soon. And then it will not be good for you here. It will be as bad as having Germans about. Now see, here is another customer of mine, who likes the early hours. I think he is an Englishman, too."

But the newcomer had already joined the group round the table and nodded a greeting to the three Belgians. The proprietor effected further introductions.

"His name is Bill. I know nothing else."

"And a very good thing too," said Bill. "Fetch me some coffee and an omelette."

He looked round at his companions as the proprietor went to his kitchen at the back of the café

"Well, two more to join our select company. And if I'm not mistaken two English soldiers on the run. What a set we are!"

"One English Air Force officer," said Bird, "and one full lance-bombardier. And that's the form."

"As for myself," said Bill, "late of the Foreign Legion. That is to say about to be late of. In short a legionnaire who is contemplating desertion. We have barracks here, you know. Discipline is very slack at the moment but even so if they thought I was deserting back to England they'd shoot me, the cads."

"You going back to England?" said Embry.

"I hope so."

"How?"

"God only knows," said Bill.

"There are no boats," said André.

"There are boats in plenty," said Leopold, "but they are not allowed to sail."

"Then we help ourselves to a boat," said Embry. "It's quite simple."

"You mean we steal one?"

"Definitely I do."

"When?"

"Tonight," said Embry.

"That's what I like to hear," said Bill.

"And how do we go about it?" asked André.

"First of all," said Embry, "we make this café our headquarters. Then we always have a meeting-place laid on. Then this afternoon we'll make a reconnaissance. I suggest we three Englishmen do it to save any language difficulties in an emergency. We'll all meet again here at five o'clock and I'll tell you what we've found and what the plan is to be."

They made their reconnaissance after lunch, making their way separately round the harbour so as not to attract attention. The harbour contained craft of all kinds; private yachts, fishing vessels of the twenty-five foot class, some felucca rigged, small motor cruisers and the usual assembly of dinghies on their outhaul moorings or buoyed off.

To Embry, leaning over the low wall that edged the quayside of the inner arm of the harbour, it seemed that none of these offered a practical proposition. In nearly every case a likely looking vessel was moored by buoy in the middle of the harbour and it would mean in the first instance seizing a dinghy to reach her, a complicated manoeuvre which was bound to be both heard and seen. The only other course would be to swim out and clamber aboard. He could hardly imagine six swimmers in a harbour as small as this completing their course without being observed. Then he saw Bird by a small jetty which jutted out from the other arm of the harbour.

He was sitting on a bollard which carried the forward mooring rope of a motor launch of some thirty-five feet tied up alongside. She was a useful looking vessel but was not, Embry felt, a privately owned craft.

Bird had taken a packet of cigarettes from his pocket and as Embry watched he saw him proffer the packet to a deck-hand leaning across the taffrail of the launch. A moment later Bird was aboard and talking to the other as if he had known him all his life. Then they went below.

It seemed to Embry that the affair could not have been left in better hands. Other things being equal, he had already decided to seize the launch.

He wandered round the harbour trying to commit to memory any outstanding features. He wondered if stealing a boat from her moorings amounted to piracy. He hoped it did. It made a pleasant addition to his already spectacular list of crimes. But it was on the foreshore that he found the open drain.

It was a large pipe, more than wide enough to hold a man. He peered in and though there was a trickle of clear water at the bottom there was neither sewage nor refuse. He had no idea for what it was intended but in one instance it would serve a very useful purpose; here, when their plan would be finally evolved, he would hide till darkness came and it was the moment to strike. It was not more than fifty yards from the jetty. It was an admirable position.

At five o'clock they all met again at the café. The plan was developed and completed.

It ran in this wise. First of all Bird reported on the vessel by the jetty. She was a Customs launch and he had fraternized with the only hand on board. A nice young chap, Bird said, and he felt a bit sorry for him in case there were accidents in the dark; nevertheless he'd been very obliging and he'd taken Bird all over the vessel. She was oil driven and her tanks were full of fuel. It appeared she was always kept in a state of immediate sea-worthiness in view of her calling. She was moored fore and aft with a single one-loop splice slipped over a bollard. She could be cast off in a matter of seconds. She was ideal for their purpose.

"But this is a miracle," said André. "The very vessel we need."

Embry motioned him to silence. He'd had a surfeit of miracles latterly.

"Very well," he said, "that's fine. Now we'll get it all worked out. Does anybody know about the local curfew?"

"It's before dark," said Leopold.

"That's a damn nuisance," said Embry, "but we'll have to take our chance. You'll all have to hide yourselves in some convenient place as near the jetty as possible. I myself have found a drain and I shall use that together with Bill here, because I suggest that he and I seize the boat, while Bird casts off. So the drill is this: hide and as soon as it is dark keep the closest watch on the launch. As soon as you see Bill and myself approach the boat, be prepared to get cracking. Bill and I will get on board first and deal with any of the crew. You others immediately follow us in case we need any reinforcements, though it doesn't look as if we shall. Bird will come last as he knows how she's moored and can cast off. Meantime Bill and I below will get down to the engines and start her up. Last of all Bird will come aboard. As soon as we're clear of the harbour we'll hold course out to sea and then after an hour we'll put about to starboard. When dawn comes we should have the coast still in view but we'll have held off sufficiently to clear any obstacles. Anyway, that's how I see it. Agreed?"

"That's fine," said Bill. "No wonder you ought to be a general."

"It's yet to be proved," said Embry, "what kind of a sailor I'll make. All right, let's go."

It was more cramped than he would have imagined in the drain and the constant trickle of water was extremely irritating. Bird in the morning had complained of his back, remarking with a sinister satisfaction that if they both didn't get proper medical attention very soon they'd be dead from septicaemia.

The round disc of light at the end of the pipe was growing dimmer. Soon it would be dusk. Bill behind him was stirring restlessly and muttering to himself. This act of piracy was, Embry thought, going to be a tricky business. He hoped his plan had been rightly conceived. Then he saw silhouetted in the disc of light a pair of legs.

He was so astonished that he nearly called out to his companion, but even before he could move he heard the shout:

"Fiche-moi le camp!"

Bill behind him heard and gasped: "What the devil's up?"

It came again: *"Fiche-moi le camp!"* and Bill grabbed Embry's ankle and asked who was telling them to get the hell out of this? Then the legs disappeared and a light was flashed in.

"It's the —— police," said Bill. "We'd better get out of this, or they may begin to shoot. They're quite half-witted. I know them."

They crawled out. Two French Air Force Special Police stood at the opening of the drain.

"You will come with us."

Bill broke into voluble French. Whatever he was saying it seemed to Embry extremely convincing but one of the policemen tapped his holster and jerked his thumb toward the town.

"Non," said Bill. *" Non . . . non. . . ."*

He recommenced his argument. The other policeman seized him by the arm.

"They won't listen to me," said Bill to Embry. "They're going to take us up before the local authorities."

"That'll fix us," said Embry.

"Qu'est-ce que vous dîtes?" asked a policeman.

"The clots don't speak English," said Bill. "Come quietly. Don't put up a show. Just do what I do."

They were marched off along the foreshore.

253

As they left the beach and gained the road Embry looked back over his shoulder and saw André a hundred yards away, hurrying across the street towards the café. At any rate the rest of the company knew what had happened but it was an awkward predicament that he and Bill were in. Any contact with police authority was highly undesirable. Though the Germans were not in Port Vendres the Italians were coming and no doubt there would be liaison between the two and all suspected persons would be very forcibly grilled.

He looked at their escort. There was an unmistakable air of second-rate troops about them. The half-shaven chin, the tufts of hair beneath the cap, the uncleaned boots. Nevertheless they were armed. They crossed the road and turned into a street lined with shops. Several passers-by turned and stared at them and one small boy put a finger to his nose and made a sound through his lips like the tearing of calico.

"When I say 'now,'" said Bill, "just follow me."

"Silence!"

They walked solemnly on.

"Now!" said Bill.

He darted down a side street with Embry after him. He heard a shout from behind but nobody fired and Bill was round a corner. As Embry followed he saw the legionnaire leap at a wall, claw at the top, then force himself over. Embry met him on the other side. They were in a small back garden. A path ran down the side of a house with green shuttered windows.

"Come on," said Bill.

He seemed to know his way as one familiar to breaking bounds. They ran down the path and into a street running sharply uphill.

"We can walk now," said Bill.

"Where are we making for?"

"My barracks. They won't have missed me yet. And the

police won't follow us there. They're a half-hearted lot."
They entered the barracks by another back wall.

"Just as well," Bill explained. "Though it's quite likely
the sentry at the guard room's asleep. We're not what we
were, you know."

He led the way across the square to a barrack block.

The room in which Embry found himself was barely
a quarter full. Many of the beds were empty or filled with
equipment or uniforms. It was almost dark by now and
the few occupants of the room were asleep. Embry chose
a bed, pulled the blankets round him, and almost before
Bill left him was himself sleeping.

He woke, wondering for a moment if he were in his
own room in the Headquarters of Brive-la-Gaillarde,
then he remembered with a start where he was and what
had happened the night before. He wondered if André
had had the sense to make contact with Bird and the
others. He had no wish, as yet, to dissolve the partnership
of friends. If last night's attempt had proved abortive, it
didn't mean that they couldn't try again. He looked at
his watch and saw it was close on seven. He rose, left the
barrack block, and, climbing back over the wall by which
they had entered, made his way down to the harbour and
the café which they had chosen as headquarters.

By eight o'clock everyone except Bill was present.

"We'll give him till nine," said Embry.

"And then?" said André.

"Perpignan," said Embry. "Perpignan because we have
got to quit this town with the Italians coming in and with
last night's escapade on our record and because there's a
British Consul at Perpignan who may help us. Where
have you left the motor-van?"

"In a field behind a haystack just out of the town."

"And how are you off for petrol?"

"Plenty of coupons. They're fakes, but they work."

At half past nine the party was seated resting at the

roadside a mile outside Port Vendres. The sun was already high and it was growing hot. There had been no sign of the legionnaire. Embry never saw Bill again. But if previously he had longed for company now it was with him in abundance, but there was more to come.

She came pedalling along the dusty road on her bicycle, dark, and young, and very pretty. It was characteristic of her that, having once made up her mind, she acted without hesitation or any false modesty. She stopped her bicycle where Embry sat in the hedge and said to him, without the least embarrassment: "Are you British or American?"

He admired her perspicacity.

"British," he said promptly. Adding: "Why?"

"Are you trying to get out of France?"

"Maybe," he said. "Now what makes you ask me that?"

"Because I am," she said bluntly.

"But you are a Frenchwoman? Why do you want to leave your own country at a time like this?"

"Yes," she said, leaning over her bicycle and staring solemnly down at him. "Yes, I'm French. But I've fought the Germans in my own fashion. It's not a kind of fighting you'd know much about, I expect. You're a soldier?"

"Air Force," said Embry.

"Ah! You do your work in the open, whereas I and my friends. . . ." She broke off. "The Germans don't like me," she said. "I've been riding away from them for days. I get rather terrified about it all sometimes, I'm afraid. All on my own. . . ."

"You'd better join us," said Embry.

She looked slowly along the group of men seated before her.

"I'd like to join you. Only. . . ."

"Well?" said Embry.

"I might be safer alone," she said slowly.

"You'll be safe with me," he said. "I'll give you my word for that."

She smiled.

"Then I'll join you. And I may be able to help you, too."

She laid the bicycle in the hedge and sat down beside him.

"Now tell me your plans," she said. "And my name's Anna-Louise."

CHAPTER TWENTY-ONE

THEY found the van intact where André had left it. As they drove to Perpignan Embry told Anna-Louise of their abortive attempt at stealing a ship.

"We were lucky not to get pinched. But we'll get one yet."

"I know the coast," she said. "We must try all the little villages and harbours."

He found the Vice-Consul without difficulty, leaving his companions with the van at the steps of the Consulate.

"Which is the best way to get out of France?" asked Embry.

"The easiest way from here would be through Spain, but the Franco-Spanish frontier is definitely closed. It may be open again in a few weeks, I don't know."

"If it's a question of weeks," said Embry, "it's no good to me. I can't wait indefinitely because I've got no money. I shall have to hire a boat. . . ."

"With no money?"

"We could just scrape up enough for that between us, if it was reasonable. Or, better still, steal one."

"They'll make it hot for you if they catch you."

"They've got to catch me first. So in case I do have any luck would you tell the British Consul at Barcelona what I'm going to do so that he can arrange with the Navy to keep a look out."

"I'll do my best," said the Consul.

When Embry returned to the van he found the party still further augmented by two Americans, both in the official uniform of war correspondents. They were, they said, very glad to meet him and they'd got the low-down on the set-up from André. So this, then, was Clifford, or Cliff for short, and pleased to shake him by the hand, and this was Wally and they'd be joining in along with the party and all the more the merrier. It seemed to Embry that they'd be needing a small liner before they'd finished.

So there were eight of them: André, Philippe, Leopold, Lance-Bombardier Bird, Wally and Cliff, Embry and Anna-Louise, on 30th June, with one motor-van to carry them and with very little money to help them on their way; and the way they chose was along the coast road running towards Marseilles, so that they could branch down from time to time to where the little fishing villages lay.

It seemed to Embry that this new kind of life of his had taken on another particular phase. In the first weeks, despite his two recaptures, Nature had, to a great extent, bidden for first place as his opponent; now it was a battle of wits, of contriving and scheming and scrapping a plan when it failed.

They worked their way as far as Sette dropping down to the little harbours. In every instance the story was the same. If a vessel were unguarded and it were practical to take her, then if she were a motor-boat she was unfuelled or, if a sailing-boat, her sails had been carried bodily away by the owner after each use.

In Sette itself, in company with André, he interviewed a shipping owner who had traded in peacetime across to the French North African coast, but all inducements were in vain. All trading was at a standstill and no one was venturing forth. Every night they slept in barns and outhouses and Anna-Louise bathed and dressed Embry's festering leg and Bird's back. Both men at night kept guard over her on either side, each with his back propped against the wall. And Anna-Louise slept safe.

But they were running short of money. It was Embry's chief concern at the time though he felt sure, with that characteristic unshakable confidence, that sooner or later they would strike lucky. He sat one morning in a café with Philippe, who later was to die tortured at the hands of the Gestapo, listening to the boy's memories of his home, while the others scoured the town and Anna-Louise had left them to shop with their last franc.

"My father thinks our party has become too big, too cumbersome."

"I'm not so sure he isn't right," said Embry.

"And these constant setbacks put people's tempers on edge."

"Don't take any notice of that," said Embry.

"Well, you don't, I know. But you are a commander, someone who leads men instinctively and therefore when anything is for the common good you keep your temper— or if it is not for the common good you lose your temper. But the cause comes first with you."

Anna-Louise returned to the café and she carried with her a great piece of cheese besides the two loaves of bread.

"See!" she said. "That will do you good and make you strong. Better than the husks and weak coffee that we have."

"Where did you get it all?" said Embry.

"I bought it. We have to live. All of us have to live."

"Where did you get the money, Anna-Louise?"

"I had what remained of my jewellery."

"You sold it?"

"Yes."

"All of it?"

"All of it, yes."

"And what did you get?"

"Two thousand francs."

"You sold your jewellery for us?"

"Yes. We can't eat jewels, but we can eat bread."

"All you had left in the world!'

"It doesn't matter. I know it was right for me to do it."

On 3rd July he passed Philippe's remark on to Bird. It was early in the morning and they were washing themselves in a little stream that flowed through the field adjoining the barn in which they had all slept. During the night the two Americans had fallen out with one another, over the temporary ownership of a pile of sacks which served as bedding, a trivial but unpleasant bickering, indicative of the mood of the party.

Embry said: "This show's getting out of hand. We've been playing about, getting nowhere."

"Too many bosses with too many ideas," said Bird.

"I think we'll split up."

"Not you and me, sir."

"Not us. We'll stick together. And maybe we'll ask Anna-Louise to come along, too."

"That's the ticket, sir."

"Then we'll go into Perpignan and see the Consul again. The situation may have changed. Anyway I'll tell him we've failed to get a boat and ask him to get in touch with the Vice-Consul at Barcelona. We want to try to get into Spain."

He announced his intention when he rejoined the others. There were protests at first but, even so, he thought he detected a certain half-heartedness in what was intended to be fervour. He knew that at the back of their minds they thought he was right. He drew Anna-Louise aside.

"Will you join Bird and me?"

She regarded him steadily, searching for an answer, as it were, in his own expression. He was as collected as she was.

"Well?"

"You both need someone to look after you."

He was amused at her necessity of having to discover some more commonplace motive than friendship to justify her choice. He wondered what would have happened to her if it had not been for himself and Bird.

"Well, will you come with us?"

"What's your plan?"

"Perpignan first to see the Consul again and then try to get in touch with Barcelona and so into Spain."

The reaction was immediate.

"Not Spain," she said.

"Of course. It's the nearest neutral, isn't it? None of our consuls in France with the situation as it is are permitted by international law to help us out of a belligerent's country. It's only in neutral countries they can really do anything practical."

"I cannot go to Spain," she said.

"Why ever not?"

"I was there before. In the Spanish War. If they recognized me. . . ." She stopped short. "What am I saying?" she said. "Oh, no! No, I could never go to Spain."

He said goodbye to them all then. The last of them to whom he spoke was Anna-Louise. She handed him a wad of five hundred francs in notes. He pocketed them with brief thanks. There was no need for any profuse show of gratitude. She had raised the money in her own way for a purpose she had duly pondered. It was an impersonal gift. It was her contribution to the cause.

"Goodbye," she said, "God look after you both."

Later in the train to Perpignan, Bird said: "Turned me up a bit, saying goodbye to Anna-Louise, sir. You don't come across many like that. Meek and mild to look at and as pretty as the day, but tough as billy-o inside. It makes you think. She never let on what she'd been up to, did she? The Jerries are after her right enough and she seems to have been in trouble in Spain. See how she shied off that. I reckon she's a secret agent of some kind. 'Cor, wouldn't my old ma like to know I've been around with a Mata Hari in real life. What's our chances of the Consul helping us?"

"I don't know," said Embry. "It depends, I should imagine, what is happening on the frontier. Everything's in a state of flux. We don't seem even to know what the armistice terms between the Germans and the French are and if they affect the situation. Anyway, we can get all that gen. from the Consul."

He was over-optimistic. They reached Perpignan only to find that the Consul had left permanently for Nice.

They went to the Préfecture, on an inspiration of Embry's. He could, he felt, just afford to make his position clear. With the only link with his own country-men gone, there was indeed little else he could do. And the English were well known in Perpignan in peacetime. The town had been, amongst others, a favourite resort with the Duke of Windsor, when Prince of Wales. Maybe English stock was good.

It appeared to be so in the very first instance when he approached the inquiry desk of the Préfecture. He spoke to a young and intelligent girl who took in the situation at a glance of Bird's battledress. She at once led Embry upstairs to the Chief of Police.

"I and my friend want to get into Spain," said Embry. "The reasons are obvious, I take it. I've been once to the English Consul, but he's now left for Nice, so I've no option but to come to you. I'm sure you'll understand."

"I understand perfectly, *monsieur*, but there is very little I can do. The frontier is closed and the terms of the armistice very definitely state that no Frenchman in any capacity can assist the enemies of Germany. My hands are completely tied."

"And I walk from St. Omer to Paris and then at last get as far as this and then get stuck. It's a bit tough," said Embry.

"There is one possibility," said the Chief.

He drew his writing-pad towards him, wrote a hurried note, placed it in an envelope and sealed it and handed it to Embry. Even at this stage and despite being in police headquarters, the affair had an air of mystery about it.

"The name is Ferrera," said the Chief, indicating the address on the envelope. "That's where he lives and the note you hold is an introduction to him. He is an Argentine in business here."

"Do you think he can help us?"

"You can try."

"You think he has some pull, some influence?"

The Chief's face was blank.

"I said you could try, *monsieur*."

"Thank you," said Embry, and left.

It was easy enough to find Señor Ferrera. It was easy to assess his income from his surroundings and his appearance. From his little dark moustache to the toe-tips of his pointed shining shoes he looked the successful business man, the financier or professional gambler, the restaurateur or an inside man on foreign exchange, anything indeed suggesting a millionaire.

He read the Chief of Police's note and then very deliberately tore it into very small fragments and dropped them into the waste-paper basket at the side of his desk.

"I see," said Señor Ferrera. "This all sounds very interesting."

He picked up the telephone.

"Give me the Grand Hotel, please."

"Do you think you can fix something?" said Embry.

"Perhaps."

"You'll earn my undying gratitude. . . ."

"I have many connexions with England. There is the

264

meat trade with the Argentine and Great Britain. And then, of course, British coal—Ah! Is that the Grand Hotel? . . . This is Señor Ferrera speaking. I want a double room . . . for two gentlemen and I will arrange matters with you when I am next in town . . . yes, that is right . . . also your waiter Felix, I would like him to attend to them for the time being . . . they will be spending much of their time in their room. . . . Yes, that is all, thank you."

He proffered a gold cigarette-case.

"No, thanks," said Embry, "I don't smoke. Did you have any luck?"

"Oh, that was just a mere matter of your accommodation. You will find the Grand Hotel very comfortable. It is where His Royal Highness the Prince of Wales liked to stay. His waiter Felix will be looking after you. You need rest and good food and I think it would be wiser for the next twelve hours or so to keep yourselves to yourselves till we see how the land lies. You know what it is these days. You never know who's who."

"I'm very grateful to you," said Embry, "but the cut of my clothes isn't quite up to the standard and my friend outside's in battle-dress. But chiefly, of course, when you're on the run you don't carry a lot of money. A bit beyond my means, I'm afraid."

"But not beyond mine, *monsieur*. That is *my* pleasure."

"How do I thank you?" said Embry. "How do I thank all these people, the poor as well as the rich, who've done so much for me?"

"You don't have to. All you have to do, *monsieur*, is very simple. Escape! Get back to England. And then when the day comes, as it will, return." He spoke with astonishing vehemence. "Return and with victory at your finger tips, drive these swine back even farther than Berlin!"

One night a hedgerow for sleeping quarters, another

night a fine château all to himself. One night a barn with a trickling stream outside, the next a palatial bed-chamber. Fine linen for coarse sacking, soft blankets for thistled hay. Grey bread and thin coffee for a bottle of Château Pontet Canet and a bowl of bouillabaisse with cannalonies to follow. A strange, strange world that a war had made.

They stayed in their room all the next day and Felix, the waiter, attended to their wants and they knew without questioning that he, too, was in this conspiracy of mercy and goodwill. But in the evening Ferrera himself arrived and took Embry aside into a private room. He had news and instructions for him.

"The position is this," he said. "The Germans have contrived a security area between Perpignan and the Spanish frontier. That is to say, even if the frontier were open it would still be difficult to get into Spain because without your papers in order this would be for you a forbidden area. Now is that quite clear?"

"Perfectly," said Embry.

"Very well! If you can reach the frontier you may find some way of getting over. That I can't tell and there I cannot help you. But I may be able to get you through this security area to the frontier."

"That's absolutely marvellous," said Embry.

"You are not there yet. We all have to take a chance on this. *Maintenant, attendez!* Tomorrow morning at eight o'clock a car will pull up fifteen yards from the left-hand side of the entrance of this hotel."

"The left-hand as from going out?"

"Precisely. As from going out. It will be a closed limousine, black, with a thin white stripe along the top of the bodywork. It will be a Renault and there will be two men in the front. The driver will wear a chauffeur's cap with a white cover. The man beside him will wear a straw panama hat. Is that perfectly clear?"

"Yes."

"As soon as the car pulls up, get in. Not a word is to be said, no greetings, no questions. As soon as you drive off, make yourselves comfortable well back in your seats. If luck is with you, you should get through to Le Perthous, which is so much on the frontier that one half of the place is in France and the other half is in Spain. The actual barrier runs across the street in the middle of the village. There you will be dropped. There is no need to thank your escort, just get out and again, without a word, depart. Now that is my answer to your request. I wish you all the good fortune in the world. Good luck to you!" He shook Embry by the hand and left.

Embry took Bird down to the lounge of the hotel in the latter part of the evening and mingled with the rest of the guests. It was characteristic of the times that scarcely anyone displayed any concern at their costumes or appearance, on the contrary, before long Embry had struck up an acquaintance with a middle-aged English-woman who had been caught by the war, as a tourist in France. The three of them shared a bottle of champagne and the woman promised to take a message to the Air Ministry, when she succeeded in reaching England, to the effect that Embry was out of German hands and on the way back.

The surroundings, the wine, the contact with a country-woman in circumstances so nearly normal, together with the promise of tomorrow, put fresh spirit into the two men.

They were in position, fifteen yards left of the entrance to the Grand Hotel at precisely eight o'clock on the following morning, 5th July. At this hour there was little traffic and few pedestrians. It was a fine bright day and the prospect of making vital progress seemed auspicious. With a reasonable element of luck they would be actually

267

at the frontier within a few hours' time, but the minutes passed by and there was no sign of a black closed car with a white stripe round its bodywork.

"Do you think we've been done in the eye, sir?" asked Bird.

"I don't think so," said Embry. "He wouldn't have gone to such lengths as he's already done only to let us down at the end. At the worst we've had a rest and a spot of comfort at his expense and we also know the name of the village to make for."

At a quarter to nine Embry was getting anxious. There was more traffic now, the town had taken its *petit déjeuner* and was astir. Moreover, their presence on the pavement had attracted the attention of several passers-by. Then at the very stroke of nine Bird tapped Embry on the arm.

They were there, the man in the white covered chauffeur's hat and the man beside him with the straw panama. They sat at the kerbside in the front seat of a black closed car with a white line round its bodywork. It was all so exact in detail as it had been described, that, together with the silent men staring stolidly in front of them, there was something both slightly fantastic and ludicrous; so that it was almost a temptation to greet them heartily to see if they were real.

Embry climbed in and Bird followed. The moment the door was closed the car started off. The two broad backs in the front seat scarcely stirred and Embry caught Bird's eye and the latter began to giggle under his breath.

"Shut up," whispered Embry.

Bird writhed into silence.

They drove out of Perpignan and no one molested them. It seemed to Embry a most extraordinary journey, so pregnant was it with purpose. They passed a police patrol without a question being raised, then they went through two villages where there were check-points. At the first they passed right through and Embry noticed that one of the police on duty turned his back; at the second block they were forced to draw up because of a small traffic block. Identification papers were being examined. It seemed to Embry that here and now was an end to this apparently best laid of schemes.

He looked at Bird, lolling back in his corner and his battle-dress appeared to fill the whole of the seat so that the merest half-wit would have known that at least one of the occupants was a British soldier. The car crawled forward a pace or two and their turn came, but instead of stopping they accelerated and drove calmly through. A few minutes later, they were on the open road again.

The end of their journey had the same strange element of mystery. The car stopped in the main street of a large village. There was no indication whether this was their destination or not, other than the stopping of the car. Neither the driver nor his companion made any attempt to move, far less to speak. Embry and Bird climbed out and the latter shut the door. The car drove off.

"I've had some pretty odd experiences," said Embry. "But that's one of the most curious. Somebody must have been pretty well squared. This must be Le Perthous. Let's get our bearings."

They walked down the main street which was remarkably busy for so small a place. The pavements were crowded and there were a considerable number of cars mostly moving forward in one direction. Embry saw the barrier across the street and the police post beside it.

It was there, immediately before him.

A barrier and a few men in uniform. That was all. But it was the frontier. It was Eldorado. It was Le Perthous, the village that shared the border. He caught at Bird's hand.

"There it is," he said.

There was no need to explain what he indicated. They stood side by side and watched the cars glide up, stop, make their identification clear and pass on. Now and again a pedestrian would move up and the same procedure followed. Once a man with a knapsack over his shoulder was turned away.

They moved forward, so they could see beyond the post. There was a wall beyond on the left, ending some fifteen yards further in a café. There were tables and chairs on the pavement outside and a man and a woman were drinking. It seemed ridiculous to think that they were in Spain while he himself and Bird were still in France. Between him and freedom, then, was only a wooden barrier. Could that be so formidable an obstacle as it was made out to be?

"Let's get to the police station," said Embry, "and find out where the Consul hangs out."

"Spain," said Bird. "Bli'me, only a flea's hop away!"

CHAPTER TWENTY-TWO

THERE were people of all nationalities at the police station. They crowded round the entrance and swarmed up the stairs, while others loitered on the pavement or lounged against the wall outside. There was a babbling of voices in many tongues, clamouring, demanding and all to the same purpose—to get out of France!

Embry pushed his way through and asked at the inquiry desk where he could find the British Vice-Consul. He felt sure his difficulties were practically at an end.

"British Consul?" The attendant spoke fair English. "There is no resident British Consul. How can *you* get in touch with *your* consul in Madrid? I do not know."

"But there must be some way," said Embry.

"There is a Mr. Dickens, who calls here three times a week."

"What's he got to do with it?"

"He comes from the consulate at Barcelona."

"That's the very man," said Embry.

"Is it?" said the attendant.

"Of course it is," said Embry. "What are his calling days?"

"I don't know."

"Oh hell!" said Embry.

He returned to the main entrance with Bird.

"Where the devil are we going to stay?" he said. "We've got to watch every penny now."

There was a movement amongst the crowd on the pavement as a car drove up. Two gendarmes ran down the steps and cleared a passage for the visitor. A tall man with an attaché case under his arm alighted from the car as the gendarmes saluted.

"This is our man," said Embry. "I'll bet you it is." He stepped forward as the other approached.

"Excuse me," said Embry, "but are you Mr. Dickens from the Consulate at Barcelona?"

"I am."

"My name is Wing Commander Embry. May I have a word with you?"

"Of course. Come along to my room."

Ten minutes later Embry had told his story.

"Remarkable," said Dickens. "But what's the next move?"

"That's what I'm asking you," said Embry.

"Of course, I'll do anything I can. But it's not going to be as easy as you think, you know. You've got to have passports to get out and into Spain, if you want to travel openly. And it's no good unless you do travel openly, because even if you did manage to slip through here which mightn't be too difficult, perhaps, then the Spanish have checking posts and patrols as far as fifteen miles within their side of the border. The first one, in fact, is only five miles over the frontier. If you were stopped and couldn't produce your authority, you'd be arrested and sent back at once."

"Well, where do we get passports?"

"The Embassy is not permitted to issue them. Our hands are tied by diplomatic custom. We can help you in every way when you're in neutral territory but it would be a grave infringement to assist you when you're still in enemy occupied territory. Of course, there are ways and means of getting passports, but then you've got to get them visa'ed, firstly by the Spanish to let you in, and then by the French to let you out."

"But this is maddening," said Embry, "I thought I'd

had everything, but now it looks as if I'm going to get strangled in red tape."

"Well, the first thing is to get quarters for you," said Dickens. "I'll arrange for you both to stay at the police station here. Meantime I'll make further enquiries when I get back to Barcelona and you do what you can at this end."

They stayed in the police station for nearly a fortnight. Dickens came and went on his regular visits but still the frontier was closed to them. It was infuriating to watch the legitimate travellers passing through and the sense of frustration increased as each day passed. Then, in a casual way, as these things occur, they chanced on two passports, but if it had been difficult to procure them it was just as difficult to resemble them.

"Your bloke," said Bird, who'd been practising before a mirror in the police station ablution benches, "has a much thicker neck than you. Squeeze yourself up a bit, sir. That's better. I think you'll pass. Passport photographs never do look like anybody, anyway."

"We'll have to get them visa'ed. Dickens told me that."

"That'll mean back to Perpignan. And how can we manage that?"

"We'll be all right with these bits of paper. Now this is the plan. We take the bus to Perpignan, buy some proper civilian clothes, have some new photos taken and exchange them with these others. The only risk we run is between here and Perpignan. If we're challenged we shall have to try to look as much like these as we can. Once we've got the new photos exchanged we're okay. After that we come on back here and go straight through without any trouble at all. It ought to be a piece of cake."

They were not challenged on their way to Perpignan. They each bought a suit and Embry added to his a dark-green felt hat with a cord round the brim and bobbins on it. Then they had their photographs taken and made the necessary exchange. The plan was proceeding excellently.

"Now for the Spanish Embassy," said Embry.

"It's nice feeling like a civvy again," said Bird.

"It won't be long till you're back with your regiment now."

"Do you think we'll get these visas all right?"

"Why on earth not?" said Embry.

"Well, because every time something crops up in our favour we generally get something to set us back."

A special room had been set apart at the Spanish Consulate for the signing of visas. There were three officials at work, each with his own cubicle and counter, while a fourth supervised the applicants as they came in. A photo of Franco hung on the wall.

Embry with both passports in his hand was about to approach the nearest official when there was a sudden shout from behind him.

The supervisor flung out an arm in wild gesticulation. He was gabbling Spanish all the time.

"What the hell's this in aid of?" said Embry.

It was clear by the repeated gestures in their direction that both Embry and Bird had committed some outrage.

"They're hopping mad," said Bird. "What the hell's the matter with them? Look at that type shaking his fist."

They were pointing now first at Embry and then at the photo of Franco on the wall. Someone raised a hand in the Fascist salute.

"Holy smoke," said Embry. "Would you believe it?"

"What's the game?" said Bird. "Shall we start to carve some of these so-and-so's up?"

"No," said Embry. "I've got it now. We didn't salute their photograph of Franco when we came in."

Without further ado he turned to the photo of Franco on the far wall and raised his hand. After a moment's hesitation Bird did likewise. There was at once a murmur of approbation round the room. The excited crowd dispersed and went about their business once more.

"I'm not surprised we're at war," said Embry, "when people can take themselves as seriously as that."

But for all the commotion they had unwittingly caused, they got no satisfaction from the visa department. They could not, they were told, have a visa for admission to Spain unless they had one permitting them to leave France.

"Then I must go to the Préfecture?" asked Embry in his pidgin French.

"Yes."

As he left the room he said to Bird: "Is there ever going to be an end to this damn nonsense?"

"Don't ask me," said Bird. "It's got me beat."

"Well, we know the Chief of Police, anyway," said Embry. "He's the chap who helped us before, so we're on safe ground there."

The ground was far from safe. The girl attendant at the Préfecture, who recognized Embry at once, told him so.

"You want a visa out of France?"

"That's right."

"Then it must be the chief to sign it. That is a pity."

"Why? He was a very good friend to us last time we were here."

"There is a change. This is a new man. He is not fond of the English."

"That shouldn't prevent him from doing his duty."

"I don't know. But I think you should go up with both passports and leave your friend outside on the street. I will follow you in."

They went upstairs to the same room where the former Chief of Police had given Embry the note of introduction to Ferrera.

The newcomer sat at his desk, pen in hand, signing

documents. It was several seconds before he looked up and Embry felt instinctively that the delay was a deliberate trick assumed in order to impress. When the Chief of Police at length laid down his pen, it was to lean back in his chair, with his finger tips pressed together, regarding Embry with cold suspicion.

"Well?" he said at last.

"I want a visa out of France."

"Let me see them."

Embry handed over the passports. There was a long silence, while the Chief of Police examined them.

"You are English?"

"Yes."

"Maybe you are an English soldier?"

"Maybe."

"Running away like the rest of your countrymen, eh?"

"If you like to put it that way."

"I do. I will do nothing for you."

The hands holding the passports began to turn in opposite directions as if to tear the flimsy cardboard.

"The English are cowards. They led us into this war, tricked us into it. Then when it went the wrong way, they ran away. I would have every Englishman left in France shot. All deserters like yourself . . ."

"Run," sounded the girl's voice behind Embry's shoulder, "Run."

He leant over the desk and in one lightning move snatched the passports from the Chief of Police's hands and fled from the room. He ran down the stairs and found Bird waiting at the edge of the pavement.

"Quick," he said. "We've got to get out of here."

Together they walked rapidly down the street, and darted round a corner but no one followed and in a little while they decided it was safe to move on. Embry told Bird what had happened.

"And we didn't get 'em signed, sir?"

"No. And it's no good going back to the Spanish Embassy without the French visa. We've had it."

"So now we are no further forward?"

"Correct. The only thing to do is to get back to Le Perthous and I'll have another go at Dickens and see if he can help, but I'm damn well browned off and I don't mind admitting it."

They caught the bus from Perpignan for Le Perthous without further incident.

So this, Embry told himself, was the outcome of all his scheming and planning, to be back where he'd started, held up relentlessly by restrictions and regulations. He saw Dickens as often as he called but discovered very little satisfaction from his visits, until one memorable morning.

The other visitor to Dickens' office on that day went by the name of Peters, who was a Gibraltarian by domicile and had known service in the R.F.C. and R.A.F. Embry was introduced.

"An official from Madrid," said Dickens and left the two men together.

Embry at first had little to say. He had had enough of officialdom, but he was to change his opinion on this occasion.

"You may be interested to know," said Peters, "that there's a price on your head. You are wanted—for murder."

"I've often wondered," said Embry, "what the charge might be for dealing with those Jerries. I was in civvies at the time—some clothes I'd borrowed including a jacket from a scarecrow. But if you've come all the way from Madrid to comfort me with that kind of news, I don't suppose you expect me to thank you."

"No. But this you can thank me for. No names, no fire picket, but I've been sent here specially to get you out of France."

"That's the finest news I've heard for weeks," said Embry.

"I haven't as yet evolved a plan, but in the end we'll think one up. Meanwhile I've got to be mighty careful as the police have their eye on me. So you'll have to be patient."

"I'll do my best," said Embry.

" There's a café opposite," said Peters. "See here."

Embry peered cautiously out of the window.

"My car is drawn up alongside," continued Peters. "I shall be off now, but I'll return either this evening or tomorrow. Meanwhile I'm going to get acquainted with the police. I shall take them into the café and buy them drinks."

He returned that evening and told Embry that not only had he bought the police drinks, but he had stood them lunch as well and they were already on very good terms.

"I think I've got an idea how to get you out of here, but it will want preparing," he said. "I shall come across the frontier two or three times a day, and I shall eat and drink in the same place. I shall leave my car in the cul-de-sac which is thirty yards from the café. I want the police to get used to that procedure."

Embry watched Peters drive off in his staff car with the Union Jack as pennant. It was such a simple thing to sit in a car and drive away. It was a commonplace thing to do—if you had the right papers. Then, in his mood of deep resentment, an opportunity occurred on 23rd July for one of them to cross the frontier by special car. But there was only room for the one.

He sent Bird.

Bird protested vehemently.

"It won't do, sir. After all we've been through together and what you had to put up with before we met—it's your place to go, sir. I can't leave you."

"You're to go, Bird; I shall get my chance. I'll meet you in Madrid."

"I'm damned if I care to leave you, sir."

"Goodbye, Bird."

"Goodbye, sir. Good luck, sir. Goodbye."

He stood with his back to the wall of the cul-de-sac by the café and close behind Peters' car. It was just before twenty to eleven of the same evening that Bird had left.

He had agreed to a desperate plan of Peters'. It was so desperate that in calmer days he would have dismissed it as foolhardy. But the frustration of every hour urged him on. He wondered if Bird were on his way to England yet. He'd always wanted to fly back, if he got away. It was growing still darker. He would act very soon now.

He thought of all that had happened in the last eight weeks. The hazards and the perils; the breaking from the Calais column; the swimming of the Somme; the morning when the Germans had captured him and how they had beaten him; the dead men lying in the farmyard while he lay at the bottom of a dunghill; the Intelligence Officer at his second recapture; Paris and the crossing of the Loire.

He thought of his great and wonderful friends who had come into his life for a little while with their splendid courage and friendship. Paul, Mrs. Roberts, Anna-Louise, Bird, and the others who, like Señor Ferrera and the woman who had milked the cow and signalled as the Calais column shuffled past, had come to his aid. Well, all his footsteps and all their loving kindness had led to a barrier and a police post on a frontier. Very well, as always, neck or nothing.

There was a deal of singing from the café. He could hear the rattle of glasses, and once or twice he thought he heard Peters' voice. There was yet another party going on in the café and once again Peters was the host and the police were his guests.

279

The door of the café opened so that a beam of light fell across the passage way. Against it Embry could see the figure of his friend. The sound of laughter and singing was suddenly louder. Then Peters was by his side.

"In here," he said.

He opened the boot of the car.

"I've got those types pretty drunk, but for heaven's sake don't make a noise and for the love of Mike don't sneeze. I shall be driving them back to their posts now. In you get."

Embry climbed into the boot. It was dark and stifling. He lay curled up, while Peters locked him in. The dust crept into his nostrils, then the car shook as it moved.

They were off! He was in the boot of the car that was going to cross the frontier. In seconds now they would be in Spain. The car stopped. For one fearful moment he thought he must have been discovered, then passengers clambered aboard.

They were still singing hilariously. He wondered what manner of song it might be and ventured to guess. He caught a whiff of the exhaust fumes as the car started up and they were off again. They stopped again, and a door opened and there were voices. A third time they stopped and again a chorus of "goodnights", but the air in the boot was getting exhausted. It was difficult to breathe and Embry's nostrils were dry and his tongue was parched. He wondered if this were to be the end of his journey, to die of suffocation. He was gasping now and only dimly aware that they were travelling in third gear. They must, he imagined, be on the hill-road, climbing the Pyrenees. There was a hammering in his head and his heart was pounding. Then on the instant the car stopped once more, the lid of the boot flew open, the sweet cool night air rushed in to greet him.

"Welcome to Spain," said Peters.

He helped Embry out of the boot.

"I'm sorry I had to stop so often," he said. "But I had a French policeman to drop at his post and a Spaniard at another, and the other one in the village itself. Now climb in alongside me."

"And where do we go?" said Embry.

"To Figueras and then Madrid."

Once they were halted by a road patrol, but the Union Jack served its purpose and they were waved on.

At Figueras they stopped for coffee. Bird was there. It was more than he could at first believe, seeing Embry in the flesh again. By the following forenoon they all reached Madrid.

"Thank you," said Embry to Peters. "That was a fine effort of yours."

"There's no need for thanks," said Peters. "It was a pleasure and an honour. *Bon Voyage*, Wing Commander. God bless you."

CHAPTER TWENTY-THREE

HE STOOD on the edge of the kerb of the fireplace of the Saloon Bar of the "Swan Hotel" in Ipswich. He wore his little green pork-pie hat with the bobbins, and the suit with its too-short sleeves and the over-long trousers which he'd bought with Lance-Bombardier Bird in Perpignan. There was a pint of beer in his hand.

There were some thirty of his fellow officers present, who had come to meet him at Ipswich station, for they had heard that he had escaped and was due home. He had walked through the black-out on the platform without seeing them, not knowing they would be there to welcome him, and then someone had recognized him and they'd all carried him off to "The Swan."

They had locked the doors of the bar behind them, because even if these were public premises, this was a private session. It was an affair to do with nobody else but themselves and the Service they represented.

Gayford, who was to die later, was there; the Intelligence Officer of his Squadron was there, and the newly appointed Adjutant to that Squadron (the writer of this record); so was the Station Adjutant, and most important of all, what were left of his comrades who had flown with him from the beginning of the war. Stokes was there. There was a message from "Hugh Pugh", who was later to command Malta in its time of grave trouble.

They didn't say very much except: "Good luck, sir," or "Cheerio, Basil" and "Here's mud in your eye", because they were not men of words and a little scared of high-sounding phrases.

Titch Pellet, the Intelligence Officer, kept wringing him by the hand, as if he wasn't sure that Embry was really present in the flesh, and he kept on saying: "My God, sir, you're back! You're *back*!" He looked as if he were going to cry, but that was probably all the liquor which he had taken.

Oswald Gayford said: "That's a natty piece of tailoring you have, my dear Basil."

Basil Embry said: "Yes. It's very characteristic. I only want a stick of onions to go with it, don't I? Then I'd be the real thing!"

It was nine weeks and five days since he had left England.

THE ESCAPE ROUTE OF WING
COMMANDER BASIL EMBRY

Now in possession of a French pass he travels by military car and passenger train to Marseilles but has to visit Perpignan and Le Perthous before getting across the frontier into Spain. This part of his journey being by regular lines of communication is not shown on the map.

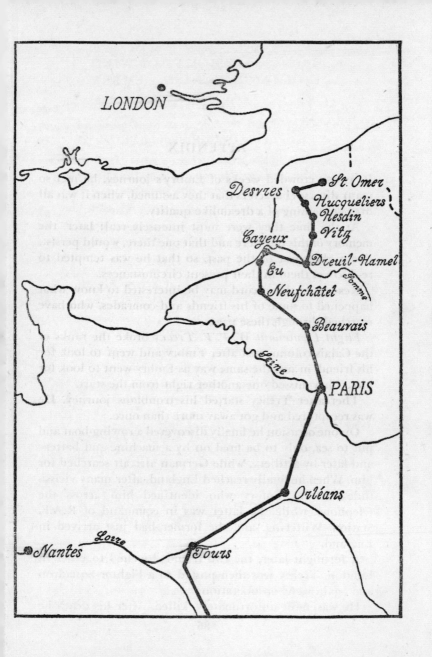

LONDON

St. Omer
Desvres
Hucqueliers
Hesdin
Vitz
Cayeux
Dreuil-Hamel
Eu
Neufchâtel
Somme
Beauvais
Seine
PARIS
Orléans
Loire
Nantes
Tours

APPENDIX

IN THOSE crowded weeks of Embry's journey, he met so many diverse characters that they assumed, when it was all over, something of a dreamlike quality.

At the time they were most intensely real; later, the memory of this one here and that one there, would persist, like a ghost out of the past, so that he was tempted to re-discover them in their present circumstances.

Readers of this record may be interested to know what happened to some of his friends and comrades, who have marched through these pages.

Flight Lieutenant W. P. F. Treacy broke the ranks of the Calais column just after Embry and went to look for his friend, in just the same way as Embry went to look for him. They missed one another right from the start.

Thereafter Treacy started his troublous journey. He was recaptured and got away more than once.

On one occasion he finally discovered a rowing-boat and put to sea, only to be fired on by a machine-gun battery and later by artillery, while German aircraft searched for him. When he finally reached England, after many vicissitudes, it was Embry who identified him across the telephone, while the latter was in command of R.A.F. Station, Wittering, and the former had just arrived in England.

A fortnight later, the two friends lunched together in London. Treacy was then posted to a Fighter Squadron and again went on operations.

He was, most unfortunately, killed. After his death he

was awarded the D.S.O. for operational exploits before he was captured. He lies buried in the Pas de Calais.

Lance Bombardier Bird reached home safely, flying, as he wanted to, from Lisbon. He is still alive.

Tom Whiting (Embry's navigator) was captured almost immediately by the Germans and was a prisoner of war throughout the rest of the war. He is still a serving officer in the R.A.F., and is today on the Headquarters Staff of Fighter Command, of which Embry is the present Commander-in-Chief.

Paul has seen Embry three times since the war. On one occasion, he and "Maman" stayed with Embry at the C-in-C's residence at Stanmore.

Mrs. Roberts, who befriended Embry in Paris, died of natural causes a few days after the liberation of Paris, but *Anna-Louise* is now happily married, with a family, in France. Embry has visited her since the war.

The French priest, who brought straw and potatoes into the church at Hucqueliers on the first night of the Calais Column march, is still at the same village. Embry recently met him again.

Embry has also recently met the lady who owned the château, near Neufchâtel, where he spent the night in the bed recently vacated by the German General. She declared that she was charmed he should have slept there!

After Embry left, the Germans returned and lived there until they were turned out of that part of France on the liberation.

André, the Belgian officer, who joined with Embry at Port Vendres, visited him later in England. André's son, *Leopold,* after the Port Vendres adventure, was missing and has never been seen again.

As for Embry himself, the story of his return has been told. After a period of leave on his arrival in England, he joined Fighter Command, and later was posted to the Desert Air Force.

Eventually, he came back to command No. 2 Group as Air Officer Commanding in the rank of Air Vice Marshal —the original Group from which he was shot down.

In the end, No. 2 Group became part of the 2nd Tactical Air Force, which was responsible for operations from Norway to Germany, from D-day onwards. Embry commanded his Group in the same rank.

The war over, Embry became Director-General of Training for the Royal Air Force; and now, in the rank of Air Marshal, is the present Commander-in-Chief of Fighter Command.

He flew operationally up to the last month of the war. He is the holder of four D.S.O.s, and four other British decorations, together with four foreign awards.

ANTHONY RICHARDSON

Chadwell Heath, Essex.
August, 1950.

A
BURNT-OUT CASE

by

GRAHAM GREENE

THE REPRINT SOCIETY : LONDON

FIRST PUBLISHED 1961
THIS EDITION PUBLISHED BY THE REPRINT SOCIETY LTD
BY ARRANGEMENT WITH WILLIAM HEINEMANN LTD 1962

PRINTED IN ENGLAND BY HAZELL WATSON AND VINEY LTD
AYLESBURY AND SLOUGH

"Io non mori', e non rimasi vivo." (I did not die, yet nothing of life remained.)

DANTE

"Within limits of normality, every individual loves himself. In cases where he has a deformity or abnormality or develops it later, his own aesthetic sense revolts and he develops a sort of disgust towards himself. Though with time, he becomes reconciled to his deformities, it is only at the conscious level. His subconscious mind, which continues to bear the mark of injury, brings about certain changes in his whole personality, making him suspicious of society."

R. V. WARDEKAR in a pamphlet on leprosy

To Docteur Michel Lechat

Dear Michel,

I hope you will accept the dedication of this novel which owes any merit it may have to your kindness and patience; the faults, failures and inaccuracies are the author's alone. Dr. Colin has borrowed from you his experience of leprosy and nothing else. Dr. Colin's leproserie is not your leproserie—which now, I fear, has probably ceased to exist. Even geographically it is placed in a region far from Yonda. Every leproserie, of course, has features in common, and from Yonda and other leproseries which I visited in the Congo and the Cameroons I may have taken superficial characteristics. From the fathers of your Mission I have stolen the Superior's cheroots—that is all, and from your Bishop the boat that he was so generous as to lend me for a journey up the Ruki. It would be a waste of time for anyone to try to identify Querry, the Ryckers, Parkinson, Father Thomas —they are formed from the flotsam of thirty years as a novelist. This is not a *roman à clef*, but an attempt to give dramatic expression to various types of belief, half-belief and non-belief, in the kind of setting, removed from world-politics and household-preoccupations, where such differences are felt acutely and find expression. This Congo is a region of the mind, and the reader will find no place called Luc on any map, nor did its Governor and Bishop exist in any regional capital.

You, if anyone, will know how far I have failed in what

I attempted. A doctor is not immune from "the long despair of doing nothing well", the *cafard* that hangs around a writer's life. I only wish I had dedicated to you a better book in return for the limitless generosity I was shown at Yonda by you and the fathers of the mission.

Affectionately yours,
Graham Greene

PART I

CHAPTER ONE

I

THE cabin-passenger wrote in his diary a parody of Descartes: "I feel discomfort, therefore I am alive," then sat pen in hand with no more to record. The captain in a white soutane stood by the open windows of the saloon reading his breviary. There was not enough air to stir the fringes of his beard. The two of them had been alone together on the river for ten days—alone, that is to say, except for the six members of the African crew and the dozen or so deck-passengers who changed, almost indistinguishably, at each village where they stopped. The boat, which was the property of the Bishop, resembled a small battered Mississippi paddle-steamer with a high nineteenth-century fore-structure, the white paint badly in need of renewal. From the saloon windows they could see the river before them unwind, and below them on the pontoons the passengers sat and dressed their hair among the logs of wood for the engine.

If no change means peace, this certainly was peace, to be found like a nut at the centre of the hard shell of discomfort—the heat that engulfed them where the river narrowed to a mere hundred metres: the shower that was always hot from the ship's engine: in the evening the mosquitoes, and in the day the tsetse flies with wings raked back like tiny jet-fighters (a board above the bank at the last village had warned them in three languages: "Zone of sleeping sickness. Be careful of the tsetse flies.") The captain read his breviary with a fly-whisk in his hand, and whenever he made a kill he held up the tiny corpse for the passenger's inspection, saying "tsetse"—it was nearly the

II

limit of their communication, for neither spoke the other's language with ease or accuracy.

This was somewhat the way in which the days passed. The passenger would be woken at four in the morning by the tinkling sound of the sanctus-bell in the saloon, and presently from the window of the Bishop's cabin, which he shared with a crucifix, a chair, a table, a cupboard where cockroaches lurked, and one picture—the nostalgic photograph of some church in Europe covered in a soutane of heavy snow, he would see the congregation going home across the gang-plank. He would watch them as they climbed the steep bank and disappeared into the bush, swinging lanterns like the carol-singers he had once seen during his stay in a New England village. By five the boat was on the move again, and at six as the sun rose he would eat his breakfast with the captain. The next three hours, before the great heat had begun, were for both men the best of the day, and the passenger found that he could watch, with a kind of inert content, the thick, rapid, khaki-coloured stream against which the small boat fought its way at about three knots, the engine, some-where below the altar and the Holy Family, groaning like an exhausted animal and the big wheel churning away at the stern. A lot of effort it seemed for so slow a progress. Every few hours a fishing-village came into sight, the houses standing high on stilts to guard them against the big rains and the rats. At times a member of the crew called up to the captain, and the captain would take his gun and shoot at some small sign of life that only he and the sailor had eyes to detect among the green and blue shadows of the forest: a baby crocodile sunning on a fallen log, or a fishing eagle which waited motionless among the leaves. At nine the heat had really begun, and the cap-tain, having finished reading his breviary, would oil his gun or kill a few more tsetse flies, and sometimes, sitting down at the dining-table with a box of beads, he would set himself the task of manufacturing cheap rosaries.

After the midday meal both men retired to their cabins as the forests sauntered by under the exhausting sun. Even when the passenger was naked it was difficult for him to sleep, and he was never finally able to decide between letting a little draught pass through his cabin or keeping the hot air out. The boat possessed no fan, and so he woke always with a soiled mouth, and while the warm water in the shower cleaned his body, it could not refresh it.

There yet remained another hour or two of peace towards the end of the day, when he sat below on a pontoon while the Africans prepared their chop in the early dark. The vampire-bats creaked over the forest and candles flickered, reminding him of the Benedictions of his youth. The laughter of the cooks went back and forth from one pontoon to the other, and it was never long before someone sang, but he couldn't understand the words.

At dinner they had to close the windows of the saloon and draw the curtains to, so that the steersman might see his way between the banks and snags, and then the pressure-lamp gave out too great a heat for so small a room. To delay the hour of bed they played *quatre cent vingt-et-un* wordlessly like a ritual mime, and the captain invariably won as though the god he believed in, who was said to control the winds and waves, controlled the dice too, in favour of his priest.

This was the moment for talk in garbled French or garbled Flemish if they were going to talk, but they never talked much. Once the passenger asked, "What are they singing, father? What kind of song? A love song?"

"No," the captain said, "not a love song. They sing only about what has happened during the day, how at the last village they bought some fine cooking-pots which they will sell for a good profit further up the river, and of course they sing of you and me. They call me the great fetishist," he added with a smile and nodded at the Holy Family and the pull-out altar over the cupboard where he kept the cartridges for his gun and his fishing-tackle. He killed a mosquito with a slap on his naked arm and said, "There is a motto in the Mongo language, 'The mosquito has no pity for the thin man'."

"What do they sing about me?"

"They are singing now, I think." He put the dice and counters away and listened. "Shall I translate for you? It is not altogether complimentary."

"Yes, if you please."

"'Here is a white man who is neither a father nor a doctor. He has no beard. He comes from a long way away—we do not know from where—and he tells no one to what place he is going nor why. He is a rich man, for he drinks whisky every evening and he smokes all the time. Yet he offers no man a cigarette'."

"That had never occurred to me."

"Of course," the captain said, "I know where you are going, but you have never told me why."

"The road was closed by floods. This was the only route."

"That wasn't what I meant."

About nine in the evening they usually, if the river had not widened and thus made navigation easy, pulled into the bank. Sometimes they would find there a rotting up-turned boat which served as shelter when it rained for unlikely passengers. Twice the captain disembarked his ancient bicycle and bounced off into the dark interior to try to obtain some cargo from a *colon* living miles away and save it from the hands of the O.T.R.A.C.O. company, the great monopolist of the river and the tributaries, and there were times, if they were not too late in tying up, when they received unexpected visitors. On one occasion a man, a woman, and a child, with sickly albino skins that came from years of heat and humidity, emerged from the thick rain-forest in an old station-wagon; the man drank a glass or two of whisky, while he and the priest complained of the price that O.T.R.A.C.O. charged for fuelling wood and spoke of the riots hundreds of miles away in the capital, while the woman sat silent holding the child's hand and stared at the Holy Family. When there were no European visitors there were always the old women, their heads tied up in dusters, their bodies wrapped in mammy-cloths, the once bright colours so faded that you could scarcely detect the printed designs of match-boxes, soda-

14

water siphons, telephones, or other gimmicks of the white man. They shuffled into the saloon on their knees and patiently waited under the roaring pressure-lamp until they were noticed. Then, with an apology to his passenger, the captain would send him to his cabin, for these were confessions that he had to hear in secret. It was the end of one more day.

<h2 style="text-align:center">2</h2>

For several mornings they were pursued by yellow butterflies which were a welcome change from the tsetses. The butterflies came tacking into the saloon as soon as it was light, while the river still lay under a layer of mist like steam on a vat. When the mist cleared they could see one bank lined with white nenuphars which from a hundred yards away resembled a regiment of swans. The colour of the water in this wider reach was pewter, except where the wheel churned the wake to chocolate, and the green reflection of the woods was not mirrored on the surface but seemed to shine up from underneath the paper-thin transparent pewter. Two men who stood in a pirogue had their legs extended by their shadows so that they appeared to be wading knee-deep in the water. The passenger said, "Look, father, over there. Doesn't that suggest to you an explanation of how Christ was thought to be walking on the water?" but the captain, who was taking aim at a heron standing behind the rank of nenuphars, did not bother to answer. He had a passion for slaughtering any living thing, as though only man had the right to a natural death.

After six days they came to an African seminary standing like an ugly red-brick university at the top of the clay bank. At this seminary the captain had once taught Greek, and so they stopped here for the night, partly for old-times sake and partly to enable them to buy wood at a cheaper price than Otraco charged. The loading began immediately—the young black seminarists were standing ready, before the ship's bell rang twice, to carry the wood on to the pontoons so that the boat might be cast off again

15

at the first hint of light. After their dinner the priests gathered in the common-room. The captain was the only one to wear a soutane. One father, with a trim pointed beard, dressed in an open khaki shirt, reminded the passenger of a young officer of the Foreign Legion he had once known in the East whose recklessness and ill-discipline had led to an heroic and wasteful death; another of the fathers might have been taken for a professor of economics, a third for a lawyer, a fourth for a doctor, but the too easy laughter, the exaggerated excitement over some simple game of cards with matches for stakes had the innocence and immaturity of isolation—the innocence of explorers marooned on an ice-cap or of men imprisoned by a war which has long passed out of hearing. They turned the radio on for the evening news, but this was just habit, the imitation of an act performed years ago for a motive they no longer remembered clearly; they were not interested in the tensions and changing cabinets of Europe, they were barely interested in the riots a few hundred miles away on the other side of the river, and the passenger became aware of his own safety among them—they would ask no intrusive questions. He was again reminded of the Foreign Legion. If he had been a murderer escaping from justice, not one would have had the curiosity to probe his secret wound.

And yet—he could not tell why—their laughter irritated him, like a noisy child or a disc of jazz. He was vexed by the pleasure which they took in small things—even in the bottle of whisky he had brought for them from the boat. Those who marry God, he thought, can become domesticated too—it's just as humdrum a marriage as all the others. The word "Love" means a formal touch of the lips as in the ceremony of the Mass, and "*Ave Maria*" like "dearest" is a phrase to open a letter. This marriage like the world's marriages was held together by habits and tastes shared in common between God and themselves—it was God's taste to be worshipped and their taste to worship, but only at stated hours like a suburban embrace on a Saturday night.

The laughter rose higher. The captain had been caught cheating, and now each priest in turn tried to outdo his neighbour by stealing matches, making surreptitious discards, calling the wrong suit—the game, like so many children's games, was about to reach an end in chaos, and would there be tears before bed? The passenger got impatiently up and walked away from them around the dreary common-room. The face of the new Pope, looking like an eccentric headmaster, stared at him from the wall. On top of a chocolate-coloured dresser lay a few *romans policiers* and a stock of missionary journals. He opened one: it reminded him of a school magazine. There was an account of a football match at a place called Oboko and an old boy was writing the first instalment of an essay called "A Holiday in Europe". A wall-calendar bore the photograph of another mission: there was the same kind of hideous church built of unsuitable brick beside a verandahed priest's house. Perhaps it was a rival school. Grouped in front of the buildings were the fathers: they were laughing too. The passenger wondered when it was that he had first begun to detest laughter like a bad smell.

He walked out into the moonlit dark. Even at night the air was so humid that it broke upon the cheek like tiny beads of rain. Some candles still burned on the pontoons and a torch moved along the upper deck, showing him where the boat was moored. He left the river and found a rough track which started behind the classrooms and led towards what geographers might have called the centre of Africa. He followed it a short way, for no reason that he knew, guided by the light of moon and stars; ahead of him he could hear a kind of music. The track brought him into a village and out the other side. The inhabitants were awake, perhaps because the moon was full: if so they had marked its exact state better than his diary. Men were beating on old tins they had salvaged from the mission, tins of sardines and Heinz beans and plum jam, and someone was playing a kind of home-made harp. Faces peered at him from behind small fires. An old

woman danced awkwardly, cracking her hips under a
piece of sacking, and again he felt taunted by the innocence of the laughter. They were not laughing at him,
they were laughing with each other, and he was abandoned, as he had been in the living-room of the seminary,
to his own region where laughter was like the unknown
syllables of an enemy tongue. It was a very poor village:
the thatch of the clay huts had been gnawed away a long
time since by rats and rain, and the women wore only old
clouts, which had once seen service for sugar or grain,
around their waists. He recognised them as pygmoids—
bastard descendants of the true pygmies. They were not
a powerful enemy. He turned and went back to the
seminary.

The room was empty, the card-game had broken up,
and he passed to his bedroom. He had become so accustomed to the small cabin that he felt defenceless in this
vast space which held only a washstand with a jug, basin
and glass, a chair, a narrow bed under a mosquito-net, and
a bottle of boiled water on the floor. One of the fathers,
who was presumably the Superior, knocked and came in.
He said, "Is there anything you want?"

"Nothing. I want nothing." He nearly added, "That
is my trouble."

The Superior looked in the jug to see whether it was
full. "You will find the water very brown," he said, "but
it is quite clean." He lifted the lid of a soap-dish to
assure himself that the soap had not been forgotten. A
brand new orange tablet lay there.

"Lifebuoy," the Superior said proudly.

"I haven't used Lifebuoy," the passenger said, "since
I was a child."

"Many people say it is good for prickly heat. But I
never suffer from that."

Suddenly the passenger found himself unable any
longer not to speak. He said, "Nor I. I suffer from nothing. I no longer know what suffering is. I have come to
an end of all that, too."

"Too?"

"Like all the rest. To the end of everything."

The Superior turned away from him without curiosity. He said, "Oh well, you know, suffering is something which will always be provided when it is required. Sleep well. I will call you at five."

CHAPTER TWO

I

DOCTOR COLIN examined the record of the man's tests
—for six months now the search for the leprosy bacilli in
smears taken from the skin had shown a negative result.
The African who stood before him with a staff under his
shoulder had lost all his toes and fingers. Doctor Colin
said, "Excellent. You are cured."

The man took a step or two nearer to the doctor's desk.
His toeless feet looked like rods and when he walked it
was as though he were engaged in pounding the path flat.
He said with apprehension, "Must I go away from here?"

Doctor Colin looked at the stump the man held out like
a piece of wood which had been roughly carved into the
beginnings of a human hand. There was a rule that the
leproserie should take contagious cases only: the cured
had to return to their villages or, if it were possible, continue what treatment was necessary as out-patients in the
hospital at Luc, the provincial capital. But Luc was
many days away whether by road or river. Colin said,
"It would be hard for you to find work outside. I will see
what can be done for you. Go and speak to the sisters."
The stump seemed useless, but it was extraordinary what
a mutilated hand could be taught to do; there was one
man in the leproserie without fingers who had been taught
to knit as well as any sister. But even success could be
saddening, for it showed the value of the material they
had so often to discard. For fifteen years the doctor had
dreamt of a day when he would have funds available for
constructing special tools to fit each mutilation, but now
he hadn't money enough even to provide decent mattresses
in the hospital.

20

"What's your name?" he asked.

"Deo Gratias."

Impatiently the doctor called out the next number.

It was a young woman with palsied fingers—a claw-hand. The doctor tried to flex her fingers, but she winced with the stab of the nerves, though she continued to smile with a kind of brave coquetry as though she thought in that way she might induce him to spare her further pain. She had made up her mouth with a mauve lipstick which went badly with the black skin, and her right breast was exposed, for she had been feeding her baby on the dispensary step. Her arm was scarred for half its length where the doctor had made an incision to release the ulnar nerve which had been strangled by its sheath. Now the girl was able with an effort to move her fingers a further degree. The doctor wrote on her card, for the sisters' attention, "Paraffin wax" and turned to the next patient.

In fifteen years Doctor Colin had only known two days hotter than this one. Even the Africans were feeling the heat, and half the usual number of patients had come to the dispensary. There was no fan, and Dr. Colin worked below a makeshift awning on the verandah: a table, a hard wooden chair, and behind him the little office that he dreaded to enter because of the insufficient ventilation. His filing cabinets were there, and the steel was hot to the touch.

Patient after patient exposed his body to him; in all the years he had never become quite accustomed to the sweet gangrenous smell of certain leprous skins, and it had become to him the smell of Africa. He ran his fingers over the diseased surface, and made his notes almost mechanically. The notes had small value, but his fingers, he knew, gave the patients comfort: they realised that they were not untouchable. Now that a cure had been found for the physical disease, he had always to remember that leprosy remained a psychological problem.

From the river Dr. Colin heard the sound of a ship's bell. The Superior passed by the dispensary on his bicycle, riding towards the beach. He waved, and the doctor raised his hand in answer. It was probably the day for the Otraco boat which was long overdue. It was supposed to call once a fortnight with mail, but they could never depend on it, for it was delayed more often than not by unexpected cargo or by a faulty pipe.

A baby began to cry and immediately like dogs all the babies around the dispensary started to howl together. "Henri," Doctor Colin called; his young African dispenser rapped out a phrase in his native tongue—"Babies to the breast" and instantaneously peace returned. At twelve-thirty the doctor broke off for the day. In the little hot office he wiped his hands with spirits.

He walked down towards the beach. He had been expecting a book to be sent him from Europe: a Japanese Atlas of Leprosy, and perhaps it had come with the mail. The long street of the leper village led towards the river: small two-roomed houses built of brick with mud huts in the yards behind. When he had arrived fifteen years ago there had been only the mud huts—now they served as kitchens, and yet still when anyone was about to die, he would retire into the yard. He couldn't die peacefully in a room furnished with a radio-set and a picture of the latest Pope; he was prepared to die only where his ancestors had died, in the darkness surrounded by the smell of dry mud and leaves. In the third yard on the left an old man was dying now, sitting in a battered deckchair, inside the shadow of the kitchen-door.

Beyond the village, just before the river came into sight, the ground was being cleared for what would one day be the new hospital-block. A gang of lepers was pounding the last square yards supervised by Father Joseph, who worked beside them, beating away himself at the ground in his old khaki pants and a soft hat which looked as though it had been washed up on the beach many years ago.

"Otraco?" Doctor Colin called out to him.

"No, the Bishop's boat," Father Joseph replied, and he paced away, feeling the ground with his feet. He had long ago caught the African habit of speaking as he moved, with his back turned, and his voice had the high African inflection. "They say there's a passenger on board."

"A passenger?"

Doctor Colin came into sight of the funnel where it stuck up between the long avenue of logs that had been cut ready for fuel. A man was walking up the avenue towards him. He raised his hat, a man of his own age, in the late fifties with a grizzled morning stubble, wearing a crumpled tropical suit. "My name is Querry," he introduced himself, speaking in an accent which Colin could not quite place as French or Flemish any more than he could immediately identify the nationality of the name.

"Dr. Colin," he said. "Are you stopping here?"

"The boat goes no further," the man answered, as if that were indeed the only explanation.

2

Once a month Doctor Colin and the Superior went into a confidential huddle over figures. The support of the leproserie was the responsibility of the Order; the doctor's salary and the cost of medicine were paid by the State. The State was the richer and the more unwilling partner, and the doctor made every effort to shift what burden he could from the Order. In the struggle with the common enemy the two of them had become close friends—Doctor Colin was even known occasionally to attend Mass, though he had long ago, before he had come to this continent of misery and heat, lost faith in any god that a priest would have recognised. The only trouble the Superior ever caused him was with the cheroot which the priest was never without, except when saying Mass and in sleep; the cheroots were strong and Dr. Colin's quarters cramped, and the ash always found a way between his pamphlets and reports. Now he had to shake the ash off the accounts he had prepared for the chief medical officer in Luc; in them he had deftly and unobtrusively transferred to the

23

State the price of a new clock and three mosquito-nets for the mission.

"I am sorry," the Superior apologised, dropping yet more ash onto an open page of the Atlas of Leprosy. The thick bright colours and the swirling designs resembled the reproduction of a Van Gogh landscape, and the doctor had been turning the pages with a purely aesthetic pleasure before the Superior joined him. "Really I am impossible," the Superior said, brushing at the page. "Worse than usual, but then I've had a visit from M. Rycker. The man upsets me."

"What did he want?"

"Oh, he wanted to find out about our visitor. And of course he was very ready to drink our visitor's whisky."

"Was it worth three days' journey?"

"Well, at least he got the whisky. He said the road had been impossible for four weeks and he had been starved of intellectual conversation."

"How is his wife—and the plantation?"

"Rycker seeks information. He never gives it. And he was anxious to discuss his spiritual problems."

"I would never have guessed he had any."

"When a man has nothing else to be proud of," the Superior said, "he is proud of his spiritual problems. After two whiskies he began to talk to me about Grace."

"What did you do?"

"I lent him a book. He won't read it, of course. He knows all the answers—six years wasted in a seminary can do a lot of harm. What he really wanted was to discover who Querry might be, where he came from, and how long he was going to stay. I would have been tempted to tell him if I had known the answer myself. Luckily Rycker is afraid of lepers, and Querry's boy happened to come in. Why did you give Querry Deo Gratias?"

"He's cured, but he's a burnt-out case, and I don't want to send him away. He can sweep a floor and make a bed without fingers or toes."

"Our visitors are sometimes fastidious."

"I assure you Querry doesn't mind. In fact he asked

24

for him. Deo Gratias was the first leper whom he saw when he came off the boat. Of course I told him the man was cured."

"Deo Gratias brought me a note. I don't think Rycker liked me touching it. I noticed that he didn't shake hands with me when he said goodbye. What strange ideas people have about leprosy, doctor."

"They learn it from the Bible. Like sex."

"It's a pity people pick and choose what they learn from the Bible," the Superior said, trying to knock the end of his cheroot into the ashtray. But he was always doomed to miss.

"What do you think of Querry, father? Why do you think he's here?"

"I'm too busy to pry into a man's motives. I've given him a room and a bed. One more mouth to feed is not an embarrassment. And to do him justice he seemed very ready to help—if there were any help that he was capable of giving. Perhaps he is only looking for somewhere quiet to rest in."

"Few people would choose a leproserie as a holiday resort. When he asked me for Deo Gratias I was afraid for a moment that we might have a leprophil on our hands."

"A leprophil? Am I a leprophil?"

"No, father. You are here under obedience. But you know very well that leprophils exist, though I daresay they are more often women than men. Schweitzer seems to attract them. They would rather wash the feet with their hair like the woman in the gospel than clean them with something more antiseptic. Sometimes I wonder whether Damien was a leprophil. There was no need for him to become a leper in order to serve them well. A few elementary precautions—I wouldn't be a better doctor without my fingers, would I?"

"I don't find it very rewarding looking for motives. Querry does no harm."

"The second day he was here, I took him to the hospital. I wanted to test his reactions. They were quite normal

25

ones—nausea not attraction. I had to give him a whiff of ether."

"I'm not as suspicious of leprophils as you are, doctor. There are people who love and embrace poverty. Is that so bad? Do we have to invent a word ending in 'phil' for them?"

"The leprophil makes a bad nurse and ends by joining the patients."

"But all the same, doctor, you've said it yourself, leprosy is a psychological problem. It may be very valuable for the leper to feel loved."

"A patient can always detect whether he is loved or whether it is only his leprosy which is loved. I don't want leprosy loved. I want it eliminated. There are fifteen million cases in the world. We don't want to waste time with neurotics, father."

"I wish you had a little time to waste. You work too hard."

But Doctor Colin was not listening. He said, "You remember that little leproserie in the bush that the nuns ran. When D.D.S. was discovered to be a cure, they were soon reduced to half a dozen patients. Do you know what one of the nuns said to me? 'It's terrible, doctor. Soon we'll have no lepers at all.' There surely was a leprophil."

"Poor woman," the Superior said. "You don't see the other side."

"What other side?"

"An old maid, without imagination, anxious to do good, to be of use. There aren't so many places in the world for people like that. And the practice of her vocation is being taken away from her by the weekly doses of D.D.S. tablets."

"I thought you didn't look for motives."

"Oh, mine's a very superficial reading like your own diagnosis, doctor. But it would be a good thing for all of us if we were even more superficial. There's no real harm in a superficial judgment, but if I begin to probe into what lies behind that desire to be of use, oh well, I might find some terrible things, and we are all tempted to stop when we reach that point. Yet if we dug further, who knows?—the terrible too might be only a few skins deep. Anyway it's safer to make superficial judgments. They can always be shrugged off. Even by the victims."

"And Querry? What of him? Superficially speaking, of course."

PART

PART II

CHAPTER ONE

I

In an unfamiliar region it is always necessary for the stranger to begin at once to construct the familiar, with a photograph perhaps, or a row of books if they are all that he has brought with him from the past. Querry had no photographs and no books except his diary. The first morning when he was woken at six by the sound of prayers from the chapel next door, he felt the panic of complete abandonment. He lay on his back listening to the pious chant, and if there had been some magic power in his signet ring, he would have twisted it and asked whatever djinn answered him to be transferred again to that place which for want of a better name he called his home. But magic, if such a thing existed at all, was more likely to lie in the rhythmical and incomprehensible chant next door. It reminded him, like the smell of a medicine, of an illness from which he had long recovered. He blamed himself for not realising that the area of leprosy was also the area of this other sickness. He had expected doctors and nurses: he had forgotten that he would find priests and nuns.

Deo Gratias was knocking on the door. Querry heard the scrape of his stump as it attempted to raise the latch. A pail of water hung on his wrist like a coat on a cloak-room knob. Querry had asked Doctor Colin before engaging him whether he suffered pain, and the doctor had reassured him, answering that mutilation was the alternative to pain. It was the palsied with their stiffened fingers and strangled nerves who suffered—suffered almost beyond bearing (you heard them sometimes crying in the night), but the suffering was in some sort a protection against mutilation. Querry did not suffer, lying on his back in bed, flexing his fingers.

And so from the first morning he set himself to build a routine, the familiar within the unfamiliar. It was the condition of survival. Every morning at seven he breakfasted with the fathers. They drifted into their common-room from whatever task they had been engaged on for the last hour, since the chanting had ceased. Father Paul and Brother Philippe were in charge of the dynamo which supplied electricity to the Mission and the leper village; Father Jean had been saying Mass at the nuns' house; Father Joseph had already started the labourers to work on clearing the ground for the new hospital; Father Thomas, with eyes sunk like stones in the pale clay of his face, swallowed his coffee in a hurry, like a nauseating medicine, and was off to superintend the two schools. Brother Philippe sat silent, taking no part in any conversation: he was older than the fathers, he could speak nothing but Flemish and he had the kind of face which seems worn away by weather and patience. As the faces began to develop features as negatives do in a hypo-bath, Querry separated himself all the more from their company. He was afraid of the questions they might ask, until he began to realise that, like the priests in the seminary on the river, they were going to ask none of any importance. Even the questions they found necessary were phrased like statements—"On Sundays a bus calls here at six-thirty if you wish to go to Mass,"—and Querry was not required to answer that he had given up attending Mass more than twenty years before. His absence was never remarked.

After breakfast he would take a book he had borrowed from the doctor's small library and go down to the bank of the river. It had widened out in this reach and was nearly a mile across. An old tin barge, rusty with long disuse, enabled him to avoid the ants; and he sat there until the sun, soon after nine, became too high for comfort. Sometimes he read, sometimes he simply watched the steady khaki flow of the stream, which carried little islands of grass and water jacinth endlessly down at the pace of

32

crawling taxis, out of the heart of Africa, towards the far-off sea.

On the other shore the great trees, with roots above the ground like the ribs of a half-built ship, stood out over the green jungle wall, brown at the top like stale cauliflowers. The cold grey trunks, unbroken by branches, curved a little this way and a little that, giving them a kind of reptilian life. Porcelain-white birds stood on the backs of coffee-coloured cows, and once for a whole hour he watched a family who sat in a pirogue by the bank doing nothing; the mother wore a bright yellow dress, the man, wrinkled like bark, sat bent over a paddle he never used, and a girl with a baby on her lap smiled and smiled like an open piano. When it was too hot to sit any longer in the sunlight he joined the doctor at the hospital or the dispensary, and when that was over half the day had safely gone. He no longer felt nausea from anything he saw, and the bottle of ether was not required. After a month he spoke to the doctor.

"You are very short-handed, aren't you, for dealing with eight hundred people?"

"Yes."

"If I could be of any use to you—I know I am not trained . . ."

"You will be leaving soon, won't you?"

"I have no plans."

"Have you any knowledge of electro-therapy?"

"No."

"You could be trained, if you were interested. Six months in Europe."

"I don't want to return to Europe," Querry said.

"Never?"

"Never. I am afraid to return." The phrase sounded in his own ears melodramatic and he tried to withdraw it. "I don't mean afraid. Just for this reason and that."

The doctor ran his fingers over the patches on a child's back. To the unpractised eye the child looked perfectly healthy. "This is going to be a bad case," Doctor Colin said. "Feel this."

Querry's hesitation was no more perceptible than the leprosy. At first his fingers detected nothing, but then they stumbled on places where the child's skin seemed to have grown an extra layer. "Have you no kind of electrical knowledge?"

"I'm sorry."

"Because I'm expecting some apparatus from Europe. It's long overdue. With it I will be able to take the temperature of the skin simultaneously in twenty places. You can't detect it with your fingers, but this nodule here is warmer than the skin around it. I hope one day to be able to forestall a patch. They are trying that in India now."

"You are suggesting things too complicated for me," Querry said. "I'm a man of one trade, one talent."

"What trade is that?" the doctor asked. "We are a city in miniature here, and there are few trades for which we could not find a place." He looked at Querry with sudden suspicion. "You are not a writer, are you? There's no room for a writer here. We want to work in peace. We don't want the press of the world discovering us as they discovered Schweitzer."

"I'm not a writer."

"Or a photographer? The lepers here are not going to be exhibits in any horror museum."

"I'm not a photographer. Believe me I want peace as much as you do. If the boat had gone any further, I would not have landed here."

"Then tell me what your trade is, and we will fit you in."

"I have abandoned it," Querry said. A sister passed on a bicycle busy about something. "Is there nothing simple I can do to earn my keep?" he asked. "Bandaging? I've had no training there either, but it can't be difficult to learn. Surely there has to be someone who washes the bandages. I could release a more valuable worker."

"That is the sisters' province. My life here would not be worth living if I interfered with their arrangements. Are you feeling restless? Perhaps next time the boat calls you could go back to the capital. There are plenty of opportunities in Luc."

"I am never going to return," Querry said.

"In that case you had better warn the fathers," the doctor said with irony. He called to the dispenser, "That's enough. No more this morning." While he washed his hands in spirits he took a look at Querry over his shoulder. The dispenser was shepherding the lepers out and they were alone. He said, "Are you wanted by the police? You needn't be afraid of telling me—or any of us. You'll find a leproserie just as safe as the Foreign Legion."

"No. I've committed no crime. I assure you there's nothing of interest in my case. I have retired, that's all. If the fathers don't want me here, I can always go on."

"You've said it yourself—the boat goes no further."

"There's the road."

"Yes. In one direction. The way you came. It's not often open though. This is the season of rains."

"There are always my feet," Querry said.

Colin looked for a smile, but there was none on Querry's face. He said, "If you really want to help me and you don't mind a rough journey you might take the second truck to Luc. The boat may not be back for weeks. My new apparatus should have arrived by now in the town. It will take you about eight days there and back—if you are lucky. Will you go? It will mean sleeping in the bush, and if the ferries are not working you'll have to return. You can hardly call it a road," he went on; he was determined that the Superior should not accuse him of persuading Querry to go. "It's only if you want to help . . . you can see how impossible it is for any of us. We can't be spared."

"Of course. I'll start right away."

It occurred to the doctor that perhaps here too was a man under obedience, but not to any divine or civil authority, only to whatever wind might blow. He said, "You could pick up some frozen vegetables too and some steak. The fathers and I could do with a change of diet.

35

There's a cold storage at Luc. Tell Deo Gratias to fetch a camp-bed from my place. If you put a bicycle in the back you could spend the first night at the Perrins', but you can't reach them by truck. They are down by the river. Then there are the Chantins about eight hours further on—unless they've gone home, I can't remember. And last of all there's always Rycker at the second ferry, about six hours from Luc. You'd get a warm welcome from him, I'm sure of that."

"I'd rather sleep in the lorry," Querry said. "I'm not a sociable man."

"I warn you, it's not an easy journey. And we could always wait for the boat."

He paused a while for Querry to answer, but all that Querry found to say was "I shall be glad to be of use." The distrust between them deadened intercourse; it seemed to the doctor that the only sentences he could find to speak with any safety had been preserved for a long time in a jar in the dispensary and smelt of formaldehyde.

2

The river drew a great bow through the bush, and generations of administrators, who had tried to cut across the arc with a road from the regional capital of Luc, had been defeated by the forest and the rain. The rain formed quagmires and swelled the tributary streams until the ferries were unusable, while at long intervals, spaced like a layer of geological time, the forest dropped trees across the way. In the deep bush trees grew unnoticeably old through centuries and here and there one presently died, lying half collapsed for a while in the ropy arms of the lianas until sooner or later they gently lowered the corpse into the only space large enough to receive it, and that was the road, narrow like a coffin or a grave. There were no hearses to drag the corpse away; if it was to be removed at all it could only be by fire.

During the rains no one ever tried to use the road; a few *colons* in the forest would then be completely isolated unless, by bicycle, they could reach the river and camp there in a fisherman's village until a boat came. Then, when the rains were over, weeks had still to pass before the local government could spare the men to build the necessary fires and clear the road. After a few years of complete neglect the road would have disappeared completely and forever. The forest would soon convert it to a surface scrawl, like the first scratches on a wall of early man, and there would remain then reptiles, insects, a few birds and primates, and perhaps the pygmoids—the only human beings in the forest who had the capacity to survive without a road.

The first night Querry stopped the truck at a turn in the road where a track led off towards the Perrins' plantation. He opened a tin of soup and a tin of Frankfurters, while Deo Gratias put up a bed for him in the back of the truck and lit the paraffin-cooker. He offered to share his food with Deo Gratias, but the man had some mess of his own ready prepared in a pot wrapped in an old rag, and the two of them sat in silence with the truck between them as though they were in separate rooms. When the meal was over Querry moved round the bonnet with the intention of saying something to Deo Gratias, but the "boy" by rising to his feet made the occasion as formal as though Querry had entered his hut in the village, and the words, whatever they were, died before they had been spoken. If the boy had possessed an ordinary name, Pierre, Jean, Marc, it might have been possible to begin some simple sentence in French, but Deo Gratias—the absurd name stuck on Querry's tongue.

He walked a little way from the truck, because he knew how far he was from sleep, up the path which led eventually to the river or to the Perrins, and he heard the thud of Deo Gratias's feet behind him. Perhaps he had followed with the idea of protecting him or perhaps because he feared to be left alone in the dark beside the truck. Querry turned with impatience because he had no wish for company, and there the man stood on his two rounded toeless feet, supported on his staff, like something

37

which had grown on that spot ages ago and to which people on one special day made offerings.

"Is this the path to the Perrins?"

The man said yes, but Querry guessed it was what Africans always replied to a question couched like that. He went back to the truck and lay down on the camp-bed. He could hear Deo Gratias settling himself for the night under the belly of the truck, and he lay on his back, staring up at where the stars ought to have been visible, but the gauze of the mosquito-net obscured them. As usual there was no silence. Silence belonged to cities. He dreamt of a girl whom he had once known and thought he loved. She came to him in tears because she had broken a vase which she valued, and she became angry with him because he didn't share her suffering. She struck him in the face, but he felt the blow no more than a dab of butter against his cheek. He said, "I am sorry, I am too far gone, I can't feel at all, I am a leper." As he explained his sickness to her he awoke.

This was a specimen of his days and nights. He had no trouble beyond the boredom of the bush. The ferries worked; the rivers were not in flood, in spite of the rain which came torrentially down on their last night. Deo Gratias made a tent over the back of the truck with a ground-sheet and lay down himself as he had done every night in the shelter of the chassis. Then the sun was out again and the track became a road a few miles out of Luc.

3

They searched a long time for the doctor's apparatus before they found a clue. The cargo-department of Otraco knew nothing of it and suggested the customs, which was no more than a wooden hut by a jetty in the tiny river port, where bat-eared dogs yapped and ran. The customs were uninterested and uncooperative, so that Querry had to dig out the European controller who was having an after-lunch siesta in a block of blue and pink modern flats by a little public garden where no one sat on the hot cement benches. The door of the apartment was opened by an African woman, tousled and sleepy, who looked as though she had been sharing the controller's siesta. The controller was an elderly Fleming who spoke very little French. The pouches under his eyes were like purses that contained the smuggled memories of a disappointing life. Querry had already become so accustomed to the bush-life that this man seemed to belong to another age and race than his own. The commercial calendar on the wall with a coloured reproduction of a painting by Vermeer, the triptych of wife and children on the locked piano, and a portrait of the man himself in a uniform of antique cut belonging to an antique war were like the deposits of a dead culture. They could be dated accurately, but no research would disclose the emotions that had once been attached to them.

The controller was very cordial and confused, as though he were anxious to hide with hospitality some secret of his siesta; he had forgotten to do up his flies. He invited Querry to sit down and take a glass, but when he heard that Querry had come from the leproserie he became restless and anxious, eyeing the chair on which Querry sat. Perhaps he expected to see the bacilli of leprosy burrowing into the upholstery. He knew nothing, he said, of any apparatus and suggested that it might be at the cathedral. When Querry stopped on the landing outside he could hear the tap running in the bathroom. The controller was obviously disinfecting his hands.

True enough the apparatus some time ago had been lodged at the cathedral, although the priest in charge, who had assumed the crates contained a holy statue or books for the father's library, at first denied all knowledge. They had gone off by the last Otraco boat and were somewhere stuck on the river. Querry drove to the cold storage. The hour of siesta was over, and he had to queue for string-beans.

The high vexed colonial voices, each angry about something different, rose around him, competing for attention. It seemed to him for a moment that he was back in

Europe, and his shoulders instinctively hunched through fear of recognition. In the crowded store he realised how on the river and in the streets of the leproserie there had been a measure of peace. "But you simply must have potatoes," a woman's voice was saying. "How dare you deny it? They came in on yesterday's plane. The pilot told me." She was obviously playing her last card, when she appealed to the European manager. "I am expecting the Governor to dinner." Surreptitiously the potatoes emerged, ready wrapped in cellophane.

A voice said, "You are Querry, aren't you?"

He turned. The man who spoke to him was tall, stooping and overgrown. He was like the kind of plant people put in bathrooms, reared on humidity, shooting too high. He had a small black moustache like a smear of city soot and his face was narrow and flat and endless, like an illustration of the law that two parallel lines never meet. He put a hot restless hand on Querry's arm. "My name is Rycker. I missed you the other day when I called at the leproserie. How did you get over here? Is a boat in?"

"I came by truck."

"You were fortunate to get through. You must stay a night at my place on your way home."

"I have to get back to the leproserie."

"They can do without you, M. Querry. They'll have to do without you. After last night's rain there'll be too much water for the ferry. Why are you waiting here?"

"I only wanted some *haricots verts* and some . . ."

"Boy! Some *haricots verts* for this master. You know you have to shout at them a little. They understand nothing else. The only alternative to staying with us is to remain here till the water goes down, and I can assure you, you won't like the hotel. This is a very provincial town. Nothing here to interest a man like you. You are *the* Querry, aren't you?" and Rycker's mouth shut trapwise, while his eyes gleamed roguishly like a detective's.

"I don't know what you mean."

"We don't all live quite out of the world like the fathers and our dubious friend the doctor. Of course this is a

40

bit of a desert, but all the same one manages—somehow—to keep in touch. Two dozen lagers, boy, and make it quick. Of course I shall respect your incognito. I will say nothing. You can trust me not to betray a guest. You'll be far safer at my place than at the hotel. Only myself and my wife. As a matter of fact it was my wife who said to me, 'Do you suppose he can possibly be *the* Querry?'"

"You've made a mistake."

"Oh no, I haven't. I can show you a photograph when you come to my house—in one of the papers that lie around in case they may prove useful. Useful! This one certainly has, hasn't it, because otherwise we would have thought you were only a relation of Querry's or that the name was pure coincidence, for who would expect to find *the* Querry holed up in a leproserie in the bush? I have to admit I am somewhat curious. But you can trust me, trust me all the way. I have serious enough problems of my own, so I can sympathise with those of another man. I've buried myself too. We'd better go outside, for in a little town like this even the walls have ears."

"I'm afraid . . . they are expecting me to return . . ."

"God rules the weather. I assure you, M. Querry, you have no choice."

CHAPTER TWO

I

HOUSE and factory overlooked the ferry; no situation could have been better chosen for a man with Rycker's devouring curiosity. It was impossible for anyone to use the road that led from the town to the interior without passing the two wide windows which were like the lenses of a pair of binoculars trained on the river. They drove under the deep blue shadows of the palm trees towards the river; Rycker's chauffeur and Deo Gratias followed in Querry's lorry.

"You see, M. Querry, how it is. The river's far too high. Not a chance to pass tonight. Who knows whether even tomorrow . . .? So we have time for some interesting talks, you and I."

As they drove through the yard of the factory, among the huge boilers abandoned to rust, a smell like stale margarine lay heavily around them. A blast of hot air struck from an open doorway, and the reflection of a furnace billowed into the waning light. "To you, of course," Rycker said, "accustomed to the factories of the West, this must appear a bit ramshackle. Though I can't remember whether you ever were closely concerned with any factories."

"No."

"There were so many spheres in which *the* Querry led the way."

He recurred again and again to the word "the" as though it were a title of nobility.

"The place functions," he said as the car bumped among the boilers, "it functions in its ugly way. We waste nothing. When we finish with the nut there's nothing left.

42

Nothing. We've crushed out the oil," he said with relish rolling the r, "and as for the husk—into the furnace with it. We don't need any other fuel to keep the furnaces alive."

They left the two cars in the yard and walked over to the house. "Marie, Marie," Rycker called, scraping the mud off his shoes, stamping across the verandah. "Marie."

A girl in blue jeans with a pretty unformed face came quickly round the corner in answer to his call. Querry was on the point of asking "Your daughter?" when Rycker forestalled him. "My wife," he said. "And here, *chérie*, is *the* Querry. He tried to deny it, but I told him we had a photograph."

"I am very glad to meet you," she said. "We will try to make you comfortable." Querry had the impression that she had learnt such occasional speeches by heart from her governess or from a book of etiquette. Now she had said her piece she disappeared as suddenly as she had come; perhaps the school-bell had rung for class.

"Sit down," Rycker said. "Marie is fixing the drinks. You can see I've trained her to know what a man needs."

"Have you been married long?"

"Two years. I brought her out after my last leave. In a post like this it's necessary to have a companion. You married?"

"Yes—that is to say I have been married."

"Of course I know you are thinking that she is very young for me. But I look ahead. If you believe in marriage you have to look to the future. I've still got twenty years of—let's call it active life ahead of me, and what would a woman of thirty be like in twenty years? A man keeps better in the tropics. Don't you agree?"

"I've never thought about it. And I don't yet know the tropics."

"There are enough problems without sex I can assure you. St. Paul wrote, didn't he, that it was better to marry than burn. Marie will stay young long enough to save me from the furnace." He added quickly, "Of course I'm only joking. We have to joke, don't we, about serious

43

things. At the bottom of my heart I believe very profoundly in love." He made the claim as some men might claim to believe in fairies.

The steward came along the verandah carrying a tray and Mme. Rycker followed him. Querry took a glass and Mme. Rycker stood at his elbow while the steward poised the syphon—a division of duties. "Will you tell me how much soda?" Mme. Rycker asked.

"And now, my dear, you'll change into a proper dress," Rycker said.

Over the whisky he turned again to what he called "Your case". He had now less the manner of a detective than of a counsel who by the nature of his profession is an accomplice after the fact. "Why are you here, Querry?"

"One must be somewhere."

"All the same, as I said this morning, no one would expect to find you working in a leproserie."

"I am not working."

"When I drove over some weeks ago, the fathers said that you were at the hospital."

"I was watching the doctor work. I stand around, that's all. There's nothing I can do."

"It seems a waste of talent."

"I have no talent."

Rycker said, "You mustn't despise us poor provincials."

When they had gone into dinner, and after Rycker had said a short grace, Querry's hostess spoke again. She said, "I hope you will be comfortable," and "Do you care for salad?" Her fair hair was streaked and darkened with sweat and he saw her eyes widen with apprehension when a black-and-white moth, with the wing-spread of a bat, swooped across the table. "You must make yourself at home here," she said, her gaze following the moth as it settled like a piece of lichen on the wall. He wondered whether she had ever felt at home herself. She said, "We don't have many visitors," and he was reminded of a child forced to entertain a caller until her mother returns. She had changed, between the whisky and the dinner, into

44

a cotton frock covered with a pattern of autumnal leaves which was like a memory of Europe.

"Not visitors like *the* Querry anyway," Rycker interrupted her. It was as though he had turned off a knob on a radio-set which had been tuned in to a lesson in deportment after he had listened enough. The sound of the voice was shut off the air, but still, behind the shy and wary eyes, the phrases were going on for no one to hear. 'The weather has been a little hot lately, hasn't it? I hope you had a good flight from Europe.'

Querry said, "Do you like the life here?" The question startled her; perhaps the answer wasn't in her phrase-book. "Oh yes," she said, "yes. It's very interesting," staring over his shoulder through the window to where the boilers stood like modern statues in the floodlit yard; then she shifted her eyes back to the moth on the wall and the gecko pointing at his prey.

"Fetch that photograph, dear," Rycker said.

"What photograph?"

"The photograph of M. Querry."

She trailed reluctantly out, making a detour to avoid the wall where the moth rested and the lizard pointed, and returned soon with an ancient copy of *Time*. Querry remembered the ten years younger face upon the cover (the issue had coincided with his first visit to New York). The artist, drawing from a photograph, had romanticised his features. It wasn't the face he saw when he shaved, but a kind of distant cousin. It reflected emotions, thoughts, hopes, profundities that he had certainly expressed to no reporter. The background of the portrait was a building of glass and steel which might have been taken for a concert-hall, or perhaps even for an *orangerie*, if a great cross planted like a belfry outside the door had not indicated it was a church.

"So you see," Rycker said, "we know all."

"I don't remember that the article was very accurate."

"I suppose the Government—or the Church—have commissioned you to do something out here?"

"No. I've retired."

45

"I thought a man of your kind never retired."

"Oh, one comes to an end, just as soldiers do and bank-managers."

When the dinner was over the girl left, like a child after the dessert. "I expect she's gone to write up her journal," Rycker said. "This is a red-letter day for her, meeting *the* Querry. She'll have plenty to put down in it."

"Does she find much to write?"

"I wouldn't know. At the beginning I used to take a quiet look, but she discovered that, and now she locks it up. I expect I teased her a little too much. I remember one entry: 'Letter from mother. Poor Maxime has had five puppies.' It was the day I was decorated by the Governor, but she forgot to put anything about the ceremony."

"It must be a lonely life at her age."

"Oh, I don't know. There are a lot of household duties even in the bush. To be quite frank, I think it's a good deal more lonely for me. She's hardly—you can see it for yourself—an intellectual companion. That's one of the disadvantages of marrying a young wife. If I want to talk about things which really interest me, I have to drive over to the fathers. A long way to go for a conversation. Living in the way I do, one has a lot of time to think things over. I'm a good Catholic, I hope, but that doesn't prevent me from having spiritual problems. A lot of people take their religion lightly, but I had six years when I was a young man with the Jesuits. If a novice master had been less unfair you wouldn't have found me here. I gathered from that article in *Time* that you are a Catholic too."

"I've retired," Querry said for the second time.

"Oh come now, one hardly retires from *that*."

The gecko on the wall leapt at the moth, missed and lay motionless again, the tiny paws spread on the wall like ferns.

"To tell you the truth," Rycker said, "I find those fathers at the leproserie an unsatisfactory lot. They are more interested in electricity and building than in

46

questions of faith. Ever since I heard you were here I've looked forward to a conversation with an intellectual Catholic."

"I wouldn't call myself that."

"In the long years I've been out here I've been thrown back on my own thoughts. Some men can manage, I suppose, with clock-golf. I can't. I've read a great deal on the subject of love."

"Love?"

"The love of God. Agape not Eros."

"I'm not qualified to talk about that."

"You underrate yourself," Rycker replied. He went to the sideboard and fetched a tray of liqueurs, disturbing the gecko who disappeared behind a reproduction of some primitive Flight into Egypt. "A glass of Cointreau," Rycker said, "or would you prefer a Van Der Hum?" Beyond the verandah Querry saw a thin figure in a gold-leafed dress move towards the river. Perhaps out of doors the moths had lost their terror.

"In the seminary I formed the habit of thinking more than most men," Rycker said. "A faith like ours, when profoundly understood, sets us many problems. For instance—no, it's not a mere instance, I'm jumping to the heart of what really troubles me, I don't believe my wife understands the true nature of Christian marriage."

Out in the darkness there was a plop-plop-plop. She must be throwing small pieces of wood into the river.

"It sometimes seems to me," Rycker said, "that she's ignorant of almost everything. I find myself wondering whether the nuns taught her at all. You saw for yourself —she doesn't even cross herself at meals when I say grace. Ignorance, you know, beyond a certain point might even invalidate a marriage in canon law. That's one of the matters I have tried in vain to discuss with the fathers. They would much prefer to talk about turbines. Now you are here . . ."

"I'm not competent to discuss it," Querry said. In the moments of silence he could hear the river flooding down.

"At least you listen. The fathers would already have

47

started talking about the new well they propose to dig. A well, Querry, a well against a human soul." He drank down his Van Der Hum and poured himself another. "They don't realise . . . just suppose that we weren't properly married, she could leave me at any time, Querry."

"It's easy to leave what you call a proper marriage, too."

"No, no. It's much more difficult. There are social pressures—particularly here."

"If she loves you . . ."

"That's no protection. We are men of the world, Querry, you and I. A love like that doesn't last. I tried to teach her the importance of loving God. Because if she loved Him, she wouldn't want to offend Him, would she? And that would be some security. I have tried to get her to pray, but I don't think she knows any prayers except the Pater Noster and the Ave Maria. What prayers do you use, Querry?"

"None—except occasionally, from habit, in a moment of danger." He added sadly, "Then I pray for a brown teddy bear."

"You are joking, I know that, but this is very serious. Have another Cointreau?"

"What's really worrying you, Rycker? A man?"

The girl came back into the light of the lamp which hung at the corner of the verandah. She was carrying a *roman policier* in the *Série Noire*. She gave a whistle that was scarcely audible, but Rycker heard it. "That damn puppy," he said. "She loves her puppy more than she loves God." Perhaps the Van Der Hum affected the logic of his transitions. He said, "I'm not jealous. It's not a man I worry about. She hasn't enough feeling for that. Sometimes she even refuses her duties."

"What duties?"

"Her duties to me. Her married duties."

"I've never thought of those as duties."

"You know very well the Church does. No one has any right to abstain except by mutual consent."

48

"I suppose there may be times when she doesn't want you."

"Then what am I supposed to do? Have I given up the priesthood for nothing at all?"

"I wouldn't talk to her too much, if I were you, about loving God," Querry said with reluctance. "She mightn't see a parallel between that and your bed."

"There's a close parallel for a Catholic," Rycker said rapidly. He put up his hand as though he were answering a question before his fellow novices. The bristles of hair between the knuckles were like a row of little moustaches.

"You seem to be very well up in the subject," Querry said.

"At the seminary I always came out well in moral theology."

"I don't fancy you need me then—or the fathers either. You have obviously thought everything out satisfactorily yourself."

"That goes without saying. But sometimes one needs confirmation and encouragement. You can't imagine, M. Querry, what a relief it is to go over these problems with an educated Catholic."

"I don't know that I would call myself a Catholic."

Rycker laughed. "What? *The* Querry? You can't fool me. You are being too modest. I wonder they haven't made you a count of the Holy Roman Empire—like that Irish singer, what was his name?"

"I don't know. I am not musical."

"You should read what they say about you in *Time.*"

"On matters like that *Time* isn't necessarily well informed. Would you mind if I went to bed? I'll have to be up early in the morning if I'm to reach the next ferry before dark."

"Of course. Though I doubt if you'll be able to cross the river tomorrow."

Rycker followed him along the verandah to his room. The darkness was noisy with frogs, and for a long while after his host had said goodnight and gone, they seemed to croak with Rycker's hollow phrases: grace: sacrament: duty: love, love, love.

49

CHAPTER THREE

I

"You want to be of use, don't you?" the doctor asked sharply. "You don't want menial jobs just for the sake of menial jobs? You aren't either a masochist or a saint."

"Rycker promised me that he would tell no one."

"He kept his word for nearly a month. That's quite an achievement for Rycker. When he came here the other day he only told the Superior in confidence."

"What did the Superior say?"

"That he would listen to nothing in confidence outside the confessional."

The doctor continued to unpack the crate of heavy electrical apparatus which had arrived at last by the Otraco boat. The lock on the dispensary door was too insecure for him to trust the apparatus there, so he unpacked it on the floor of his living-room. One could never be certain of the African's reaction to anything unfamiliar. In Leopoldville six months before, when the first riots broke out, the attack had been directed at the new glass-and-steel hospital intended for African patients. The most monstrous rumours were easily planted and often believed. It was a land where Messiahs died in prison and rose again from the dead: where walls were said to fall at the touch of finger-nails sanctified by a little holy dust. A man whom the doctor had cured of leprosy wrote him a threatening letter once a month; he really believed that he had been turned out of the leproserie, not because he was cured, but because the doctor had personal designs on the half acre of ground on which he used to grow bananas. It only needed someone, in malice or ignorance, to suggest that the new machines were intended to torture the patients and some fools would break into the dispensary and destroy them. Yet in our century you could hardly call them fools. Hola Camp, Sharpeville, and Algiers had justified all possible belief in European cruelty.

So it was better, the doctor explained, to keep the machines out of sight at home until the new hospital was finished. The floor of his sitting-room was covered with straw from the crates.

"The position of the power-plugs will have to be decided now." The doctor asked, "Do you know what this is?"

"No."

"I've wanted it for so long," the doctor said, touching the metal shape tenderly as a man might stroke the female flank of one of Rodin's bronzes. "Sometimes I despaired. The papers I have had to fill in, the lies I've told. And here at last it *is*."

"What does it do?"

"It measures to one twenty-thousandth of a second the reaction of the nerves. One day we are going to be proud of this leproserie. Of you too and the part you will have played."

"I told you I've retired."

"One never retires from a vocation."

"Oh yes, make no mistake, one does. One comes to an end."

"What are you here for then? To make love to a black woman?"

"No. One comes to an end of that too. Possibly sex and a vocation are born and die together. Let me roll bandages or carry buckets. All I want is to pass the time."

"I thought you wanted to be of use."

"Listen," Querry said and then fell silent.

"I *am* listening."

"I don't deny my profession once meant a lot to me. So have women. But the use of what I made was never important to me. I wasn't a builder of council-houses or factories. When I made something I made it for my own pleasure."

"Is that the way you loved women?" the doctor asked, but Querry hardly heard him. He was talking as a hungry man eats.

"Your vocation is quite a different one, doctor. You are concerned with people. I wasn't concerned with the people who occupied my space—only with the space."

"I wouldn't have trusted your plumbing then."

"A writer doesn't write for his readers, does he? Yet he has to take elementary precautions all the same to make them comfortable. My interest was in space, light, proportion. New materials interested me only in the effect they might have on those three. Wood, brick, steel, concrete, glass—space seems to alter with what you use to enclose it. Materials are the architect's plot. They are not his motive for work. Only the space and the light and the proportion. The subject of a novel is not the plot. Who remembers what happened to Lucien de Rubempré in the end?"

"Two of your churches are famous. Didn't you care what happened inside them—to people?"

"The acoustics had to be good of course. The high altar had to be visible to all. But people hated them. They said they weren't designed for prayer. They meant that they were not Roman or Gothic or Byzantine. And in a year they had cluttered them up with their cheap plaster saints; they took out my plain windows and put in stained glass dedicated to dead pork-packers who had contributed to diocesan funds, and when they had destroyed my space and my light, they were able to pray again, and they even became proud of what they had spoilt. I became what they called a great Catholic architect, but I built no more churches, doctor."

"I am not a religious man, I don't know much about these things, but I suppose they had a right to believe their prayers were more important than a work of art."

"Men have prayed in prison, men have prayed in slums and concentration camps. It's only the middle-classes who demand to pray in suitable surroundings.

52

Sometimes I feel sickened by the word prayer. Rycker used it a great deal. Do you pray, doctor?"

"I think the last time I prayed was before my final medical exam. And you?"

"I gave it up a long time ago. Even in the days when I believed, I seldom prayed. It would have got in the way of work. Before I went to sleep, even if I was with a woman, the last thing I had always to think about was work. Problems which seemed insoluble would often solve themselves in sleep. I had my bedroom next to my office, so that I could spend two minutes in front of the drawing-board the last thing of all. The bed, the bidet, the drawing-board, and then sleep."

"It sounds a little hard on the woman."

"Self-expression is a hard and selfish thing. It eats everything, even the self. At the end you find you haven't even got a self to express. I have no interest in anything any more, doctor. I don't want to sleep with a woman nor design a building."

"Have you no children?"

"I once had, but they disappeared into the world a long time ago. We haven't kept in touch. Self-expression eats the father in you, too."

"So you thought you could just come and die here?"

"Yes. That *was* in my mind. But chiefly I wanted to be in an empty place, where no new building or woman would remind me that there was a time when I was alive, with a vocation and a capacity to love—if it was love. The palsied suffer, their nerves feel, but I am one of the mutilated, doctor."

"Twenty years ago we might have been able to offer you your death, but now we deal only in cures. D.D.S. costs three shillings a year. It's much cheaper than a coffin."

"Can you cure me?"

"Perhaps your mutilations haven't gone far enough yet. When a man comes here too late the disease has to burn itself out." The doctor laid a cloth tenderly over his machine. "The other patients are waiting. Do you want

53

to come or would you like to sit here thinking of your own case? It's often the way with the mutilated—they want to retire too, out of sight."

The air in the hospital lay heavily and sweetly upon them: it was never moved by a fan or a breeze. Querry was conscious of the squalor of the bedding—cleanliness was not important to the leper, only to the healthy. The patients brought their own mattresses which they had probably possessed for a lifetime—rough sacking from which the straw had escaped. The bandaged feet lay in the straw like ill-wrapped packages of meat. On the verandah the walking cases sat out of the sun—if you could call a walking case a man who, when he moved, had to support his huge swollen testicles with both hands. A woman with palsied eye-lids who could not close her eyes or even blink sat in a patch of shade out of the merciless light. A man without fingers nursed a baby on his knee, and another man lay flat on the verandah with one breast long and drooping and teated like a woman's. There was little the doctor could do for any of these; the man with elephantiasis had too weak a heart for an operation, and though he could have sewn up the woman's eye-lids, she had refused to have it done from fear, and as for the baby it would be a leper too in time. Nor could he help those in the first ward who were dying of tuberculosis or the woman who dragged herself between the beds, her legs withered with polio. It had always seemed to the doctor unfair that leprosy did not preclude all other diseases (leprosy was enough for one human being to bear) and yet it was from the other diseases that most of his patients died. He passed on and Querry tagged at his heels, saying nothing.

In the mud kitchen at the back of one of the lepers' houses an old man sat in the dark on an ancient deck-chair. He made an effort to rise when the doctor crossed the yard, but his legs wouldn't support him and he made a gesture of courteous apology. "High blood pressure," the doctor said softly. "No hope. He has come to his kitchen to die." His legs were as thin as a child's and he

54

wore a clout like a baby's napkin round the waist for decency. Querry had seen where his clothes had been left neatly folded in the new brick cottage under the Pope's portrait. A holy medal lay in the hollow of his breast among the scarce grey hairs. He had a face of great kindness and dignity, a face that must have always accepted life without complaint, the face of a saint. Now he enquired after the doctor's health as though it were the doctor who was sick, not he.

"Is there anything that I can fetch you?" the doctor asked, and no, the old man replied, he had everything he needed. He wanted to know whether the doctor had heard recently from his family and he made enquiries after the health of the doctor's mother.

"She has been in Switzerland, in the mountains. A holiday in the snow."

"Snow?"

"I forgot. You have never seen snow. It is frozen vapour, frozen mist. The air is so cold that it never melts and it lies on the ground white and soft like the feathers of a *pique-bœuf*, and the lakes are covered with ice."

"I know what ice is," the old man said proudly. "I have seen ice in a refrigerator. Is your mother old like me?"

"Older."

"Then she ought not to travel far away from her home. One should die in one's own village if it is possible." He looked sadly at his own thin legs. "They will not carry me or I should walk to mine."

"I would arrange for a lorry to take you," the doctor said, "but I don't think you would stand the journey."

"It would be too much trouble for you," the old man said, "and in any case there is no time because I am going to die tomorrow."

"I will tell the Superior to come and see you as soon as he can."

"I do not wish to be any trouble to him. He has many duties. I will not be dead till the evening."

By the old deck-chair stood a bottle with a Johnny

Walker label. It contained a brown liquid and some withered plants tied together with a loop of beads. "What has he got there," Querry asked after they left him, "in the bottle?"

"Medicine. Magic. An appeal to his god, Nzambe."

"I thought he was a Catholic."

"If I sign a form I call myself a Catholic too. So does he. I believe in nothing most of the time. He half believes in Christ and half believes in Nzambe. There's not much difference between us as far as Catholicism is concerned. I only wish I were as good a man."

"Will he really die tomorrow?"

"I think so. They have a wonderful knack of knowing."

In the dispensary a leper with bandaged feet stood waiting with a small boy in her arms. Every rib in the child's body showed. It was like a cage over which a dark cloth has been flung at night to keep a bird asleep, and like a bird his breath moved under the cloth. It was not leprosy that would kill him, the doctor said, but sicklaemia, an incurable disease of the blood. There was no hope. The child would not live long enough even to become a leper, but there was no point in telling the mother that. He touched the little hollow chest with his finger, and the child winced away. The doctor began to abuse the woman in her own language, and she argued unconvincingly back, clutching the boy against her hip. The boy stared passively over the doctor's shoulder with sad frog-like eyes as though nothing that anyone said would ever concern him seriously again. When the woman had gone, Doctor Colin said, "She promises it won't happen any more. But how can I tell?"

"What happen?"

"Didn't you see the little scar on his breast? They have been cutting a pocket in his skin to put their native medicines in. She says it was the grandmother who did it. Poor child. They won't let him die in peace without pain. I told her that if it happened again, I would cease treating her for leprosy, but I daresay they won't let me see the

56

boy a second time. In that state he's as easy to hide as a needle."

"Can't you put him in the hospital?"

"You've seen what sort of a hospital I've got. Would you want a boy of yours to die there? Next," he called angrily, "next," and the next was a child too, a boy of six years old. His father accompanied him, and his fingerless fist rested on the boy's shoulder to give him comfort. The doctor turned the child round and ran his hand over the young skin.

"Well," he said, "you should be noticing things by this time. What do you think of this case?"

"One of his toes has gone already."

"That's not important. He's had jiggers and they've neglected them. It happens often in the bush. No—here's the first patch. The leprosy has just begun."

"Is there no way to protect the children?"

"In Brazil they take them away at birth, and thirty per cent of the babies die. I prefer a leper to a dead child. We'll cure him in a couple of years." He looked up quickly at Querry and away again. "One day—in the new hospital—I'll have a special children's ward and dispensary. I'll anticipate the patch. I'll live to see leprosy in retreat. Do you know there are some areas, a few hundred miles from here, where one in five of the people are lepers? I dream of movable prefabricated hospitals. War has changed. In 1914 generals organised battles from country-houses, but in 1944 Rommel and Montgomery fought from moving caravans. How can I convey what I want to Father Joseph? I can't draw. I can't even design one room to the best advantage. I'll only be able to tell him what's wrong after the hospital is built. He's not even a builder. He's a good bricklayer. He's putting one brick on another for the love of God like they used to build monasteries. So you see I need you," Doctor Colin said. The boy's four toes wriggled impatiently on the cement floor, waiting for the meaningless conversation between the white men to reach a conclusion.

57

Querry wrote in his journal: "I haven't enough feeling left for human beings to do anything for them out of pity." He carefully recalled the scar on the immature breast and the four toes, but he was unmoved; an accumulation of pinpricks cannot amount to the sensation of pain. A storm was on the way, and the flying ants swarmed into the room, striking against the light until he shut the window. Then they fell on the cement floor and lost their wings and ran this way and that as though they were confused at finding themselves so suddenly creatures of earth not air. With the window closed the wet heat increased and he had to put blotting paper under his wrist to catch the sweat.

He wrote, in an attempt to make clear his motives to Dr. Colin: "A vocation is an act of love: it is not a professional career. When desire is dead one cannot continue to make love. I've come to the end of desire and to the end of a vocation. Don't try to bind me in a loveless marriage and to make me imitate what I used to perform with passion. And don't talk to me like a priest about my duty. A talent—we used to learn that lesson as children in scripture-lessons—should not be buried when it still has purchasing power, but when the currency has changed and the image has been superseded and no value is left in the coin but the weight of a wafer of silver, a man has every right to hide it. Obsolete coins, like corn, have always been found in graves."

The notes were rough and disjointed: he had no talent to organise his thought in words. He ended: "What I have built, I have always built for myself, not for the glory of God or the pleasure of a purchaser. Don't talk to me of human beings. Human beings are not my country. And haven't I offered anyway to wash their filthy bandages?"

He tore the pages out and sent them by Deo Gratias to Dr. Colin. At the end a half-sentence had been thrust out into the void—"I will do anything for you in reason, but don't ask me to try to revive . . ." like a plank from a ship's deck off which a victim has been thrust.

Dr. Colin came to his room later and tossed the letter, scrumpled into a paper-ball, on to his table. "Scruples," the doctor said impatiently. "Just scruples."

"I tried to explain . . ."

"Who cares?" the doctor said, and that question "Who cares?" went echoing obsessively on in Querry's brain like a line of verse learnt in adolescence.

He had a dream that night from which he woke in terror. He was walking down a long railway-track, in the dark, in a cold country. He was hurrying because he had to reach a priest and explain to him that, in spite of the clothes he was wearing, he was a priest also and he must make his confession and obtain wine with which to celebrate Mass. He was under orders of some kind from a superior. He had to say his Mass now, that night. Tomorrow would be too late. He would lose his chance forever. He came to a village and left the railway-track (the small station was shuttered and deserted: perhaps the whole branch line had been closed long since by the authorities) and presently found himself outside the priest's door, heavy and mediaeval, studded with great nails the size of Roman coins. He rang and was admitted. A lot of chattering pious women surrounded the priest, but he was friendly and accessible in spite of them. Querry said, "I must see you at once, alone. There is something I have to tell you," and already he began to feel the enormous relief and security of his confession. He was nearly home again. The priest took him aside into a little room where a decanter of wine stood on a table, but before he had time to speak the holy women came billowing in through the curtain after them, full of little pious jests and whimsicalities. "But we must be alone," Querry cried, "I have to speak to you," and the priest pushed the women back through the curtain, and they swayed for a moment to and fro like clothes on hangers in a cupboard. All the same the two of them were sufficiently alone now for him to speak, and with his eyes on the wine he was able at last really to begin. "Father . . ." but at that moment, when he was about to lose the burden of his fear and responsibility, a second priest entered the room and taking the father on one side began to explain to him how he had run short of wine and had come to borrow his, and still talking he picked up the decanter from the table. Then Querry broke down. It was as though he had had an appointment with hope at this turn of the road and had arrived just too late. He let out a cry like that of an animal in pain and woke. It was raining hard on all the tin roofs, and when the lightning flashed he could see the small white cell that his mosquito-net made, the size of a coffin, and in one of the leper-houses nearby a quarrel had begun between a man and a woman. He thought, 'I was too late,' and an obsessional phrase bobbed up again, like a cork attached to some invisible fishing-net below the water, 'Who cares?' 'Who cares?'

When the morning came at last he went to the carpenter in the leproserie and showed him how to make the kind of desk and drawing-board that he required, and only when that was done did he seek out Doctor Colin to tell him of his decision.

"I am glad," Dr. Colin said, "for you."

"Why for me?"

"I know nothing about you," Doctor Colin said, "but we are all made much the same way. You have been trying an impossible experiment. A man can't live with nothing but himself."

"Oh yes, he can."

"Sooner or later he would kill himself."

"If he had enough interest," Querry replied.

60

CHAPTER FOUR

I

AFTER two months a measure of natural confidence had
grown between Querry and Deo Gratias. At first it was
based only on the man's disabilities. Querry was not
angry with him when he spilt water; he kept his temper
when one of his drawings was smeared by ink from a
broken bottle. It takes a long time to learn even the
simplest tasks without fingers and toes, and in any case a
man who cares for nothing finds it difficult—or absurd—
to be angry. There was one occasion when the crucifix
which the fathers had left hanging on Querry's wall was
broken by some maladroitness on the part of the mutilated
man and he expected Querry to react as he might have
reacted himself if a fetish of his own had been carelessly
or heartlessly destroyed. It was easy for him to mistake
indifference for sympathy.

One night when the moon was full Querry became
aware of the man's absence as one might become aware
of some hitherto unnoticed object missing from a mantelpiece in a temporary home. His ewer had not been filled
and the mosquito-net had not been drawn down, and
later, as he was on his way to the doctor's house, where
he had to discuss a possible cut in the cost of building,
he met Deo Gratias stumbling with his staff down the
central road of the leproserie as quickly as he was able
on toeless feet. The man's face was wet with sweat and
when Querry spoke to him he swerved away into someone's backyard. When Querry returned half-an-hour
later he stood there still, like a tree-stump that the owner
had not bothered to move. The sweat looked like traces
of the night's rain on the bark and he appeared to be

listening to something a long way off. Querry listened too, but he could hear nothing except the rattle of the crickets and the swelling diapason of the frogs. In the morning Deo Gratias had not returned, and Querry felt an unimportant disappointment that the servant had not spoken a word to him before he left. He told the doctor that the boy had gone. "If he doesn't come back to-morrow will you find me another?"

"I don't understand," Doctor Colin said. "I only gave him the job so that he might stay in the leproserie. He had no wish to go." Later that day a leper picked up the man's staff from a path that led into the thickest bush, and brought it to Querry's room where he was at work, taking advantage of the last light.

"But how do you know that the staff is his? All the mutilated lepers have them," Querry asked and the man simply repeated that it belonged to Deo Gratias—no argument, no reason, just one more of the things they knew that he knew nothing about.

"You think some accident has happened to him?"

Something, the man said in his poor French, had happened, and Querry got the impression that an accident was what the man feared least of all.

"Why don't you go and look for him then?" Querry asked.

There was not enough light left, the man said, under the trees. They would have to wait till morning.

"But he's been gone already nearly twenty-four hours. If there has been an accident we have waited long enough. You can take my torch."

The morning would be better, the man repeated, and Querry saw that he was scared.

"If I go with you, will you come?"

The man shook his head, so Querry went alone.

He could not blame these people for their fears: a man had to believe in nothing if he was not to be afraid of the big bush at night. There was little in the forest to appeal to the romantic. It was completely empty. It had never been humanised, like the woods of Europe, with witches and charcoal-burners and cottages of marzipan; no one had ever walked under these trees lamenting lost love, nor had anyone listened to the silence and communed like a lake-poet with his heart. For there was no silence; if a man here wished to be heard at night he had to raise his voice to counter the continuous chatter of the insects as in some monstrous factory where thousands of sewing-machines were being driven against time by myriads of needy seamstresses. Only for an hour or so, in the midday heat, silence fell, the siesta of the insect.

But if, like these Africans, one believed in some kind of divine being, wasn't it just as possible for a god to exist in this empty region as in the empty spaces of the sky where men had once located him? These woody spaces would remain unexplored, it seemed likely now, for longer than the planets. The craters of the moon were already better known than the forest at the door that one could enter any day on foot. The sharp sour smell of chlorophyl from rotting vegetation and swamp-water fell like a dentist's mask over Querry's face.

It was a stupid errand. He was no hunter. He had been bred in a city. He couldn't possibly hope to discover a human track even in daylight, and he had accepted too easily the evidence of the staff. Shining his torch on this side and that he elicited only stray gleams and flashes among the foliage which might have been the reflection of eyes, but were more probably little pools of rainwater caught in the curls of the leaves. He must have been walking now for half an hour, and he had probably covered a mile along the narrow path. Once his finger slipped on the trigger of the torch and in the moment of darkness he walked off the twisting path slap into the forest-wall. He thought: I have no reason to believe that my battery will see me home. He continued to digest the thought as he walked further in. He had said to Doctor Colin to explain the reason for his stay, "the boat goes no further", but it is always possible to go a little deeper on one's own feet. He called "Deo Gratias! Deo Gratias!" above the noise of the insects, but the absurd name which sounded like an invocation in a church received no response.

His own presence here was hardly more explicable than that of Deo Gratias. The thought of his servant lying injured in the forest waiting for the call or footstep of any human being would perhaps at an earlier time have vexed him all night until he was forced into making a token-gesture. But now that he cared for nothing, perhaps he was being driven only by a vestige of intellectual curiosity. What had brought Deo Gratias here out of the safety and familiarity of the leproserie? The path, of course, might be leading somewhere—to a village perhaps where Deo Gratias had relations—but he had already learned enough of Africa to know that it was more likely to peter out—to be the relic of a track made by men who had come searching for caterpillars to fry; it might well mark the furthest limit of human penetration. What was the meaning of the sweat he had seen pouring down the man's face? It might have been caused by fear or anxiety or even, in the heavy river-heat, by the pressure of thought. Interest began to move painfully in him like a nerve that has been frozen. He had lived with inertia so long that he examined his "interest" with clinical detachment.

He must have been walking now, he told himself, over an hour. How had Deo Gratias come so far without his staff on mutilated feet? He felt more than ever doubtful whether the battery would last him home. Nonetheless, he went on. He realised how foolish he had been not to tell the doctor or one of the fathers where he was going in case of accident, but wasn't an accident perhaps exactly what he was seeking? In any case he went on, while the mosquitoes droned to the attack. There was no point in waving them away. He trained himself to submit.

Fifty yards further he was startled by a harsh animal sound—the kind of grunt he could imagine a wild boar giving. He stopped and moved his waning light in a circle round him. He saw that many years ago this path must have been intended to lead somewhere, for in front of him were the remains of a bridge made from the trunks of trees that had long ago rotted. Two more steps and he would have fallen down the gap, not a great fall, a matter of feet only, into a shallow overgrown marsh, but for a man mutilated in hands and feet, far enough: the light shone on the body of Deo Gratias, half in the water, half out. He could see the tracks made in the wet and slippery ground by hands like boxing gloves which had tried to catch hold. Then the body grunted again, and Querry climbed down beside it.

Querry couldn't tell whether Deo Gratias was conscious or not. His body was too heavy to lift, and he made no effort to co-operate. He was warm and wet like a hummock of soil; he felt like part of the bridge that had fallen in many years ago. After ten minutes of struggle Querry managed to drag his limbs out of the water—it was all he could do. The obvious thing now, if his torch would last long enough, was to fetch help. Even if the Africans refused to return with him two of the fathers would certainly aid him. He made to climb up on to the bridge and Deo Gratias howled, as a dog or a baby might howl. He raised a stump and howled, and Querry realised that he was crippled with fear. The fingerless hand fell on Querry arm like a hammer and held him there.

There was nothing to be done but wait for the mornii The man might die of fear, but neither of them wor die from damp or mosquito-bites. He settled him down as comfortably as he could by the boy and by last light of the torch examined the rocky feet. As fai he could tell an ankle was broken—that seemed to be Soon the light was so dim that Querry could see the sh of the filament in the dark, like a phosphorescent wo then it went out altogether. He took Deo Gratias's h to reassure him, or rather laid his own hand down be it; you cannot "take" a fingerless hand. Deo Gra grunted twice, and then uttered a word. It sounded "Pendélé". In the darkness the knuckles felt like a that has been eroded for years by the weather.

"We both had a lot of time to think," Querry said to Doctor Colin. "It wasn't light enough to leave him till about six. I suppose it was about six—I had forgotten to wind my watch."

"It must have been a long bad night."

"One has had worse alone." He seemed to be searching his memory for an example. "Nights when things end. Those are the interminable nights. In a way you know this seemed a night when things begin. I've never much minded physical discomfort. And after about an hour when I tried to move my hand, he wouldn't let it go. His fist lay on it like a paper-weight. I had an odd feeling that he needed me."

"Why odd?" Doctor Colin asked.

"Odd to me. I've needed people often enough in my life. You might accuse me of having used people more than I have ever loved them. But to be needed is a different sensation, a tranquillizer, not an excitement. Do you know what the word 'Pendélé' means? Because after I moved my hand he began to talk. I had never properly listened to an African talking before. You know how one listens with half an ear, as one does to children. It wasn't easy to follow the mixture of French and whatever language it is that Deo Gratias speaks. And this word 'Pendélé' continually cropped up. What does it mean, doctor?"

"I've an idea that it means something the same as *Bunkasi*—and that means pride, arrogance, perhaps a kind of dignity and independence if you look at the good side of the word."

"It's not what he meant. I am certain he meant a place —somewhere in the forest, near water, where something of great importance to him was happening. He had felt strangled his last day in the leproserie; of course he didn't use the word 'strangled', he told me there wasn't enough air, he wanted to dance and shout and run and sing. But, poor fellow, he couldn't run or dance and the fathers would have taken a poor view of the kind of songs he wanted to sing. So he set out to find this place beside the water. He had been taken there once by his mother when he was a child, and he could remember how there had been singing and dancing and games and prayers."

"But Deo Gratias comes from hundreds of miles away."

"Perhaps there is more than one Pendélé in the world."

"A lot of people left the leproserie three nights ago. They've most of them come back. I expect they had some kind of witchcraft going on. He started too late and he couldn't catch up with them."

"I asked him what prayers. He said they prayed to Yezu Klisto and someone called Simon. Is that the same as Simon Peter?"

"No, not quite the same. The fathers could tell you about Simon. He died in gaol nearly twenty years ago. They think he'll rise again. It's a strange Christianity we have here, but I wonder whether the Apostles would find it as difficult to recognise as the collected works of Thomas Aquinas. If Peter could have understood those, it would have been a greater miracle than Pentecost, don't you think? Even the Nicaean Creed—it has the flavour of higher mathematics to me."

"That word Pendélé runs in my head."

"We always connect hope with youth," Doctor Colin said, "but sometimes it can be one of the diseases of age. The cancerous growth you find unexpectedly in the dying after a deep operation. These people here are all dying—oh, I don't mean of leprosy, I mean of us. And their last disease is hope."

"You'll know where to look for me," Querry said, "if I should be missing." An unexpected sound made the doctor look up; Querry's face was twisted into the rictus of a laugh. The doctor realised with astonishment that Querry had perpetrated a joke.

PART III

CHAPTER ONE

I

M. AND Mme. Rycker drove into town for cocktails with the Governor. In a village by the road stood a great wooden cage on stilts where once a year at a festival a man danced above the flames lit below; in the bush thirty kilometres before they had passed something sitting in a chair constructed out of a palm-nut and woven fibres into the rough and monstrous appearance of a human being. Inexplicable objects were the fingerprints of Africa. Naked women smeared white with grave-clay fled up the banks as the car passed, hiding their faces.

Rycker said, "When Mme. Guelle asks you what you will drink, say a glass of Perrier."

"Not an *orange pressée*?"

"Not unless you can see a jug of it on the sideboard. We mustn't inconvenience her."

Marie Rycker took the advice seriously in and then turned her eyes from her husband and stared away at the dull forest wall. The only path that led inside was closed with fibre-mats for a ceremony no white man must see.

"You heard what I said, darling?"

"Yes. I will remember."

"And the *canapés*. Don't eat too many of them like you did last time. We haven't come to the Residence to take a meal. It creates a bad impression."

"I won't touch a thing."

"That would be just as bad. It would look as though you had noticed they were stale. They usually are."

The little medal of Saint Christopher jingle-jangled like a fetish below the windscreen.

"I am frightened," the girl said. "It is all so complicated and Mme. Guelle does not like me."

"It isn't that she doesn't like you," Rycker explained kindly. "It is only that last time, you remember, you began to leave before the wife of the Commissioner. Of course, we are not bound by these absurd colonial rules, but we don't want to seem pushing and it is generally understood that as leading *commerçants* we come after the Public Works. Watch for Mme. Cassin to leave."

"I never remember any of their names."

"The very fat one. You can't possibly miss her. By the way if Querry should be there don't be shy of inviting him for the night. In a place like this one longs for intelligent conversation. For the sake of Querry I would even put up with that atheist Doctor Colin. We could make up another bed on the verandah."

But neither Querry nor Colin was there.

"A Perrier if you are sure it's no trouble," Marie Rycker said. Everybody had been driven in from the garden, for it was the hour when the D.D.T. truck cannoned a stinging hygienic fog over the town.

Mme. Guelle graciously brought the Perrier with her own hands. "You are the only people," she said, "who seem to have met M. Querry. The mayor would have liked him to sign the Golden Book, but he seems to spend all his time in that sad place out there. Now you perhaps could pry him out for all our sakes."

"We don't really know him," Marie Rycker said. "He spent the night with us when the river was in flood, that's all. He wouldn't have stayed otherwise. I don't think he wants to see people. My husband promised not to tell . . ."

"Your husband was quite right to tell *us*. We should have looked such fools, having *the* Querry in our own territory without being aware of it. How did he strike you, dear?"

"I hardly spoke to him."

"His reputation in certain ways is very bad they tell me. Have you read the article in *Time*? Oh yes, of course, your husband showed it to us. Not of course that they

72

write of *that*. It's only what they say in Europe. One has to remember though that some of the great saints of the Church passed through a certain period of—how shall I put it?"

"Do I hear you talking of saints, Mme. Guelle?" Rycker asked. "What excellent whisky you always have."

"Not exactly saints. We were discussing M. Querry."

"In my opinion," Rycker said, raising his voice a little like a monitor in a noisy classroom, "he may well be the greatest thing to happen in Africa since Schweitzer, and Schweitzer after all is a Protestant. I found him a most interesting companion when he stayed with us. And have you heard the latest story?" Rycker asked the room at large, shaking the ice in his glass like a hand-bell. "He went out into the bush two weeks ago, they say, to find a leper who had run away. He spent the whole night with him in the forest, arguing and praying, and he persuaded the man to return and complete his treatment. It rained in the night and the man was sick with fever, so he covered him with his body."

"What an unconventional thing to do," Mme. Guelle said. "He's not, is he . . . ?"

The Governor was a very small man with a short-sight which gave him an appearance of moral intensity; physically he had the air of looking to his wife for protection, but like a small nation, proud of its culture, he was an unwilling satellite. He said, "There are more saints in the world than the Church recognises." This remark stamped with official approval what might otherwise have been regarded as an eccentric or even an ambiguous action.

"Who is this man Querry?" the Director of Public Works asked the Manager of Otraco.

"They say he's a world-famous architect. You should know. He comes into your province."

"He's not here officially, is he?"

"He's helping with the new hospital at the leproserie."

"But I passed those plans months ago. They don't need an architect. It's a simple building job."

73

"The hospital," Rycker said, interrupting them and drawing them within his circle, "you can take it from me, is only a first step. He is designing a modern African church. He hinted at that to me himself. He's a man of great vision. What he builds lasts. A prayer in stone. There's Monseigneur coming in. Now we shall learn what the Church thinks of Querry."

The Bishop was a tall rakish figure with a neatly trimmed beard and the roving eye of an old-fashioned cavalier of the boulevards. He generously avoided putting out his hand to the men so that they might escape a genuflection. Women however liked to kiss his ring (it was a form of innocent flirtation), and he readily allowed it.

"So we have a saint among us, Monseigneur," Mme. Guelle said.

"You honour me too much. And how is the Governor? I don't see him here."

"He's gone to unlock some more whisky. To tell the truth, Monseigneur, I was not referring to you. I'd be sorry to see you become a saint—for the time being, that is."

"An Augustinian thought," the Bishop said obscurely.

"We were talking about Querry, *the* Querry," Rycker explained. "A man in that position burying himself in a leproserie, spending a night praying with a leper in the bush—you must admit, Monseigneur, that self-sacrifices like that are rare. What do you think?"

"I am wondering, does he play bridge?" Just as the Governor's comment had given administrative approval to Querry's conduct, so the Bishop's question was taken to mean that the Church in her wise and traditional fashion reserved her opinion.

The Bishop accepted a glass of orange juice. Marie Rycker looked at it sadly. She had parked her Perrier and didn't know what to do with her hands. The Bishop said to her kindly, "You should learn bridge, Mme. Rycker. We have too few players round here now."

"I am frightened of cards, Monseigneur."

"I will bless the pack and teach you myself." Marie

Rycker was uncertain whether the Bishop was joking; she tried out an unnoticeable kind of smile.

Rycker said, "I can't imagine how a man of Querry's calibre can work with that atheist Colin. That's a man, you can take it from me, who doesn't know the meaning of the word charity. Do you remember last year when I tried to organise a Lepers' Day? He would have nothing to do with it. He said he couldn't afford to accept charity. Four hundred dresses and suits had been accumulated and he refused to distribute them, just because there weren't enough to go round. He said he would have had to buy the rest out of his own pocket to avoid jealousy— why should a leper be jealous? You should talk to him one day, Monseigneur, on the nature of charity."

But Monseigneur had moved on, his hand under Marie Rycker's elbow.

"Your husband seems very taken up with this man Querry," he said.

"He thinks he may be somebody he can talk to."

"Are you so silent?" the Bishop asked, teasing her gently as though he had indeed picked her up outside a café on the boulevards.

"I can't talk about his subjects."

"What subjects?"

"Free Will and Grace and—Love."

"Come now—love . . . you know about that, don't you?"

"Not that kind of love," Marie Rycker said.

2

By the time the Ryckers came to go—they had to wait a long time for Mme. Cassin—Rycker had drunk to the margin of what was dangerous; he had passed from excessive amiability to dissatisfaction, the kind of cosmic dissatisfaction which, after probing faults in others' characters, went on to the examination of his own. Marie Rycker knew that if he could be induced at this stage to take a sleeping-pill all might yet be well; he would probably reach unconsciousness before he reached religion which, like the open doorway in a red-lamp district, led inevitably to sex.

"There are times," Rycker said, "when I wish we had a more spiritual bishop."

"He was kind to me," Marie Rycker said.

"I suppose he talked to you of cards."

"He offered to teach me bridge."

"I suppose he knew that I had forbidden you to play."

"He couldn't. I've told no one."

"I will not have my wife turned into a typical *colon*."

"I think I am one already." She added in a low voice, "I don't want to be different."

He said sharply, "Spending all their time in small talk . . ."

"I wish I could. How I wish I could. If anyone could only teach me that . . ."

It was always the same. She drank nothing but Perrier, and yet the alcohol on his breath would make her talk as though the whisky had entered her own blood, and what she said then was always too close to the truth. Truth, which someone had once written made us free, irritated Rycker as much as one of his own hang-nails. He said, "What nonsense. Don't talk like that for effect. There are times when you remind me of Mme. Guelle." The night sang discordantly at them from either side of the road, and the noises from the forest were louder than the engine. She had a longing for all the shops which climbed uphill along the rue de Namur: she tried to look through the lighted dashboard into a window full of shoes. She stretched out her foot beside the brake and said in a whisper, "I take size six."

"What did you say?"

"Nothing."

In the light of the headlamp she saw the cage strutting by the road like a Martian.

"You are getting into a bad habit of talking to yourself."

She said nothing. She couldn't tell him, "There is no

one else to speak to," about the pâtisserie at the corner, the day when Sister Thérèse broke her ankle, the *plage* in August with her parents.

"A lot of it is my own fault," Rycker said, reaching his second stage. "I realise that. I have failed to teach you the real values as I see them. What can you expect from the manager of a palm-oil factory? I was not meant for this life. I should have thought even you could have seen that." His vain yellow face hung like a mask between her and Africa. He said, "When I was young I wanted to be a priest." He must have told her this, after drinks, at least once a month since they married, and every time he spoke she remembered their first night in the hotel at Antwerp, when he had lifted his body off her like a half-filled sack and dumped it at her side, and she, feeling some tenderness because she thought that in some way she had failed him, touched his shoulder (which was hard and round like a swede in the sack), and he asked her roughly, "Aren't you satisfied? A man can't go on and on." Then he had turned on his side away from her: the holy medal that he always wore had got twisted by their embrace and now lay in the small of his back, facing her like a reproach. She wanted to defend herself: 'It was you who married me. I know about chastity too—the nuns taught me.' But the chastity she had been taught was something which she connected with clean white garments and light and gentleness, while his was like old sackcloth in a desert.

"What did you say?"

"Nothing."

"You are not even interested when I tell you my deepest feelings."

She said miserably, "Perhaps it was a mistake."

"Mistake?"

"Marrying me. I was too young."

"You mean I am too old to give you satisfaction."

"No—no. I didn't mean . . ."

"You know only one kind of love, don't you? Do you suppose that's the kind of love the saints feel?"

77

"I don't know any saints," she said desperately.

"You don't believe I am capable in my small way of going through the Dark Night of the Soul? I am only your husband who shares your bed . . ."

She whispered, "I don't understand. Please, I don't understand."

"What don't you understand?"

"I thought that love was supposed to make you happy."

"Is that what they taught you in the convent?"

"Yes."

He made a grimace at her, breathing heavily, and the coupé was filled momentarily with the scent of Vat 69. They passed beside the grim constructed figure in the chair; they were nearly home.

"What are you thinking?" he asked.

She had been back in the shop in the rue de Namur watching an elderly man who was gently, so gently, easing her foot into a stiletto-heeled shoe. So she said, "Nothing."

Rycker said in a voice suddenly kind, "That is the opportunity for prayer."

"Prayer?" She knew, but without relief, that the quarrel was over, for from experience she knew too that, after the rain had swept by, the lightning always came nearer.

"When I have nothing else to think of, I mean that I *have* to think of, I always say a Pater Noster, an Ave Maria or even an Act of Contrition."

"Contrition?"

"That I have been unjustly angry with a dear child whom I love." His hand fell on her thigh and his fingers kneaded gently the silk of her skirt, as though they were seeking some muscle to fasten on. Outside the rusting abandoned cylinders showed they were approaching the house; they would see the lights of the bedrooms when they turned.

She wanted to go straight to her room, the small hot uninviting room where he sometimes allowed her to be alone during her monthly or unsafe periods, but he stopped

78

her with a touch; she hadn't really expected to get away with it. He said, "You aren't angry with me, Mawie?" He always lisped her name childishly at the moments when he felt least childish.

"No. It's only—it wouldn't be safe." Her hope of escape was that he feared a child.

"Oh come. I looked up the calendar before I came out."

"I've been so irregular the last two months." Once she had bought a douche, but he had found it and thrown it away and afterwards he had lectured her on the enormity and unnaturalness of her act, speaking so long and emotionally on the subject of Christian marriage that the lecture had ended on the bed.

He put his hand below her waist and propelled her gently in the direction he required. "Tonight," he said, "we'll take a risk."

"But it's the worst time. I promise . . ."

"The Church doesn't intend us to avoid all risk. The safe period mustn't be abused, Mawie."

She implored him, "Let me go to my room for a moment. I've left my things there," for she hated undressing in front of his scrutinising gaze. "I won't be long. I promise I won't be long."

"I'll be waiting for you," Rycker promised.

She undressed as slowly as she dared and took a pyjama jacket from under her pillow. There was no room here for anything but a small iron bed, a chair, a wardrobe, a chest-of-drawers. On the chest was a photograph of her parents—two happy elderly people who had married late and had one child. There was a picture postcard of Bruges sent by a cousin, and an old copy of *Time*. Underneath the chest she had hidden a key and now she unlocked the bottom drawer. Inside the drawer was her secret museum: a too-clean Missal which she had been given at the time of her first communion, a sea-shell, the programme of a concert in Brussels, M. André Lejeune's Catholic History of Europe in one volume for the use of schools, and an exercise book containing an essay which she had written during her last term (she had

79

received the maximum marks) on the Wars of Religion. Now she added to her collection the old copy of *Time*. Querry's face covered M. Lejeune's History: it lay, a discord, among the relics of childhood. She remembered Mme. Guelle's words exactly: "His reputation in certain ways is very bad." She locked the drawer and hid the key—it was unsafe to delay any further. Then she walked along the verandah to *their* room, where Rycker was stretched naked inside the mosquito tent of the double-bed under the wooden body on the cross. He looked like a drowned man fished up in a net—hair lay like seaweed on his belly and legs; but at her entrance he came immediately to life, lifting the side of the tent. "Come, Mawie," he said. A Christian marriage, how often she had been told it by her religious instructors, symbolised the marriage of Christ and his Church.

CHAPTER TWO

I

THE Superior with old-fashioned politeness ground out his cheroot, but Mme. Rycker was no sooner seated than absentmindedly he lit another. His desk was littered with hardware catalogues and scraps of paper on which he had made elaborate calculations that always came out differently, for he was a bad mathematician—multiplication with him was an elaborate form of addition and a series of subtractions would take the place of long division. One page of a catalogue was open at the picture of a bidet which the Superior had mistaken for a new kind of footbath. When Mme. Rycker entered he was trying to calculate whether he could afford to buy three dozen of these for the leproserie: they were just the thing for washing leprous feet.

"Why, Mme. Rycker, you are an unexpected visitor. Is your husband . . ."

"No."

"It's a long way to come alone."

"I had company as far as the Perrins'. I spent the night there. My husband asked me to bring you two drums of oil."

"How very kind of him."

"I am afraid we do too little for the leproserie."

It occurred to the Superior that he might ask the Ryckers to supply a few of the novel foot-baths, but he was uncertain how many they could afford. To a man without possessions any man with money appears rich—should he ask for one foot-bath or the whole three dozen? He began to turn the photographs towards Marie Rycker, cautiously, so that it might look as though he were only fiddling with his papers. It would be so much easier for him to speak if she were to exclaim, "What an interesting new foot-bath," so that he could follow up by saying——

Instead of that she confused him by changing the subject. "How are the plans for the new church, father?"

"New church?"

"My husband told me you were building a wonderful new church as big as a cathedral, in an African style."

"What an extraordinary idea. If I had the money for that"—not with all his scraps of paper could he calculate the cost of a "church like a cathedral"—"why, we could build a hundred houses, each with a foot-bath." He turned the catalogue a little more towards her. "Doctor Colin would never forgive me for wasting money on a church."

"I wonder why my husband . . . ?"

Was it possibly a hint, the Superior wondered, that the Ryckers were prepared to finance . . . He could hardly believe that the manager of a palm-oil factory had made himself sufficiently rich, but Mme. Rycker of course might have been left a fortune. Her inheritance would certainly be the talk of Luc, but he only made the journey to the town once a year. He said, "The old church, you know, will serve us a long time yet. Only half our people are Catholics. Anyway it's no use having a great church if the people still live in mud huts. Now our friend Querry sees a way of cutting the cost of a cottage by a quarter. We were such amateurs here until he came."

"My husband has told everyone that Querry is building a church."

"Oh no, we have better uses for him than that. The new hospital too is a long way from being finished. Any money we can beg or steal must go to equipping it. I've just been looking at these catalogues . . ."

"Where is M. Querry now?"

"Oh, I expect he's working in his room, unless he's with the doctor."

"Everybody was talking about him at the Governor's two weeks ago."

"Poor M. Querry."

A small black child hardly more than two feet high walked into the room without knocking, coming in like a scrap of shadow from the noonday glare outside. He was quite naked and his little tassel hung like a bean-pod below the pot-belly. He opened a drawer in the Superior's desk and pulled out a sweet. Then he walked out again.

"They were being quite complimentary," Mme. Rycker said. "Is it true—about this boy getting lost . . . ?"

"Something of the sort happened. I don't know what *they* are saying."

"That he stayed all night and prayed . . ."

"M. Querry is hardly a praying man."

"My husband thinks a lot of him. There are so few people my husband can talk to. He asked me to come here and invite . . ."

"We are very grateful for the two drums of oil. What you have saved us with those, we can spend . . ." He turned the photograph of the bidet a little further towards Mme. Rycker.

"Do you think I could speak to him?"

"The trouble is, Mme. Rycker, this is his hour for work."

She said imploringly, "I only want to be able to tell my husband that I've asked him," but her small toneless voice contained no obvious appeal and the Superior was looking elsewhere, at a feature of the foot-bath which he did not fully understand. "What do you think of that?" he asked.

"What?"

"This foot-bath. I want to get three dozen for the hospital."

He looked up because of her silence and was surprised to see her blushing. It occurred to him that she was a very pretty child. He said, "Do you think . . . ?"

She was confused, remembering the ambiguous jokes of

her more dashing companions at the convent. "It's not really a foot-bath, father."

"What else could it be for then?"

She said with the beginnings of humour, "You'd better ask the doctor—or M. Querry." She moved a little in her chair, and the Superior took it for a sign of departure.

"It's a long ride back to the Perrins', my dear. Can I offer you a cup of coffee, or a glass of beer?"

"No. No, thank you."

"Or a little whisky?" In all the long years of his abstinence the Superior had never learnt that whisky was too strong for the midday sun.

"No, thank you. Please, father, I know you are busy. I don't want to be a nuisance, but if I could just see M. Querry and ask him . . ."

"I will give him your message, my dear. I promise I won't forget. See, I am writing it down." He hesitated which sum to disfigure with the memo—"Querry-Rycker." It was impossible for him to tell her that he had given his promise to Querry to leave him undisturbed, "particularly by that pious imbecile, Rycker."

"It won't do, father. It won't do. I promised I'd see him myself. He won't believe I've tried." She broke off and the Superior thought, 'I really believe she was going to ask me for a note, the kind of note children take to school, saying that they have been genuinely ill.'

"I'm not even sure where he is," the Superior said, emphasising the word 'sure' to avoid a lie.

"If I could just look for him."

"We can't have you wandering around in this sun. What would your husband say?"

"That's what I am afraid of. He'll never believe that I did my best." She was obviously close to tears and this made her look younger, so that it was easy to discount the tears as the facile meaningless grief of childhood.

"I tell you what," the Superior said, "I will get him to telephone—when the line is in order."

"I know that he doesn't like my husband," she said with sad frankness.

84

"My dear child, it's all in your imagination." He was at his wit's end. He said, "Querry's a strange fellow. None of us really knows him. Perhaps he likes none of us."

"He stays with you. He doesn't avoid you."

The Superior felt a stab of anger against Querry. These people had sent him two drums of oil. Surely they deserved in return a little civility. He said, "Stay here. I'll see if Querry's in his room. We can't have you looking all over the leproserie . . ."

He left his study and turning the corner of the verandah made for Querry's room. He passed the rooms of Father Thomas and Father Paul which were distinguished from each other by nothing more personal than an individual choice of crucifix and a differing degree of untidiness: then the chapel: then Querry's room. It was the only one in the place completely bare of symbols, bare indeed of almost everything. No photographs of a community or a parent. The room struck the Superior even in the heat of the day as cold and hard, like a grave without a cross. Querry was sitting at his table, a letter before him, when the Superior entered. He didn't look up.

"I'm sorry to disturb you," the Superior said.

"Sit down, father. Just a moment while I finish this." He turned the page and said, "How do you end your letters, father?"

"It depends. Your brother in Christ perhaps?"

"*Toute à toi*. I remember I used to put that phrase too. How false it sounds now."

"You have a visitor. I've kept my word and defended you to the last ditch. I can do no more. I wouldn't have disturbed you otherwise."

"I'm glad you came. I don't relish being alone with this. You see—the mail has caught up with me. How did anyone know I was here? Does that damned local *Journal* in Luc circulate even in Europe?"

"Mme. Rycker is here, asking for you."

"Oh well, at least it's not her husband."

He picked up the envelope. "Do you see, she's even

got the post box number right. What patience. She must have written to the Order."

"Who is she?"

"She was once my mistress. I left her three months ago, poor woman—and that's hypocrisy. I feel no pity. I'm sorry, father. I didn't mean to embarrass you."

"You haven't. It's Mme. Rycker who has done that. She brought us two drums of oil and she wants to speak to you."

"Am I worth that much?"

"Her husband sent her."

"Is that the custom here? Tell him I'm not interested."

"She's only brought you an invitation, poor young woman. Can't you see her and thank her and say no? She seems half-afraid to go back unless she can say that she has talked to you. You aren't afraid of her, are you?"

"Perhaps. In a way."

"Forgive me for saying it, M. Querry, but you don't strike me as a man who is afraid of women."

"Have you never come across a leper, father, who is afraid of striking his fingers because he knows they won't hurt any more?"

"I've known men rejoice when the feeling returns— even pain. But you have to give pain a chance."

"One can have a mirage of pain. Ask the amputated. All right, father, bring her in. It's a great deal better than seeing her wretched husband anyway."

The Superior opened the door, and there the girl was on the threshold, in the glare of sun, caught with her mouth open, like someone surprised by a camera in a night-club, looking up in the flash, with an ungainly grimace of pain. She turned sharply round and walked away to where her car was parked and they heard her inefficient attempts at starting. The Superior followed her. A line of women returning from the market delayed him. He scampered a little way after the car, the cheroot still in his mouth and his white sun-helmet tip-tilted, but she drove away under the big arch which bore the name of the leproserie, her boy watching his antics curiously through the side-window. He came limping back because he had stubbed a toe.

"Silly child," he said, "why didn't she stay in my room? She could have spent the night with the nuns. She'll never get to the Perrins' by dark. I only hope her boy's reliable."

"Do you suppose she heard?"

"Of course she heard. You didn't exactly lower your voice when you spoke of Rycker. If you love a man it can't be very pleasant to hear how unwelcome . . ."

"And it's far worse, father, when you don't love him at all."

"Of course she loves him. He's her husband."

"Love isn't one of the commonest characteristics of marriage, father."

"They're both Catholics."

"Nor is it of Catholics."

"She's a very good young woman," the Superior said obstinately.

"Yes, father. And what a desert she must live in out there alone with that man." He looked at the letter which lay on his desk and that phrase of immolation which everyone used and some people meant—"*toute à toi*". It occurred to him that one could still feel the reflection of another's pain when one had ceased to feel one's own. He put the letter in his pocket: it was fair at least that he should feel the friction of the paper. "She's been taken a long way from Pendélé," he said.

"What's Pendélé?"

"I don't know—a dance at a friend's house, a young man with a shiny simple face, going to Mass on Sunday with the family, falling asleep in a single bed perhaps."

"People have to grow up. We are called to more complicated things than that."

"Are we?"

" 'When we are a child we think as a child'."

"I can't match quotations from the Bible with you, father, but surely there's also something about having to be as little children if we are to inherit . . . We've grown up rather badly. The complications have become too complex—we should have stopped with the amoeba—no, long before that with the silicates. If your god wanted an adult world he should have given us an adult brain."

"We most of us make our own complications, M. Querry."

"Why did he give us genitals then if he wanted us to think clearly? A doctor doesn't prescribe marijuana for clear thought."

"I thought you said you had no interest in anything."

"I haven't. I've come through to the other side, to nothing. All the same I don't like looking back," he said and the letter crackled softly as he shifted.

"Remorse is a kind of belief."

"Oh no, it isn't. You try to draw everything into the net of your faith, father, but you can't steal all the virtues. Gentleness isn't Christian, self-sacrifice isn't Christian, charity isn't, remorse isn't. I expect the caveman wept to see another's tears. Haven't you even seen a dog weep? In the last cooling of the world, when the emptiness of your belief is finally exposed, there'll always be some bemused fool who'll cover another's body with his own to give it warmth for an hour more of life."

"You believe that? But once I remember you saying you were incapable of love."

"I am. The awful thing is I know it would be my body someone would cover. Almost certainly a woman. They have a passion for the dead. Their missals are stuffed with memorial cards."

The Superior stubbed out his cheroot and then lit another as he moved towards the door. Querry called after him, "I've come far enough, haven't I? Keep that girl away and her bloody tears." He struck his hand furiously on the table because it seemed to him that he had used a phrase applicable only to the stigmata.

When the Superior had gone Querry called to Deo Gratias. The man came in propped on his three toeless feet. He looked to see if the wash-basin needed emptying.

"It's not that," Querry said. "Sit down. I want to ask you something."

The man put down his staff and squatted on the ground. Even the act of sitting was awkward without toes or fingers. Querry lit a cigarette and put it in the man's mouth. He said, "Next time you try to leave here, will you take me with you?"

The man made no answer. Querry said, "No, you needn't answer. Of course you won't. Tell me, Deo Gratias, what was the water like? Like the big river out there?"

The man shook his head.

"Like the lake at Bikoro?"

"No."

"What was it like, Deo Gratias?"

"It fell from the sky."

"A waterfall?" But the word had no meaning to Deo Gratias in this flat region of river and deep bush.

"You were a child in those days on your mother's back. Were there many other children?"

He shook his head.

"Tell me what happened?"

"*Nous étions heureux*," Deo Gratias said.

PART IV

CHAPTER ONE

I

QUERRY and Doctor Colin sat on the steps of the hospital in the cool of the early day. Every pillar had its shadow and every shadow its crouching patient. Across the road the Superior stood at the altar saying Mass, for it was a Sunday morning. The church had open sides, except for a lattice of bricks to break the sun, so that Querry and Colin were able to watch the congregation cut into shapes like a jig-saw pattern, the nuns on chairs in the front row and behind them the lepers sitting on long benches raised a foot from the ground, built of stone because stone could be disinfected more thoroughly and quickly than wood. At this distance it was a gay scene with the broken sun spangled on the white nuns' robes and the bright mammy cloths of the women. The rings which the women wore round their thighs jingled like rosaries when they knelt to pray, and all the mutilations were healed by distance and by the brickwork which hid their feet. Beyond the doctor on the top step sat the old man with elephantiasis, his scrotum supported on the step below. They talked in a whisper, so that their voices would not disturb the Mass which went on across the way—a whisper, a tinkle, a jingle, a shuffle, private movements of which they had both almost forgotten the meaning, it was so long since they had taken any part.

"Is it really impossible to operate?" Querry asked.

"Too risky. His heart mightn't stand the anaesthetic."

"Has he got to carry that thing around then till death?"

"Yes. It doesn't weigh as much as you would think. But it seems unfair, doesn't it, to suffer all that and leprosy too."

93

In the church there was a sigh and a shuffle as the congregation sat. The doctor said, "One day I'll screw some money out of someone and have a few wheel-chairs made for the worst cases. He would need a special one, of course. Could a famous ecclesiastical architect design a chair for swollen balls?"

"I'll get you out a blueprint," Querry said.

The voice of the Superior reached them from across the road. He was preaching in a mixture of French and Creole; even a Flemish phrase crept in here and there, and a word or two that Querry assumed to be Mongo or some other tongue of the river tribes.

"And I tell you truth I was ashamed when this man he said to me, 'You Klistians are all big thieves—you steal this, you steal that, you steal all the time. Oh, I know you don't steal money. You don't creep into Thomas Olo's hut and take his new radio-set, but you are thieves all the same. Worse thieves than that. You see a man who lives with one wife and doesn't beat her and looks after her when she gets a bad pain from medicines at the hospital, and you say that's Klistian love. You go to the courthouse and you hear a good judge, who say to the piccin that stole sugar from the white man's cupboard, 'You're a very sorry piccin. I not punish you, and you, you will not come here again. No more sugar palaver,' and you say that's Klistian mercy. But you are a mighty big thief when you say that—for you steal this man's love and that man's mercy. Why do you not say when you see man with knife in his back bleeding and dying, 'There's Klistian anger'?"

"I really believe he's answering something I said to him," Querry said with a twitch of the mouth that Colin was beginning to recognise as a rudimentary smile, "but I didn't put it quite like that."

"Why not say when Henry Okapa got a new bicycle and someone came and tore his brake, 'There's Klistian envy.' You are like a man who steals only the good fruit and leaves the bad fruit rotting on the tree.

"All right. You tell me I'm number one thief, but I

94

say you make big mistake. Any man may defend himself before his judge. All of you in this church, you are my judges now, and this is my defence."

"It's a long time since I listened to a sermon," Doctor Colin said. "It brings back the long tedious hours of childhood, doesn't it?"

"You pray to Yezu," the Superior was saying. He twisted his mouth from habit as though he were despatching a cheroot from one side to the other. "But Yezu is not just a holy man. Yezu is God and Yezu made the world. When you make a song you are in the song, when you bake bread you are in the bread, when you make a baby you are in the baby, and because Yezu made you, he is in you. When you love it is Yezu who loves, when you are merciful it is Yezu who is merciful. But when you hate or envy it is not Yezu, for everything that Yezu made is good. Bad things are not there— they are nothing. Hate means no love. Envy means no justice. They are just empty spaces, where Yezu ought to be."

"He begs a lot of questions," Doctor Colin said.

"Now I tell you that when a man loves, he must be Klistian. When a man is merciful he must be Klistian. In this village do you think you are the only Klistians— you who come to church? There is a doctor who lives near the well beyond Marie Akimbu's house and he prays to Nzambe and he makes bad medicine. He worships a false God, but once when a piccin was ill and his father and mother were in the hospital he took no money; he gave bad medicine but he took no money: he made a big God palaver with Nzambe for the piccin but took no money. I tell you then he was a Klistian, a better Klistian than the man who broke Henry Okapa's bicycle. He not believe in Yezu, but he a Klistian. I am not a thief, who steal away his charity to give to Yezu. I give back to Yezu only what Yezu made. Yezu made love, he made mercy. Everybody in the world has something that Yezu made. Everybody in the world is that much a Klistian. So how can I be a thief? There is no man so wicked he never once in his life show in his heart something that God made."

"That would make us both Christians," Querry said. "Do you feel a Christian, Colin?"

"I'm not interested," Colin said. "I wish Christianity could reduce the price of cortisone, that's all. Let's go."

"I hate simplifications," Querry said, and sat on.

The Superior said, "I do not tell you to do good things for the love of God. That is very hard. Too hard for most of us. It is much easier to show mercy because a child weeps or to love because a girl or a young man pleases your eye. That's not wrong, that's good. Only remember that the love you feel and the mercy you show were made in you by God. You must go on using them and perhaps if you pray Klistian prayers it makes it easier for you to show mercy a second time and a third time . . ."

"And to love a second and a third girl," Querry said.

"Why not?" the doctor asked.

"Mercy . . . love . . ." Querry said. "Hasn't he ever known people to kill with love and kill with mercy? When a priest speaks those words they sound as though they had no meaning outside the vestry and the guild-meetings."

"I think that is the opposite of what he's trying to say."

"Does he want us to blame God for love? I'd rather blame man. If there is a God, let him be innocent at least. Come away, Colin, before you are converted and believe yourself an unconscious Christian."

They rose and walked past the mutter of the Credo towards the dispensary.

"Poor man," Colin said. "It's a hard life, and he doesn't get many thanks. He does his best for everybody. If he believes I'm a crypto-Christian it's convenient for me, isn't it? There are many priests who wouldn't be happy to work with an atheist for a colleague."

"He should have learnt from you that it's possible for an intelligent man to make his life without a god."

"My life is easier than his—I have a routine that fills my day. I know when a man is cured by the negative skin-tests. There are no skin-tests for a good action. What were your motives, Querry, when you followed your boy into the forest?"

"Curiosity. Pride. Not Klistian love, I assure you."

Colin said, "All the same you talk as if you'd lost something you'd loved. I haven't. I think I have always liked my fellow men. Liking is a great deal safer than love. It doesn't demand victims. Who is your victim, Querry?"

"I have none now. I'm safe. I'm cured, Colin," he added without conviction.

2

Father Paul took a helping of what was meant to be a cheese soufflé, then poured himself out a glass of water to ease it down. He said, "Querry is wise today to lunch with the doctor. Can't you persuade the sisters to vary the *plat du jour*? Sunday after all is a feast-day."

"This is meant to be a treat for us," the Superior said. "They believe we look forward to it all through the week. I wouldn't like to disillusion the poor things. They use a lot of eggs."

All the cooking for the priests' house was done by the nuns and the food had to be carried a quarter of a mile in the sun. It had never occurred to the nuns that this might be disastrous for soufflés and omelettes and even for after-dinner coffee.

Father Thomas said, "I do not think Querry minds much about his food." He was the only priest in the leproserie with whom the Superior felt ill at ease; he still seemed to carry with him the strains and anxieties of the seminary. He had left it longer ago than any of the others, but he seemed doomed to a perpetual and unhappy youth; he was ill at ease with men who had grown up and were more concerned over the problems of the electric-light plant or the quality of the brickmaking than over the pursuit of souls. Souls could wait. Souls had eternity.

"Yes, he's a good enough guest," the Superior said,

steering a little away from the course that he suspected Father Thomas wished to pursue.

"He's a remarkable man," Father Thomas said, struggling to regain direction.

"We have enough funds now," the Superior said at large, "for an electric fan in the delivery-ward."

"We'll have air-conditioning in our rooms yet," Father Jean said, "and a drug-store and all the latest movie magazines including pictures of Brigitte Bardot." Father Jean was tall, pale and concave with a beard which struggled like an unpruned hedge. He had once been a brilliant moral theologian before he joined the order and now he carefully nurtured the character of a film-fan, as though it would help him to wipe out an ugly past.

"I'd rather have a boiled egg for Sunday lunch," Father Paul said.

"You wouldn't like stale eggs boiled," Father Jean said, helping himself to more soufflé; in spite of his cadaverous appearance he had a Flemish appetite.

"They wouldn't be stale," Father Joseph said, "if they only learnt to manage the chickens properly. I'd be quite ready to put some of my men on to building them proper houses for intensive production. It would be easy enough to carry the electric power down from their houses . . ."

Brother Philippe spoke for the first time. He was always reluctant to intrude on the conversation of men who he considered belonged to another less mundane world. "Electric fans, chicken houses; be careful, father, or you will be overloading the dynamos before you've done."

The Superior was aware that Father Thomas was smouldering at his elbow. He said tactfully, "And the new classroom, father? Have you everything that's needed?"

"Everything but a catechist who knows the first thing about his faith."

"Oh well, so long as he can teach the alphabet. First things first."

"I should have thought the Catechism was rather more important than the alphabet."

"Rycker was on the telephone this morning," Father Jean said, coming to the Superior's rescue.

"What did he want?"

"Querry of course. He said he had a message—something about an Englishman, but he refused to give it. He threatened to be over one day soon, when the ferries are working again. I asked him if he could bring me some film-magazines, but he said he didn't read them. He also wants to borrow Father Garrigou-Lagrange on Predestination."

"There are moments," the Superior said with moderation, "when I almost regret M. Querry's arrival."

"Surely we should be very glad," Father Thomas said, "of any small inconvenience he may bring us. We don't live a very troubled life." The helping of soufflé he had taken remained untasted on his plate. He kneaded a piece of bread into a hard pellet and washed it down like a pill. "You can't expect people to leave us alone while he is here. It's not only that he's a famous man. He's a man of profound faith."

"I hadn't noticed it," Father Paul said. "He wasn't at Mass this morning." The Superior lit another cheroot.

"Oh yes he was. I can tell you his eyes never left the altar. He was sitting across the way with the sick. That's as good a way of attending Mass as sitting up in front with his back to the lepers, isn't it?"

Father Paul opened his mouth to reply, but the Superior stopped him with a covert wink. "At any rate it is a charitable way of putting it," the Superior said. He balanced his cheroot on the edge of his plate and rose to give thanks. Then he crossed himself and picked up his cheroot again. "Father Thomas," he said, "can you spare me a minute?"

He led the way to his room and installed Father Thomas in the one easy chair that he kept for visitors by the filing-cabinet. Father Thomas watched him tensely, sitting bolt upright, like a cobra watching a mongoose. "Have a cheroot, father?"

"You know I don't smoke."

"Of course. I'm sorry. I was thinking of someone else. Is that chair uncomfortable? I'm afraid the springs may have gone. It's foolish having springs in the tropics, but it was given us with a lot of junk . . ."

"It's quite comfortable, thank you."

"I'm sorry you don't find your catechist satisfactory. It's not so easy to find a good one now that we have three classes for boys. The nuns seem to manage better than we do."

"Only if you consider Marie Akimbu a suitable teacher."

"She works very hard I'm told by Mother Agnes."

"Certainly, if you call having a baby every year by a different man hard work. I can't see that it's right allowing her to teach with her cradle in the class. She's pregnant again. What kind of an example is that?"

"Oh well, you know, *autres pays autres mœurs*. We are here to help, father, not condemn, and I don't think we can teach the sisters their business. They know the young woman better than we do. Here, you must remember, there are few people who know their own fathers. The children belong to the mother. Perhaps that's why they prefer us, and the Mother of God, to the Protestants." The Superior searched for words. "Let me see, father, you've been with us now—it must be over two years?"

"Two years next month."

"You know you don't eat enough. That soufflé wasn't exactly inviting . . ."

"I have no objection to the soufflé. I happen to be fasting for a private intention."

"Of course you have your confessor's consent?"

"It wasn't necessary for just one day, father."

"The soufflé day was a good day to choose then, but you know this climate is very difficult for Europeans, especially at the beginning. By the time our leave comes at the end of six years we have become accustomed to it. Sometimes I almost dread going home. The first years . . . one mustn't drive oneself."

"I am not aware of driving myself unduly, father."

"Our first duty, you know, is to survive, even if that means taking things a little more easily. You have a great spirit of self-sacrifice, father. It's a wonderful quality, but it's not always what's required on the battlefield. The good soldier doesn't court death."

"I am quite unaware . . ."

"We all of us have a feeling of frustration sometimes. Poor Marie Akimbu, we have to take the material we have to hand. I'm not sure that you'd find better material in some of the parishes of Liège, though sometimes I've wondered whether perhaps you might be happier there. The African mission is not for everyone. If a man feels himself ill-adapted here, there's no defeat in asking for a transfer. Do you sleep properly, father?"

"I have enough sleep."

"Perhaps you ought to have a check-up with Doctor Colin. It's wonderful what a pill will do at the right time."

"Father, why are you so against M. Querry?"

"I hope I'm not. I'm unaware of it."

"What other man in his position—he's world-famous, father, even though Father Paul may never have heard of him—would bury himself here, helping with the hospital?"

"I don't look for motives, Father Thomas. I hope I accept what he does with gratitude."

"Well, I do look for motives. I've been talking to Deo Gratias. I hope I would have done what he did, going out at night into the bush looking for a servant, but I doubt . . ."

"Are you afraid of the dark?"

"I'm not ashamed to say that I am."

"Then it would have needed more courage in your case. I have still to find what does frighten M. Querry."

"Well, isn't that heroic?"

"Oh no. I am disturbed by a man without fear as I would be by a man without a heart. Fear saves us from so many things. Not that I'm saying, of course, that M. Querry . . ."

"Does it show a lack of heart staying beside his boy all night, praying for him?"

"They are telling that story in the city, I know, but did he pray? It's not what M. Querry told the doctor."

"I asked Deo Gratias. He said yes. I asked him what prayers—the Ave Maria, I asked him? He said yes."

"Father Thomas, when you have been in Africa a little longer, you will learn not to ask an African a question which may be answered by yes. It is their form of courtesy to agree. It means nothing at all."

"I think after two years I can tell when an African is lying."

"Those are not lies. Father Thomas, I can well understand why you are attracted to Querry. You are both men of extremes. But in our way of life, it is better for us not to have heroes—not live heroes, that is. The saints should be enough for us."

"You are not suggesting there are not live saints?"

"Of course not. But don't let's recognise them before the Church does. We shall be saved a lot of disappointment that way."

3

Father Thomas stood by his netted door staring through the wire-mesh at the ill-lighted avenue of the leproserie. Behind him on his table he had prepared a candle and the flame shone palely below the bare electric globe; in five minutes all the lights would go out. This was the moment he feared; prayers were of no avail to heal the darkness. The Superior's words had reawakened his longing for Europe. Liège might be an ugly and brutal city, but there was no hour of the night when a man, lifting his curtain, could not see a light shining on the opposite wall of the street or perhaps a late passer-by going home. Here at ten o'clock, when the dynamos ceased working, it needed an act of faith to know that the forest had not come up to the threshold of the room. Sometimes it seemed to him that he could hear the leaves brushing on the mosquito-wire. He looked at his watch—four minutes to go.

He had admitted to the Superior that he was afraid of the dark. But the Superior had brushed away his fear as of no account. He felt an enormous longing to confide, but it was almost impossible to confide in men of his own Order, any more than a soldier could admit his cowardice to another soldier. He couldn't say to the Superior, "Every night I pray that I won't be summoned to attend someone dying in the hospital or in his kitchen, that I won't have to light the lamp of my bicycle and pedal through the dark." A few weeks ago an old man had so died, but it was Father Joseph who went out to find the corpse where it sat in a rickety deck-chair with some fetish or other for Nzambe placed in its lap and a holy medal round its neck; he had given conditional absolution by the light of the bicycle-lamp because there were no candles to be found.

He believed that the Superior grudged the admiration he felt for Querry. His companions, it seemed to him, spent their lives with small concerns which they could easily discuss together—the cost of foot-baths, a fault in the dynamo, a holdup at the brick-kiln, but the things which worried him he could discuss with no one. He envied the happily married man who had a ready confidante at bed and board. Father Thomas was married to the Church and the Church responded to his confidence only in the clichés of the confessional. He remembered how even in the seminary his confessor had checked him whenever he had gone further than the platitudes of his problem. The word "scruple" was posted like a traffic sign in whichever direction the mind drove. 'I want to talk, I want to talk,' Father Thomas cried silently to himself as all the lights went out and the beat of the dynamos stopped. Somebody came down the verandah in the dark; the steps passed the room of Father Paul and would have passed his own if he had not called out, "Is it you, M. Querry?"

"Yes."

"Won't you come in for a moment?"

Querry opened the door and came into the small radiance of the candle. He said, "I've been explaining to the Superior the difference between a bidet and a foot-bath."

"Please won't you sit down? I can never sleep so early as this, and my eyes are not good enough to read by candle-light." Already in one sentence he had admitted more to Querry than he had ever done to his Superior, for he knew that the Superior would only too readily have given him a torch and permission to read for as long as he liked after the lights went out, but that permission would have drawn attention to his weakness. Querry looked for a chair. There was only one and Father Thomas began to pull back the mosquito-net from the bed.

"Why not come to my room?" Querry asked. "I have some whisky there."

"Today I am fasting," Father Thomas said. "Please take the chair. I will sit here." The candle burnt straight upwards to its smoky tip like a crayon. "I hope you are happy here," Father Thomas said.

"Everyone has been very kind to me."

"You are the first visitor to stay here since I came."

"Is that so?"

Father Thomas's long narrow nose was oddly twisted at the end; it gave him the effect of smelling sideways at some elusive odour. "Time is needed to settle in a place like this." He laughed nervously. "I'm not sure that I'm settled myself yet."

"I can understand that," Querry said mechanically for want of anything better to say, but the bromide was swallowed like wine by Father Thomas.

"Yes, you have great understanding. I sometimes think a layman has more capacity for understanding than a priest. Sometimes," he added, "more faith."

"That's certainly not true in my case," Querry said.

"I have told this to no one else, " Father Thomas said as though he were handing over some precious object which would leave Querry forever in his debt. "When I finished at the seminary I sometimes thought that only by martyrdom could I save myself—if I could die before I lost everything."

"One doesn't die, "Querry said.

"I wanted to be sent to China, but they wouldn't accept me."

"Your work here must be just as valuable," Querry said, dealing out his replies quickly and mechanically like cards.

"Teaching the alphabet?" Father Thomas shifted on the bed and the drape of mosquito-net fell over his face like a bride's veil or a beekeeper's. He turned it back and it fell again, as though even an inanimate object had enough consciousness to know the best moment to torment.

"Well, it's time for bed," Querry said.

"I'm sorry. I know I'm keeping you up. I'm tiring you."

"Not at all," Querry said. "Besides I sleep badly."

"You do? It's the heat. I can't sleep for more than a few hours."

"I could let you have some pills."

"Oh no, no, thank you. I must learn somehow—this is the place God has sent me to."

"Surely you volunteered?"

"Of course, but if it hadn't been His will . . ."

"Perhaps it's His will that you should take a nembutal. Let me fetch you one."

"It does me so much more good just to talk to you for a little. You know in a community one doesn't talk—about anything important. I'm not keeping you from your work, am I?"

"I can't work by candlelight."

"I'll release you very soon," Father Thomas said, smiling weakly, and then fell silent again. The forest might be approaching, but for once he had a companion. Querry sat with his hands between his knees waiting. A mosquito hummed near the candle-flame. The dangerous desire to confide grew in Father Thomas's mind like the pressure of an orgasm. He said, "You won't understand how much one needs, sometimes, to have one's faith fortified by talking to a man who believes."

Querry said, "You have the fathers."

"We talk only about the dynamo and the schools." He said, "Sometimes I think if I stay here I'll lose my faith altogether. Can you understand that?"

"Oh yes, I can understand that. But I think it's your confessor you should talk to, not me."

"Deo Gratias talked to you, didn't he?"

"Yes. A little."

"You make people talk. Rycker . . ."

"God forbid." Querry moved restlessly on the hard chair. "What I would say to you wouldn't help you at all. You must believe that. I'm not a man of—faith."

"You are a man of humility," Father Thomas said. "We've all noticed that."

"If you knew the extent of my pride . . ."

"Pride which builds churches and hospitals is not so bad a pride."

"You mustn't use me to buttress your faith, father. I'd be the weak spot. I don't want to say anything that could disturb you more—but I've nothing for you—nothing. I wouldn't even call myself a Catholic unless I were in the army or in a prison. I am a legal Catholic, that's all."

"We both of us have our doubts," Father Thomas said. "Perhaps I have more than you. They even come to me at the altar with the Host in my hands."

"I've long ceased to have doubts. Father, if I must speak plainly, I don't believe at all. Not at all. I've worked it out of my system—like women. I've no desire to convert others to disbelief, or even to worry them. I want to keep my mouth shut, if only you'd let me."

"You can't think what a lot of good our conversation has done me," Father Thomas said with excitement. "There's not a priest here to whom I can talk as we're talking. One sometimes desperately needs a man who has experienced the same weaknesses as oneself."

"But you've misunderstood me, father."

"Don't you see that perhaps you've been given the grace

of aridity? Perhaps even now you are walking in the footsteps of St. John of the Cross, the *noche oscura*."

"You are so very far from the truth," Querry said, making a movement with his hands of bewilderment or rejection.

"I've watched you here," Father Thomas said, "I am capable of judging a man's actions." He leant forward until his face was not very far from Querry's and Querry could smell the lotion Father Thomas used against mosquito-bites. "For the first time since I came to this place, I feel I can be of use. If you ever have the need to confess, always remember I am here."

"The only confession I am ever likely to make," Querry said, "would be to an examining magistrate."

"Ha, ha." Father Thomas caught the joke in mid-air and confiscated it like a schoolboy's ball under his soutane. He said, "Those doubts you have. I can assure you I know them too. But couldn't we perhaps go over together the philosophical arguments . . . to help us both?"

"They wouldn't help me, father. Any sixteen-year-old student could demolish them, and anyway I need no help. I don't want to be harsh, father, but I don't wish to believe. I'm cured."

"Then why do I get more sense of faith from you than from anyone here?"

"It's in your own mind, father. You are looking for faith and so I suppose you find it. But I'm not looking. I don't want any of the things I've known and lost. If faith were a tree growing at the end of the avenue, I promise you I'd never go that way. I don't mean to say anything to hurt you, father. I would help you if I could. If you feel in pain because you doubt, it is obvious that you are feeling the pain of faith, and I wish you luck."

"You really do understand, don't you?" Father Thomas said, and Querry could not restrain an expression of tired despair. "Don't be irritated. Perhaps I know you better than you do yourself. I haven't found so much understanding, 'not in all Israel' if you can call the community that. You have done so much good. Perhaps—

another night—we could have a talk again. On our problems—yours and mine."

"Perhaps, but——"

"And pray for me, M. Querry. I would value your prayers."

"I don't pray."

"I have heard differently from Deo Gratias," Father Thomas said, fetching up a smile like a liquorice-stick, dark and sweet and prehensile. He said, "There are interior prayers, the prayers of silence. There are even unconscious prayers when men have goodwill. A thought from you may be a prayer in the eyes of God. Think of me occasionally, M. Querry."

"Of course."

"I would like to be of help to you as you have been to me." He paused as though he were waiting for some appeal, but Querry only put a hand to his face and brushed away the sticky tendrils which a spider had left dangling between him and the door. "I shall sleep tonight," Father Thomas said, threateningly.

CHAPTER TWO

I

ABOUT twice a month the Bishop's boat was due to come in with the heavier provisions for the leproserie, but sometimes many weeks went by without a visit. They waited for it with forced patience; perhaps the captain of the Otraco boat which brought the mail would also bring news of her small rival—a snag in the river might have pierced its bottom: it might be stranded on a mud-bank; perhaps the rudder had been twisted in collision with a fallen tree-trunk; or the captain might be down with fever or have been appointed a professor of Greek by the Bishop who had not yet found a priest to take his place. It was not a very popular job among members of the Order. No knowledge of navigation was required, not even of machinery, for the African mate was in virtual charge of the engine and the bridge. Four weeks of loneliness on the river every trip, the attempt at each halt to discover some cargo which had not been pledged to Otraco, such a life compared unfavourably with employment at the cathedral in Luc or even at a seminary in the bush.

It was dusk when the inhabitants of the leproserie heard the bell of the long-overdue boat; the sound came to Colin and Querry where they sat over the first drink of the evening on the doctor's verandah. "At last," Colin said, finishing his whisky, "if only they have brought the new X-ray . . ."

White flowers had opened with twilight on the long avenue; fires were being lit for the evening meal, and the mercy of darkness was falling at last over the ugly and the deformed. The wrangles of the night had not yet begun, and peace was there, something you could touch like a petal or smell like wood-smoke. Querry said to Colin, "You know I am happy here." He closed his mouth on the phrase too late; it had escaped him on the sweet evening air like an admission.

2

"I remember the day you came," Colin said. "You were walking up this road and I asked you how long you were going to stay. You said—do you remember? ——"

But Querry was silent and Colin saw that he already regretted having spoken at all.

The white boat came slowly round the bend of the river; a lantern was alight at the bow, and the pressure-lamp was burning in the saloon. A black figure, naked except for a loin-cloth, was poised with a rope on the pontoon, preparing to throw it. The fathers in their white soutanes gathered on the verandah like moths round a treacle-jar, and when Colin looked behind him he could see the glow of the Superior's cheroot following them down the road.

Colin and Querry halted at the top of the steep bank above the river. An African dived in from the pontoon and swam ashore as the engines petered out. He caught the rope and made it fast around a rock and the topheavy boat eased in. A sailor pushed a plank across for a woman who came ashore carrying two live turkeys on her head; she fussed with her mammy-cloths, draping and redraping them about her waist.

"The great world comes to us," Colin said.

"What do you mean?"

The captain waved from the window of the saloon. Along the narrow deck the door of the Bishop's cabin was closed, but a faint light shone through the mosquito-netting.

"Oh, you never know what the boat may bring. After all, it brought you."

"They seem to have a passenger," Querry said.

The captain gesticulated to them from the window; his

arm invited them to come aboard. "Has he lost his voice?" the Superior said, joining them at the top of the bank, and cupping his hands he yelled as loudly as he could, "Well, captain, you are late." The sleeve of a white soutane moved in the dusk; the captain had put a finger to his lips. "In God's name," the Superior said, "has he got the Bishop on board?" He led the way down the slope and across the gang-plank.

Colin said, "After you." He was aware of Querry's hesitation. He said, "We'll have a glass of beer. It's the custom," but Querry made no move. "The captain will be glad to see you again," he went on, his hand under Querry's elbow to help him down the bank. The Superior was picking his way among the women, the goats and the cooking-pots, which littered the pontoon, towards the iron ladder by the engine.

"What you said about the world?" Querry said. "You don't really suppose, do you . . . ?" and he broke off with his eyes on the cabin that he had once occupied, where the candle-flame was wavering in the river-draught.

"It was a joke," Colin said. "I ask you—does it look like the great world?" Night which came in Africa so quickly had wiped the whole boat out, except the candle in the Bishop's cabin, the pressure-lamp in the saloon where two white figures silently greeted each other, and the hurricane-lamp at the foot of the ladder where a woman sat preparing her husband's chop.

"Let's go," Querry said.

At the top of the ladder the captain greeted them. He said, "So you are still here, Querry. It is a pleasure to see you again." He spoke in a low voice; he might have been exchanging a confidence. In the saloon the beer was already uncapped and awaiting them. The captain shut the door and for the first time raised his voice. He said, "Drink up quickly, Doctor Colin. I have a patient for you."

"One of the crew?"

"Not one of the crew," the captain said, raising his glass. "A real passenger. I've only had two real passengers in two years, first there was M. Querry and now this man. A passenger who pays, not a father."

"Who is he?"

"He comes from the great world," the captain said, echoing Colin's phrase. "It has been difficult for me. He speaks no Flemish and very little French, and that made it yet more complicated when he went down with fever. I am very glad to be here," he said and seemed about to lapse into his more usual silence.

"Why has he come?" the Superior asked.

"How do I know? I tell you—he speaks no French."

"Is he a doctor?"

"He is certainly not a doctor or he wouldn't be so frightened of a little fever."

"Perhaps I should see him right away," Colin said. "What language does he speak?"

"English. I tried him in Latin," the captain said. "I even tried him in Greek, but it was no good."

"I can speak English," Querry said with reluctance.

"How is his fever?" Colin asked.

"This is the worst day. Tomorrow it will be better. I said to him, 'Finitum est,' but I think he believed that I meant he was dying."

"Where did you pick him up?"

"At Luc. He had some kind of introduction to the Bishop—from Rycker, I think. He had missed the Otraco boat."

Colin and Querry went down the narrow deck to the Bishop's cabin. Hanging at the end of the deck was the misshapen lifebelt looking like a dried eel, the steaming shower, the lavatory with the broken door, and beside it the kitchen-table and the hutch where two rabbits munched in the dark; nothing, except presumably the rabbits, had changed. Colin opened the cabin-door, and there was the photograph of the church under snow, but in the rumpled bed which Querry had somehow imagined would still bear, like a hare's form, his own impression, lay the naked body of a very fat man. His neck as he lay on his back was forced into three ridges like gutters and the sweat filled them and drained round the curve of his head on to the pillow.

"I suppose we'll have to take him ashore," Colin said. "If there's a spare room at the fathers'." On the table stood a Rolleiflex-camera and a portable Remington, and inserted in the typewriter was a sheet of paper on which the man had begun to type. When Querry brought the candle closer he could read one sentence in English: "The eternal forest broods along the banks unchanged since Stanley and his little band". It petered out without punctuation. Colin lifted the man's wrist and felt his pulse. He said, "The captain's right. He'll be up in a few days. This sleep marks the end."

"Then why not leave him here?" Querry said.

"Do you know him?"

"I've never seen him before."

"I thought you sounded afraid," Colin said. "We can hardly ship him back if he's paid his passage here."

The man woke as Colin dropped his wrist. "Are you the doctor?" he asked in English.

"Yes. My name is Doctor Colin."

"I'm Parkinson," the man said firmly as though he were the sole survivor of a whole tribe of Parkinsons. "Am I dying?"

"He wants to know if he is dying," Querry translated.

Colin said, "You will be all right in a few days."

"It's bloody hot," Parkinson said. He looked at Querry. "Thank God there's someone here at last who speaks English." He turned his head towards the Remington and said, "The white man's grave."

"Your geography's wrong. This is not West Africa," Querry corrected him with dry dislike.

"They won't know the bloody difference," Parkinson said.

"And Stanley never came this way," Querry went on, without attempting to disguise his antagonism.

"Oh yes he did. This river's the Congo, isn't it?"

"No. You left the Congo a week ago after Luc."

The man said again ambiguously, "They won't know the bloody difference. My head's splitting."

113

"He's complaining about his head," Querry told Colin.

"Tell him I'll give him something when we've taken him ashore. Ask him if he can walk as far as the fathers'. He would be a terrible weight to carry."

"Walk!" Parkinson exclaimed. He twisted his head and the sweat-gutters drained on to the pillow. "Do you want to kill me? It would be a bloody good story, wouldn't it, for everyone but me. Parkinson buried where Stanley once . . ."

"Stanley was never here," Querry said.

"I don't care whether he was or not. Why keep bringing it up? I'm bloody hot. There ought to be a fan. If the chap here is a doctor, why can't he take me to a proper hospital?"

"I doubt if you'd like the hospital we have," Querry said. "It's for lepers."

"Then I'll stay where I am."

"The boat returns to Luc tomorrow."

Parkinson said, "I can't understand what the doctor says. Is he a good doctor? Can I trust him?"

"Yes, he's a good doctor."

"But they never tell the patient, do they?" Parkinson said. "My old man died thinking he only had a duodenal ulcer."

"You are not dying. You have got a touch of malaria, that's all. You are over the worst. It would be much easier for all of us if you'd walk ashore. Unless you want to return to Luc."

"When I start a job," Parkinson said obscurely, "I finish a job." He wiped his neck dry with his fingers. "My legs are like butter," he said. "I must have lost a couple of stone. It's the strain on the heart I'm afraid of."

"It's no use," Querry told Colin. "We'll have to have him carried."

"I will see what can be done," Colin said and left them. When they were alone, Parkinson said, "Can you use a camera?"

"Of course."

"With a flash bulb?"

114

"Yes."

He said, "Would you do me a favour and take some pictures of me carried ashore? Get as much atmosphere in as you can—you know the kind of thing, black faces gathered round looking worried and sympathetic."

"Why should they be worried?"

"You can easily fix that," Parkinson said. "They'll be worried enough anyway in case they drop me—and *they* won't know the difference."

"What do you want the picture for?"

"It's the kind of thing they like to have. You can't mistrust a photograph, or so people think. Do you know, since you came into the cabin and I could talk again, I've been feeling better? I'm not sweating so much, am I? And my head . . ." He twisted it tentatively and gave a groan again. "Oh well, if I hadn't had this malaria, I daresay I'd have had to invent it. It gives the right touch."

"I wouldn't talk so much if I were you."

"I'm bloody glad the boat-trip's over, I can tell you that."

"Why have you come here?"

"Do you know a man called Querry?" Parkinson said.

The man had struggled round onto his side. The reflection from the candle shone back from the dribbles and pools of sweat so that the face appeared like a too-travelled road after rain. Querry knew for certain he had never seen the man before, and yet he remembered how Doctor Colin had said to him, "The great world comes to us."

"Why do you want Querry?" he asked.

"It's my job to want him," Parkinson said. He groaned again. "It's no bloody picnic this. You wouldn't lie to me, would you, about the doctor? And what he said?"

"No."

"It's my heart, as I told you. Two stone in a week. This too too solid flesh is surely melting. Shall I tell you a secret? The daredevil Parkinson is sometimes damned afraid of death."

"Who are you?" Querry asked. The man turned his face away with irritable indifference and closed his eyes. Soon he was asleep again.

He was still asleep when they carried him off the boat wrapped in a piece of tarpaulin like a dead body about to be committed to the deep. It needed six men to lift him and they got in each other's way, so that once as they struggled up the bank, a man slipped and fell. Querry was in time to prevent the body falling. The head rammed his chest and the smell of hair-oil poisoned the night. He wasn't used to supporting such a weight and he was breathless and sweating as they got the body over the rise and came on Father Thomas standing there holding a hurricane-lamp. Another African took Querry's place and Querry walked behind at Father Thomas's side. Father Thomas said, "You shouldn't have done that—a weight like that, in this heat—it's rash at your age. Who is he?"

"I don't know. A stranger."

Father Thomas said, "Perhaps a man can be judged by his rashness." The glow of the Superior's cheroot approached them through the dark. "You won't find much rashness here," Father Thomas went angrily on. "Bricks and mortar and the monthly bills—that's what we think about. Not the Samaritan on the road to Jericho."

"Nor do I. I just took a hand for a few minutes, that's all."

"We could all learn from you," Father Thomas said, taking Querry's arm above the elbow as though he were an old man who needed the support of a disciple.

The Superior overtook them. He said, "I don't know where we are going to put him. We haven't a room free."

"Let him share mine. There's room for the two of us," Father Thomas said, and he squeezed Querry's arm as if he wished to convey to him, 'I at least have learnt your lesson. I am not as my brothers are.'

CHAPTER THREE

I

DOCTOR COLIN had before him a card which carried the outline-drawing of a man. He had made the drawing himself; the cards he had ordered in Luc because he despaired of obtaining any like them from home. The trouble was they cost too little; the invoices had fallen like fine dust through the official tray that sifted his requests for aid. There was nobody on the lower levels of the Ministry at home with authority to allow an expenditure of six hundred francs, and nobody with courage enough to worry a senior officer with such a paltry demand. Now whenever he used the charts he felt irritated by his own bad drawings. He ran his fingers over a patient's back and detected a new thickening of the skin below the left shoulder-blade. He drew the shading on his chart and called "Next." Perhaps he might have forestalled that patch if the new hospital had been finished and the new apparatus installed for taking the temperature of the skin. 'It is not a case of what I have done,' he thought, 'but what I am going to do.' This optimistic phrase had an ironic meaning for Doctor Colin.

When he first came to this country, there was an old Greek shopkeeper living in Luc—a man in his late seventies who was famous for his reticence. A few years before he had married a young African woman who could neither read nor write. People wondered what kind of contact they could have, at his age, with his reticence and her ignorance. One day he saw his African clerk bedding her down at the back of the warehouse behind some sacks of coffee. He said nothing at all, but next day he went to the bank and took out his savings. Most of the savings he put in an envelope and posted in at the door of the local orphanage which was always chock-a-block with unwanted half-castes. The rest he took with him up the hill behind the courthouse to a garage which sold ancient cars, and there he bought the cheapest car they could sell him. It was so old and so cheap that even the manager, perhaps because he too was a Greek, had scruples. The car could only be trusted to start on top of a hill, but the old man said that didn't matter. It was his ambition to drive a car once before he died—his whim if you liked to call it that. So they showed him how to put it into gear and how to accelerate, and shoving behind they gave him a good running start. He rode down to the square in Luc where his store was situated and began hooting as soon as he got there. People stopped to look at the strange sight of the old man driving his first car, and as he passed the store his clerk came out to see the fun. The old man drove all round the square a second time—he couldn't have stopped the car anyway because it would not start on the flat. Round he came with his clerk waving in the doorway to encourage him, then he twisted the wheel, trod down on the accelerator and drove straight over his clerk into the store, where the car came to the final halt of all time up against the cash register. Then he got out of the car, and leaving it just as it was, he went into his parlour and waited for the police to arrive. The clerk was not dead, but both his legs were crushed and the pelvis was broken and he wouldn't be any good for a woman ever again. Presently the Commissioner of Police walked in. He was a young man and this was his first case and the Greek was highly respected in Luc. "What have you done?" he demanded when he came into the parlour. "It is not a case of what have I done," the old man said, "but of what I am going to do," and he took a gun from under the cushion and shot himself through the head. Doctor Colin since those days had often found comfort in the careful sentence of the old Greek storekeeper.

He called again, "Next." It was a day of extreme heat and humidity and the patients were languid and few. It had never ceased to surprise the doctor how human beings never became acclimatised to their own country; an African suffered from the heat like any European, just as a Swede he once knew suffered from the long winter night as though she had been born in a southern land. The man who now came to stand before the doctor would not meet his eyes. On the chart he was given the name of Attention, but now any attention he had was certainly elsewhere.

"Trouble again like the other night?" the doctor asked.

The man looked over the doctor's shoulder as if someone he feared were approaching and said, "Yes." His eyes were heavy and bloodshot; he pushed his shoulders forward on either side of his sunken chest as though they were the corners of a book he was trying to close.

"It will be over soon," the doctor said. "You must be patient."

"I am afraid," the man said in his own tongue. "Please when night comes let them bind my hands."

"Is it as bad as that?"

"Yes. I am afraid for my boy. He sleeps beside me."

The D.D.S. tablets were not a simple cure. Reactions from the drug were sometimes terrible. When it was only a question of pain in the nerves you could treat a patient with cortisone, but in a few cases a kind of madness came over the mind in the hours of darkness. The man said, "I am afraid of killing my boy."

The doctor said, "This will pass. One more night, that's all. Remember you have just to hold on. Can you read the time?"

"Yes."

"I will give you a clock that shines so that you can read it in the dark. The trouble will start at eight o'clock. At eleven o'clock you will feel worse. Don't struggle. If we tie your hands you will struggle. Just look at the clock. At one you will feel very bad, but then it will begin to pass. At three you will feel no worse than you do now, and after that less and less—the madness will go. Just look at the clock and remember what I say. Will you do that?"

"Yes."

"Before dark I will bring you the clock."

"My child . . ."

"Don't worry about your child. I will tell the sisters to look after him till the madness has gone. You must just watch the clock. As the hands move the madness will move too. And at five the clock will ring a bell. You can sleep then. Your madness will have gone. It won't come back."

He tried to speak with conviction, but he felt the heat blurring his intonation. When the man had gone he felt that something had been dragged out of him and thrown away. He said to the dispenser, "I can't see anyone today."

"There are only six more."

"Am I the only one who must not feel the heat?" But he felt some of the shame of a deserter as he walked away from his tiny segment of the world's battlefield.

Perhaps it was shame that led his steps towards another patient. As he passed Querry's room he saw him busied at his drawing-board; he went on and came to Father Thomas's room. Father Thomas too had taken the morning off—his schools like the dispensary would have been all but emptied by the heat. Parkinson sat on the only chair, wearing the bottom of his pyjamas: the cord looked as if it were tied insecurely round an egg. Father Thomas was talking excitedly, as Colin entered, in what even the doctor recognised to be very odd English. He heard the name "Querry." There was hardly space to stand between the two beds.

"Well," Colin said, "you see, M. Parkinson, you are not dead. One doesn't die of a small fever."

"What's he saying?" Parkinson asked Father Thomas. "I'm tired of not understanding. What was the good of the Norman Conquest if we don't speak the same language now?"

"Why has he come here, Father Thomas? Have you found that out?"

"He is asking me a great many questions about Querry."

"Why? What business is it of his?"

"He told me that he had come here specially to talk to him."

"Then he would have done better to have gone back with the boat because Querry won't talk."

"Querry, that's right, Querry," Parkinson said. "It's stupid of him to pretend to hide away. No one really wants to hide from Montagu Parkinson. Aren't I the end of every man's desire? Quote. Swinburne."

"What have you told him, father?"

Father Thomas said defensively, "I've done no more than confirm what Rycker told him."

"Rycker! Then he's been listening to a pack of lies."

"Is the story of Deo Gratias a lie? Is the new hospital a lie? I hope that I have been able to put the story in the right context, that's all."

"What is the right context?"

"The Catholic context," Father Thomas replied.

The Remington portable had been set up on Father Thomas's table beside the crucifix. On the other side of the crucifix, like the second thief, the Rolleiflex hung by its strap from a nail. Dr. Colin looked at the typewritten sheet upon the table. He could read English more easily than he could speak it. He read the heading: 'The Recluse of the Great River,' then looked accusingly at Father Thomas. "Do you know what this is about?"

"It is the story of Querry," Father Thomas said.

"This nonsense!"

Colin looked again at the typewritten sheet. 'That is the name which the natives have given to a strange newcomer in the heart of darkest Africa.' Colin said, "*Qui êtes-vous?*"

"Parkinson," the man said. "I've told you already. Montagu Parkinson." He added with disappointment, "Doesn't the name mean anything at all to you?"

Lower down the page Colin read, 'three weeks by boat to reach this wild territory. Struck down after seven days by the bites of tsetse flies and mosquitoes I was carried ashore unconscious. Where once Stanley battled his way with Maxim guns, another fight is being waged—this time in the cause of the African—against the deadly infection of leprosy . . . woke from my fever to find myself a patient in a leper hospital . . .'

"But these are lies," Colin said to Father Thomas.

"What's he grousing about?" Parkinson asked.

"He says that what you have written there is—not altogether true."

"Tell him it's more than the truth," Parkinson said. "It's a page of modern history. Do you really believe Caesar said '*Et tu, Brute*'? It's what he ought to have said and someone on the spot—old Herodotus, no, he was the Greek, wasn't he, it must have been someone else, Suetonius perhaps, spotted what was needed. The truth is always forgotten. Pitt on his deathbed asked for Bellamy's Pork Pies, but history altered that." Even Father Thomas could not follow the convolutions of Parkinson's thoughts. "My articles have to be remembered like history. At least from one Sunday to another. Next Sunday's instalment, 'The Saint with a Past'."

"Do you understand a word of all this, father?" Colin asked.

"Not very much," Father Thomas admitted.

"Has he come here to make trouble?"

"No, no. Nothing like that. Apparently his paper sent him to Africa to write about some disturbances in British territory. He arrived too late, but by that time we had our own trouble in the capital, so he came on."

"Not even knowing French?"

"He had a first-class return ticket to Nairobi. He told me that his paper could not afford two star writers in Africa, so they cabled him to move on into our territory. He was too late again, but then he heard some rumours of Querry. He said that he had to bring *something* back. When he got to Luc he happened at the Governor's to meet Rycker."

"What does he know of Querry's past? Even we . . ."

Parkinson was watching the discussion closely; his eyes travelled from one face to another. Here and there a word must have meant something to him and he drew his rapid, agile, erroneous conclusions.

"It appears," Father Thomas said, "that the British newspapers have what they call a *morgue*. He has only to cable them and they will send him a précis of all that has ever been published about Querry."

"It's like a police persecution."

"Oh, I'm convinced they'll find nothing to his discredit."

"Have neither of you," Parkinson asked sorrowfully, "heard my name Montagu Parkinson? Surely it's memorable enough." It was impossible to tell whether he was laughing at himself.

Father Thomas began to answer him. "To be quite truthful until you came . . ."

"My name is writ in water. Quote. Shelley," Parkinson said.

"Does Querry know what it's all about?" Colin asked Father Thomas.

"Not yet.

"He was beginning to be happy here."

"You mustn't be hasty," Father Thomas said. "There is another side to all of this. Our leproserie may become famous—as famous as Schweitzer's hospital, and the British, one has heard, are a generous people."

Perhaps the name Schweitzer enabled Parkinson to catch at Father Thomas's meaning. He brought quickly out, "My articles are syndicated in the United States, France, Germany, Japan and South America. No other living journalist . . ."

"We have managed without publicity until now, father," Colin said.

"Publicity is only another name for propaganda. And we have a college for that in Rome."

"Perhaps it is more fitted for Rome, father, than Central Africa."

"Publicity can be an acid test for virtue. Personally I am convinced that Querry . . ."

"I have never enjoyed blood-sports, father. And a man-hunt least of all."

"You exaggerate, doctor. A great deal of good can come from all of this. You know how you have always lacked money. The mission can't provide it. The State will not. Your patients deserve to be considered."

"Perhaps Querry is also a patient," Colin said.

"That's nonsense. I was thinking of the lepers—you have always dreamt of a school for rehabilitation, haven't you, if you could get the funds. For those poor burnt-out cases of yours."

"Querry may be also a burnt-out case," the doctor said. He looked at the fat man in the chair. "Where now will he be able to find *his* therapy? Limelight is not very good for the mutilated."

The heat of the day and the anger they momentarily felt for each other made them careless, and it was only Parkinson who saw that the man they were discussing was already over the threshold of Father Thomas's room.

"How are you, Querry?" Parkinson said. "I didn't recognise you when I met you on the boat."

Querry said, "Nor I you."

"Thank God," Parkinson said, "you aren't finished like the riots were. I've caught up with one story anyway. We've got to have a talk, you and I."

2

"So that's the new hospital," Parkinson said. "Of course I don't know about these things, but there seems to me nothing very original . . ." He bent over the plans and said with the obvious intention of provoking, "It reminds me of something in one of our new satellite towns. Hemel Hempstead perhaps. Or Stevenage."

"This is not architecture," Querry said. "It's a cheap building job. Nothing more. The cheaper the better, so long as it stands up to heat, rain and humidity."

"Do they require a man like you for that?"

"Yes. They have no builder here."

"Are you going to stay till it's finished?"

"Longer than that."

124

"Then what Rycker told me must be partly true."

"I doubt if anything that man says could ever be true."

"You'd need to be a kind of a saint, wouldn't you, to bury yourself here."

"No. Not a saint."

"Then what are you? What are your motives? I know a lot about you already. I've briefed myself," Parkinson said. He sat his great weight down on the bed and said confidingly, "You aren't exactly a man who loves his fellows, are you? Leaving out women, of course." There is a strong allurement in corruption and there was no doubt of Parkinson's; he carried it on the surface of his skin like phosphorus, impossible to mistake. Virtue had died long ago within that mountain of flesh for lack of air. A priest might not be shocked by human failings, but he could be hurt or disappointed; Parkinson would welcome them. Nothing would ever hurt Parkinson save failure or disappoint him but the size of a cheque.

"You heard what the doctor called me just now—one of the burnt-out cases. They are the lepers who lose everything that can be eaten away before they are cured."

"You are a whole man as far as one can see," said Parkinson, looking at the fingers resting on the drawing-board.

"I've come to an end. This place, you might say, is the end. Neither the road nor the river go any further. You have been washed up here too, haven't you?"

"Oh, no, I came with a purpose."

"I was afraid of you on the boat, but I'm afraid of you no longer."

"I can't understand what you had to fear. I'm a man like other men."

"No," Querry said, "you are a man like me. Men with vocations are different from the others. They have more to lose. Behind all of us in various ways lies a spoilt priest. You once had a vocation, admit it, if it was only a vocation to write."

"That's not important. Most journalists begin that

way." The bed bent below Parkinson's weight as he shifted his buttocks like sacks.

"And end your way?"

"What are you driving at? Are you trying to insult me? I'm beyond insult, Mr. Querry."

"Why should I insult you? We are two of a kind. I began as an architect and I am ending as a builder. There's little pleasure in that kind of progress. Is there pleasure in *your* final stage, Parkinson?" He looked at the typewritten sheet that he had picked up in Father Thomas's room and carried in with him.

"It's a job."

"Of course."

"It keeps me alive," Parkinson said.

"Yes."

"It's no use saying I'm like you. At least, I enjoy life."

"Oh yes. The pleasures of the senses. Food, Parkinson?"

"I have to be careful." He took the dangling corner of the mosquito-net to mop his forehead with. "I weigh eighteen stone."

"Women, Parkinson?"

"I don't know why you are asking me these questions. I came to interview *you*. Of course I screw a bit now and then, but there comes a time in every man's life . . ."

"You're younger than I am."

"My heart's not all that strong."

"You really have come to an end like me, haven't you, Parkinson, so here we find ourselves together. Two burnt-out cases. There must be many more of us in the world. We should have a masonic sign to recognise each other."

"I'm not burnt-out. I have my work. The biggest syndication . . ." He seemed determined to prove that he was dissimilar to Querry. Like a man presenting his skin to a doctor he wanted to prove that there was no thickening, no trace of a nodule, nothing that might class him with the other lepers.

"There was a time," Querry said, "when you would not have written that sentence about Stanley."

"It's a small mistake in geography, that's all. One has to dramatise. It's the first thing they teach a reporter on the *Post*—he has to make every story stand up. Anyway no one will notice."

"Would you write the real truth about me?"

"There are laws of libel."

"I would never bring an action. I promise you that." He read the advance announcement aloud. 'The Past of a Saint. What a saint!"

"How do you know that Rycker's not right about you? We none of us really know ourselves."

"We have to if we are to be cured. When we reach the furthest point, there's no mistaking it. When the fingers are gone and the toes too and the smear-reactions are all negative, we can do no more harm. Would you write the truth, Parkinson, even if I told it to you? I know you wouldn't. You aren't burnt-out after all. You are still infectious."

Parkinson looked at Querry with bruised eyes. He was like a man who has reached the limit of the third degree, when there is nothing else to do but admit everything. "They would sack me if I tried," he said. "It's easy enough to take risks when you are young. To think I am further off from heaven etc. etc. Quote. Edgar Allan Poe."

"It wasn't Poe."

"Nobody notices things like that."

"What is the past you have given me?"

"Well, there was the case of Anne Morel, wasn't there? It even reached the English papers. After all you had an English mother. And you had just completed that modern church in Bruges."

"It wasn't Bruges. What story did they tell about that?"

"That she killed herself for love of you. At eighteen. For a man of forty."

"It was more than fifteen years ago. Do papers have so long a memory?"

"No. But the *morgue* serves us instead. I shall describe

in my best Sunday-paper style how you came here in expiation . . ."

"Papers like yours invariably make small mistakes. The woman's name was Marie and not Anne. She was twenty-five and not eighteen. Nor did she kill herself for love of me. She wanted to escape me. That was all. So you see I am expiating nothing."

"She wanted to escape the man she loved?"

"Exactly that. It must be a terrible thing for a woman to make love nightly with an efficient instrument. I never failed her. She tried to leave me several times, and each time I got her to come back. You see it hurt my vanity to be left by a woman. I always wanted to do the leaving."

"How did you bring her back?"

"Those of us who practise one art are usually adept at another. A painter writes. A poet makes a tune. I happened in those days to be a good actor for an amateur. Once I used tears. Another time an overdose of nembutal, but not, of course, a dangerous dose. Then I made love to a second woman to show her what she was going to miss if she left me. I even persuaded her that I couldn't do my work without her. I made her think that I would leave the Church if I hadn't her support to my faith—she was a good Catholic, even in bed. In my heart of course I had left the Church years before, but she never realised that. I believed a little of course, like so many do, at the major feasts, Christmas and Easter, when memories of childhood stir us to a kind of devotion. She always mistook it for the love of God."

"All the same there must be some reason that you came out here, among the lepers . . ."

"Not in expiation, Mr. Parkinson. There were plenty of women after Marie Morel as there had been women before her. Perhaps for ten more years I managed to believe in my own emotion—'my dearest love', '*toute à toi*' and all the rest. One always tries not to repeat the same phrases, just as one tries to preserve some special position in the act of sex, but there are only thirty-two positions according to Aretine and there are less than that number of endearing words, and in the end most women reach their climax most easily in the commonest position of all and with the commonest phrase upon the tongue. It was only a question of time before I realised that I didn't love at all. I've never really loved. I'd only accepted love. And then the worst boredom settled in. Because if I had deceived myself with women I had deceived myself with work too."

"No one has ever questioned your reputation."

"The future will. Somewhere in a back street of Brussels now there's a boy at a drawing-board who will show me up. I wish I could see the cathedral he will build . . . No, I don't. Or I wouldn't be here. He'll be no spoilt priest. He'll pass the novice-master."

"I don't know what you are talking about, Querry. Sometimes you talk like Rycker."

"Do I? Perhaps he has the Masonic sign too . . ."

"If you are so bored, why not be bored in comfort? A little apartment in Brussels or a villa in Capri. After all, you are a rich man, Querry."

"Boredom is worse in comfort. I thought perhaps out here there would be enough pain and enough fear to distract. . . ." He looked at Parkinson. "Surely *you* can understand me if anyone can."

"I can't understand a word."

"Am I such a monster that even you . . . ?"

"What about your work, Querry? Whatever you say, you can't be bored with that. You've been a raging success."

"You mean money? Haven't I told you that the work wasn't good enough? What were any of my churches compared with the cathedral at Chartres? They were all signed with my name of course—nobody could mistake a Querry for a Corbusier, but which one of us knows the architect of Chartres? He didn't care. He worked with love not vanity—and with belief too, I suppose. To build a church when you don't believe in a god seems a little indecent, doesn't it? When I discovered I was doing that,

I accepted a commission for a city hall, but I didn't believe in politics either. You never saw such an absurd box of concrete and glass as I landed on the poor city square. You see I discovered what seemed only to be a loose thread in my jacket—I pulled it and all the jacket began to unwind. Perhaps it's true that you can't believe in a god without loving a human being or love a human being without believing in a god. They use the phrase 'make love,' don't they? But which of us are creative enough to 'make' love? We can only be loved—if we are lucky."

"Why are you telling me this, Mr. Querry—even if it's true?"

"Because at least you are someone who won't mind the truth, though I doubt whether you'll ever write it. Perhaps—who knows?—I might persuade you to drop altogether this absurd pious nonsense that Rycker talks about me. I am no Schweitzer. My God, he almost tempts me to seduce his wife. That at least might change his tune."

"Could you?"

"It's an awful thing when experience and not vanity makes one say yes."

Parkinson made an oddly humble gesture. He said, "Let me have men about me that are fat. Quote. Shakespeare. I got that one right anyway. As for me I wouldn't even know how to begin."

"Begin with readers of the *Post*. You are famous among your readers and fame is a potent aphrodisiac. Married women are the easiest, Parkinson. The young girl too often has her weather-eye open on security, but a married woman has already found it. The husband at the office, the children in the nursery, a condom in the bag. Say that she's been married at twenty, she's ready for a limited excursion before she's reached thirty. If her husband is young too, don't be afraid; she may have had enough of youth. With a man of my age and yours she needn't expect jealous scenes."

"What you are talking about doesn't have much to do

with love, does it? You said you'd been loved. You complained of it if I remember right. But I probably don't. As you realise well enough, I'm only a bloody journalist."

"Love comes quickly enough with gratitude, only too quickly. The loveliest of women feels gratitude, even to an ageing man like me, if she learns to feel pleasure again. Ten years in the same bed wither the little bud, but now it blooms once more. Her husband notices the way she looks. Her children cease to be a burden. She takes an interest again in housekeeping as she used to in the old days. She confides a little in her intimate friends, because to be the mistress of a famous man increases her self-respect. The adventure is over. Romance has begun."

"What a cold-blooded bastard you are," Parkinson said with deep respect, as though he were talking of the *Post's* proprietor.

"Why not write that instead of this pious nonsense you are planning?"

"I couldn't. My newspaper is for family reading. Although of course that word the Past has a certain meaning. But it means abandoned follies, doesn't it? not abandoned virtues. We'll touch on Mlle. Morel—delicately. And there was somebody else, wasn't there, called Grison?"

Querry didn't answer.

"It's no use denying things now," Parkinson said. "Grison is mummified in the *morgue* too."

"Yes, I do remember him. I don't care to because I don't like farce. He was a senior employee in the Post Office. He challenged me to a duel after I had left his wife. One of those bogus modern duels where nobody fires straight. I was tempted to break the conventions and to wing him, but his wife would have mistaken it for passion. Poor man, he was quite content so long as we were together, but when I left her he had to suffer such scenes with her in public . . . She had much less mercy on him than I had."

"It's odd that you admit all this to me," Parkinson said. "People are more cautious with me as a rule. Except that

I remember once there was a murderer—he talked as much as you."

"Perhaps it's the mark of a murderer, loquacity."

"They didn't hang this chap and I pretended to be his brother and visited him twice a month. All the same I'm puzzled by your attitude. You didn't strike me when I saw you first as exactly a talking man."

"I have been waiting for you, Parkinson, or someone like you. Not that I didn't fear you too."

"Yes, but why?"

"You are my looking-glass. I can talk to a looking-glass, but one can be a little afraid of one too. It returns such a straight image. If I talked to Father Thomas as I've talked to you, he'd twist my words."

"I'm grateful for your good opinion."

"A good opinion? I dislike you as much as I dislike myself. I was nearly happy when you arrived, Parkinson, and I've only talked to you now so that you'll have no excuse to stay. The interview is over, and you've never had a better one. You don't want my opinion, do you, on Gropius? Your public hasn't heard of Gropius."

"All the same I jotted down some questions," Parkinson said. "We might get on to those now that we've cleared the way."

"I said the interview was over."

Parkinson leaned forward on the bed and then swayed back like a Chinese wobbling toy made in the likeness of the fat God of Prosperity. He said, "Do you consider that the love of God or the love of humanity is your principal driving force, M. Querry? What in your opinion is the future of Christianity? Has the Sermon on the Mount influenced your decision to give your life to the lepers? Who is your favourite saint? Do you believe in the efficacy of prayer?" He began to laugh, the great belly rolling like a dolphin. "Do miracles still occur? Have you yet visited Fatima?"

He got off the bed. "We can forget the rest of the crap. 'In his bare cell in the heart of the dark continent one of the greatest of modern architects and one of the most famous Catholics of his day bared his conscience to the correspondent of the *Post*. Montagu Parkinson, who was on the spot last month in South Korea, is on the spot again. He will reveal to our readers in his next instalment how remorse for the past is Querry's driving force. Like many a recognised saint Querry is atoning for a reckless youth by serving others. Saint Francis was the gayest spark in all the gay old city of Firenze—Florence to you and me'."

Parkinson went out into the hard glare of the Congo day, but he hadn't said enough. He returned and put his face close up against the net and blew his words through it in a fine spray. "'Next Sunday's instalment: A girl dies for love.' I don't like you any more than you like me, Querry, but I'm going to build you up. I'll build you up so high they'll raise a statue to you by the river. In the worst possible taste, you know the sort of thing, you won't be able to avoid it because you'll be dead and buried —you on your knees surrounded by your bloody lepers teaching them to pray to the god you don't believe in and the birds shitting on your hair. I don't mind you being a religious fake, Querry, but I'll show you that you can't use me to ease your bleeding conscience. I wouldn't be surprised if there weren't pilgrims at your shrine in twenty years, and that's how history's written, believe you me. *Exegi monumentum*. Quote. Virgil.'

Querry took from his pocket the meaningless letter with the all-inclusive phrase which might, of course, be genuine. The letter had not come to him from one of the women Parkinson had mentioned: the *morgue* of the *Post* was not big enough to hold all possible bodies. He read it through again in the mood that Parkinson had elicited. "Do you remember?" She was one of those who would never admit that when an emotion was dead, the memory of the occasion was dead as well. He had to take her memories on trust, because she had always been a truthful woman. She reminded him of a guest who claims one particular matchbox as her own out of the debris of a broken party.

He went to his bed and lay down. The pillow gathered

heat under his neck, but this noonday he couldn't face the sociabilities of lunch with the fathers. He thought: there was only one thing I could do and that is reason enough for being here. I can promise you, Marie, *toute à toi*, all of you, never again from boredom or vanity to involve another human being in my lack of love. I shall do no more harm, he thought, with the kind of happiness a leper must feel when he is freed at last by his seclusion from the fear of passing on contagion to another. For years he had not thought of Marie Morel; now he remembered the first time he had heard her name spoken. It was spoken by a young architectural student whom he had been helping with his studies. They had come back together from a day at Bruges into the neon-lighted Brussels evening and they had passed the girl accidentally outside the northern station. He had envied a little his dull undistinguished companion when he saw her face brighten under the lamps. Has anyone ever seen a man smile at a woman as a woman smiles at the man she loves, fortuitously, at a bus-stop, in a railway carriage, at some chain-store in the middle of buying groceries, a smile so naturally joyful, without premeditation and without caution? The converse, of course, is probably true also. A man can never smile quite so falsely as the girl in a brothel-parlour. But the girl in the brothel, Querry thought, is imitating something true. The man has nothing to imitate.

He soon had no cause to feel envy for his companion of that night. Even in those early days he had known how to alter the direction of a woman's need to love. Woman? She was not even as old as the architectural student whose name he couldn't now remember—an ugly name like Hoghe. Unlike Marie Morel the former student was probably still alive, building in some suburb his bourgeois villas—machines for living in. Querry addressed him from the bed. "I am sorry. I really believed that I meant you no harm. I really thought in those days I acted from love." There is a time in life when a man with a little acting ability is able to deceive even himself.

PART V

CHAPTER ONE

I

IT is characteristic of Africa the way that people come and go, as though the space and emptiness of an undeveloped continent encourage drift; the high tide deposits the flotsam on the edge of the shore and sweeps it away again in its withdrawal, to leave elsewhere. No one had expected Parkinson, he had come unannounced, and a few days later he went again, carrying his Rolleiflex and Remington down to the Otraco boat bound for some spot elsewhere. Two weeks later a motor-boat came up the river in the late evening carrying a young administrator who played a game of liar-dice with the fathers, drank one glass of whisky before bed, and left behind him, as if it had been the sole intention of his voyage, a copy of an English journal, the *Architectural Review*, before departing without so much as breakfast into the grey and green immensity. (The review contained—apart from the criticism of a new arterial road—some illustrations of a hideous cathedral newly completed in a British colony. Perhaps the young man thought that it would serve as a warning to Querry.) Again a few weeks went unnoticed by—a few deaths from tuberculosis, the hospital climbing a few feet higher from its foundations—and then two policemen got off the Otraco boat to make enquiries about a Salvation Army leader who was wanted in the capital. He was said to have persuaded the people of a neighbouring tribe to sell their blankets to him because they would be too heavy to wear at the Resurrection of the Dead and then to give him the money back so that he might keep it for them in a secure place where no thieves would break in and steal. As a recompense he had given certificates insuring them

137

against the danger of being kidnapped by the Catholic and Protestant missionaries who, he said, were exporting bodies with the help of witchcraft wholesale to Europe in sealed railway trucks where they were turned into canned food labelled Best African Tunny. The policemen could learn nothing of the fugitive at the leproserie, and they departed again on the same boat two hours later, floating away with the small islands of water-jacinth at the same speed and in the same direction, as though they were all a part of nature too.

Querry in time began to forget Parkinson. The great world had done its worst and gone, and a kind of peace descended. Rycker stayed aloof, and no echo from any newspaper-article out of distant Europe came to disturb Querry. Even Father Thomas moved away for a while from the leproserie to a seminary in the bush from which he hoped to obtain a teacher for yet another new class. Querry's feet were becoming familiar with the long laterite road that stretched between his room and the hospital; in the evening, when the worst heat was over, the laterite glowed, like a night-blooming flower, in shades of rose and red.

The fathers were unconcerned with private lives. A husband, after he had been cured, left the leproserie and his wife moved into the hut of another man, but the fathers asked no questions. One of the catechists, a man who had reached the limit of mutilation, having lost nose, fingers, toes (he looked as though he had been lopped, scraped and tidied by a knife), fathered a baby with the woman, crippled by polio, who could only crawl upon the ground dragging her dwarfed legs behind her. The man brought the baby to the Church for baptism and there it was baptised Emanuel—there were no questions and no admonitions. The fathers were too busy to bother themselves with what the Church considered sin (moral theology was the subject they were least concerned with). In Father Thomas some thwarted instinct might be seen deviously at work, but Father Thomas was no longer there to trouble the leproserie with his scruples and anxieties.

The doctor was a less easy character to understand. Unlike the fathers he had no belief in a god to support him in his hard vocation. Once when Querry made a comment on his life—a question brought to his mind by the sight of some pitiable and squalid case, the doctor looked up at him with much the same clinical eye with which he had just examined the patient. He said, "Perhaps if I tested your skin now I would get a second negative reaction."

"What do you mean?"

"You are showing curiosity again about another human being."

"Who was the first?" Querry asked.

"Deo Gratias. You know I have been luckier in my vocation than you."

Querry looked down the long row of worn-out mattresses where bandaged people lay in the awkward postures of the bedridden. The sweet smell of sloughed skin was in the air. "Lucky?" he said.

"It needs a very strong man to survive an introspective and solitary vocation. I don't think you were strong enough. I know I couldn't have stood your life."

"Why does a man choose a vocation like this?" Querry asked.

"He's chosen. Oh, I don't mean by God. By accident. There is an old Danish doctor still going the rounds who became a leprologist late in life. By accident. He was excavating an ancient cemetery and found skeletons there without finger-bones—it was an old leper-cemetery of the fourteenth century. He X-rayed the skeletons and he made discoveries in the bones, especially in the nasal area, which were quite unknown to any of us—you see most of us haven't the chance to work with skeletons. He became a leprologist after that. You will meet him at any international conference on leprosy carrying his skull with him in an airline's overnight bag. It has passed through a lot of douaniers' hands. It must be rather a shock, that skull, to them, but I believe they don't charge duty on it."

"And you, Doctor Colin? What was your accident?"

"Only the accident of temperament, perhaps," the doctor replied evasively. They came out together into the unfresh and humid air. "Oh, don't mistake me. I had no death wish as Damien had. Now that we can cure leprosy, we shall have fewer of those vocations of doom, but they weren't uncommon once." They began to cross the road to the shade of the dispensary where the lepers waited on the steps; the doctor halted in the hot centre of the laterite. "There used to be a high suicide-rate among leprologists—I suppose they couldn't wait for that positive test they all expected some time. Bizarre suicides for a bizarre vocation. There was one man I knew quite well who injected himself with a dose of snake-venom, and another who poured petrol over his furniture and his clothes and then set himself alight. There is a common feature, you will have noticed, in both cases—unnecessary suffering. That can be a vocation too."

"I don't understand you."

"Wouldn't you rather suffer than feel discomfort? Discomfort irritates our ego like a mosquito-bite. We become aware of ourselves, the more uncomfortable we are, but suffering is quite a different matter. Sometimes I think that the search for suffering and the remembrance of suffering are the only means we have to put ourselves in touch with the whole human condition. With suffering we become part of the Christian myth."

"Then I wish you'd teach me how to suffer," Querry said. "I only know the mosquito-bites."

"You'll suffer enough if we stand here any longer," Dr. Colin said and he drew Querry off the laterite into the shade. "Today I am going to show you a few interesting eye-cases." He sat at his surgery-table and Querry took the chair beside him. Only on the linen masks that children wear at Christmas had he seen such scarlet eyes, representing avarice or senility, as now confronted them. "You only need a little patience," Dr. Colin said. "Suffering is not so hard to find," and Querry tried to remember who it was that had said much the same to him months ago. He was irritated by his own failure of memory.

"Aren't you being glib about suffering?" he asked. "That woman who died last week . . ."

"Don't be too sorry for those who die after some pain. It makes them ready to go. Think of how a death sentence must sound when you are full of health and vigour." Dr. Colin turned away from him to speak in her native tongue to an old woman whose palsied eyelids never once moved to shade the eyes.

That night, after taking dinner with the fathers, Querry strolled over to the doctor's house. The lepers were sitting outside their huts to make the most of the cool air which came with darkness. At a little stall, lit by a hurricane-lamp, a man was offering for five francs a handful of caterpillars he had gathered in the forest. Somebody was singing a street or two away, and by a fire Querry came upon a group of dancers gathered round his boy Deo Gratias, who squatted on the ground and used his fists like drum-sticks to beat the rhythm on an old petrol-tin. Even the bat-eared dogs lay quiet as though carved on tombs. A young woman with bare breasts kept a rendez-vous where a path led away into the forest. In the moonlight the nodules on her face ceased for a while to exist, and there were no patches on her skin. She was any young girl waiting for a man.

To Querry after his outbreak to the Englishman it seemed that some persistent poison had been drained from his system. He could remember no evening peace to equal this since the night when he had given the last touches to the first plans, perhaps the only ones, which had completely satisfied him. The owners, of course, had spoilt the building afterwards as they spoiled everything. No building was safe from the furniture, the pictures, the human beings that it would presently contain. But first there had been this peace. *Consummatum est:* pain over and peace falling round him like a little death.

When he had drunk his second whisky he said to the doctor, "When a smear-test is negative, does it always stay so?"

"Not always. It's too early to loose the patient on the

world until the tests have been negative—oh, for six months. There are relapses even with our present drugs."

"Do they sometimes find it hard to be loosed?"

"Very often. You see they become attached to their hut and their patch of land, and of course for the burnt-out cases life outside isn't easy. They carry the stigma of leprosy in their mutilation. People are apt to think once a leper, always a leper."

"I begin to find your vocation a little easier to understand. All the same—the fathers believe they have the Christian truth behind them, and it helps them in a place like this. You and I have no such truth. Is the Christian myth that you talked about enough for you?"

"I want to be on the side of change," the doctor said. "If I had been born an amoeba who could think, I would have dreamed of the day of the primates. I would have wanted anything I did to contribute to that day. Evolution, as far as we can tell, has lodged itself finally in the brains of man. The ant, the fish, even the ape has gone as far as it can go, but in our brain evolution is moving— my God—at what a speed! I forget how many hundreds of millions of years passed between the dinosaurs and the primates, but in our own lifetime we have seen the change from diesel to jet, the splitting of the atom, the cure of leprosy."

"Is change so good?"

"We can't avoid it. We are riding a great ninth evolutionary wave. Even the Christian myth is part of the wave, and perhaps, who knows, it may be the most valuable part. Suppose love were to evolve as rapidly in our brains as technical skill has done. In isolated cases it may have done, in the saints . . . if the man really existed, in Christ."

"You can really comfort yourself with all that?" Querry asked. "It sounds like the old song of progress."

"The nineteenth century wasn't as far wrong as we like to believe. We have become cynical about progress because of the terrible things we have seen men do during the last forty years. All the same through trial and error

142

the amoeba did become the ape. There were blind starts and wrong turnings even then, I suppose. Evolution today can produce Hitlers as well as St. John of the Cross. I have a small hope, that's all, a very small hope, that someone they call Christ was the fertile element, looking for a crack in the wall to plant its seed. I think of Christ as an amoeba who took the right turning. I want to be on the side of the progress which survives. I'm no friend of pterodactyls."

"But if we are incapable of love?"

"I'm not sure such a man exists. Love is planted in man now, even uselessly in some cases, like an appendix. Sometimes of course people call it hate."

"I haven't found any trace of it in myself."

"Perhaps you are looking for something too big and too important. Or too active."

"What you are saying seems to me every bit as superstitious as what the fathers believe."

"Who cares? It's the superstition I live by. There was another superstition—quite unproven—Copernicus had it —that the earth went round the sun. Without that superstition we shouldn't be in a position now to shoot rockets at the moon. One has to gamble on one's superstitions. Like Pascal gambled on his." He drank his whisky down.

"Are you a happy man?" Querry asked.

"I suppose I am. It's not a question that I've ever asked myself. Does a happy man ever ask it? I go on from day to day."

"Swimming on your wave," Querry said with envy. "Do you never need a woman?"

"The only one I ever needed," the doctor said, "is dead."

"So that's why you came out here."

"You are wrong," Colin said. "She's buried a hundred yards away. She was my wife."

CHAPTER TWO

I

IN the last three months the hospital had made great progress. It was no longer a mere ground-plan looking like the excavation of a Roman villa; the walls had risen; the window-spaces were there waiting for wire nets. It was even possible to estimate the time when the roof would be fixed. The lepers worked more rapidly as the end came in sight. Querry was walking through the building with Father Joseph; they passed through non-existent doors like revenants, into rooms that did not yet exist, into the future operating-theatre, the X-ray room, the fire-proof room with the vats of paraffin wax for the palsied hands, into the dispensary, into the two main wards.

"What will you do," Father Joseph said, "when this is finished?"

"What will you, father?"

"Of course it's for the Superior and the doctor to decide, but I would like to build a place where the mutilated can learn to work—occupational therapy, I suppose they call it at home. The sisters do what they can with individuals, especially the mutilated. No one wants to be a special case. They would learn much quicker in a class where they could joke a bit."

"And after that?"

"There's always more building to be done for the next twenty years, if only lavatories."

"Then there'll always be something for me to do, father."

"An architect like you is wasted on the work we have here. These are only builders' jobs."

"I have become a builder."

144

"Don't you ever want to see Europe again?"

"Do you, father?"

"There's a big difference between us. Europe is much the same as this for those of our Order—a group of buildings, very like the ones we have here, our rooms aren't any different, nor the chapel (even the Stations are the same), the same classrooms, the same food, the same clothes, the same kind of faces. But surely to you Europe means more than that—theatres, friends, restaurants, bars, books, shops, the company of your equals—the fruits of fame whatever that means."

Querry said, "I am content here."

It was nearly time for the midday meal, and they walked back together towards the mission, passing the nuns' house and the doctor's and the small shabby cemetery. It was not kept well—the service of the living took up too much of the fathers' time. Only on All Souls night was the graveyard properly remembered when a lamp or a candle shone on every grave, pagan and Christian. About half the graves had crosses, and they were as simple and uniform as those of the mass dead in a war-cemetery. Querry knew now which grave belonged to Mme. Colin. It stood crossless and a little apart, but the only reason for the separation was to leave space for Doctor Colin to join her.

"I hope you'll find room for me there too," Querry said. "I won't rate a cross. "

"We shall have trouble with Father Thomas over that. He'll argue that once baptized you are always a Christian."

"I would do well to die then before he returns."

"Better be quick about it. He will be back sooner than we think." Even his brother priests were happier without Father Thomas; it was impossible not to feel a grudging pity for so unattractive a man.

Father Joseph's warning proved wise too quickly. Absorbed in examining the new hospital they had failed to hear the bell of the Otraco boat. Father Thomas was already ashore with the cardboard-box in which he carried all his personal belongings. He stood in the doorway of his room and greeted them as they passed. He had the curious and disquieting air of receiving them like guests.

"Well, Father Joseph, you see that I am back before my time."

"We do see," Father Joseph said.

"Ah, M. Querry, I have something very important to discuss with you."

"Yes?"

"All in good time. Patience. Much has happened while I have been away."

"Don't keep us on tenterhooks," Father Joseph said.

"At lunch, at lunch," Father Thomas replied, carrying his cardboard-box elevated like a monstrance into his room.

As they passed the next window they could see the Superior standing by his bed. He was pushing a hairbrush, a sponge-bag and a box of cheroots into his khaki knapsack, a relic of the last war which he carried with him across the world like a memory. He took the cross from his desk and packed it away wrapped in a couple of handkerchiefs. Father Joseph said, "I begin to fear the worst."

The Superior at lunch sat silent and preoccupied. Father Thomas was on his right. He crumbled his bread with the closed face of importance. Only when the meal was over did the Superior speak. He said, "Father Thomas has brought me a letter. The Bishop wants me in Luc. I may be away some weeks or even months and I am asking Father Thomas to act for me during my absence. You are the only one, father," he added, "with the time to look after the accounts." It was an apology to the other fathers and a hidden rebuke to the pride which Father Thomas was already beginning to show— he had very little in common with the doubting pitiful figure of a month ago. Perhaps even a temporary promotion could cure a failing vocation.

"You know you can trust me," Father Thomas said.

"I can trust everyone here. My work is the least

important in the place. I can't build like Father Joseph or look after the dynamos like Brother Philippe."

"I will try not to let the school suffer," Father Thomas said.

"I am sure you will succeed, father. You will find that my work will take up very little of your time. A superior is always replaceable."

The more bare a life is, the more we fear change. The Superior said grace and looked around for his cheroots, but he had already packed them. He accepted a cigarette from Querry, but he wore it as awkwardly as he would have worn a suit of lay clothes. The fathers stood unhappily around unused to departures. Querry felt like a stranger present at some domestic grief.

"The hospital will be finished, perhaps, before I return," the Superior said with a certain sadness.

"We will not put up the roof-tree till you are back," Father Joseph replied.

"No, no, you must promise me to delay nothing. Father Thomas, those are my last instructions. The roof-tree at the earliest moment and plenty of champagne— if you can find a donor—to celebrate."

For years in their quiet unchanging routine they had been apt to forget that they were men under obedience, but now, suddenly, they were reminded of it. Who knew what was intended for the Superior, what letters might not have passed between the Bishop and the General in Europe? He spoke of returning in a few weeks (the Bishop, he had explained, had summoned him for a consultation), but all of them were aware that he might never return. Decisions might already have been taken elsewhere. They watched him now unobtrusively, with affection, as one might watch a dying man (only Father Thomas was absent: he had already gone to move his papers into the other's room), and the Superior in turn looked at them and the bleak refectory in which he had spent his best years. It was true what Father Joseph had said. The buildings, wherever he went, would always be very much the same; the refectories would vary as little as colonial airports, but for that very reason a man became more accustomed to the minute differences. There would always be the same coloured reproduction of the Pope's portrait, but this one had a stain in the corner where the leper who made the frame had spilt the walnut colouring. The chairs too had been fashioned by lepers, who had taken as a model the regulation kind supplied to the junior grade of government-officials, a kind you would find in every mission, but one of the chairs had become unique by its unreliability; they had always kept it against the wall since a visiting priest, Father Henri, had tried to imitate a circus-trick by balancing on the back. Even the bookcase had an individual weakness: one shelf slanted at an angle, and there were stains upon the wall that reminded each man of something. The stains on a different wall would evoke different pictures. Wherever one went one's companions would have much the same names (there are not so many saints in common use to choose from), but the new Father Joseph would not be quite the same as the old.

From the river came the summons of the ship's bell. The Superior took the cigarette out of his mouth and looked at it as though he wondered how it had come there. Father Joseph said, "I think we should have a glass of wine . . ." He rummaged in the cupboard for a bottle and found one which had been two-thirds finished some weeks ago on the last major feast-day. However there was a thimbleful left for all. "*Bon voyage*, father." The ship's bell rang again. Father Thomas came to the door and said, "I think you should be off now, father."

"Yes. I must fetch my knapsack."

"I have it here," Father Thomas said.

"Well then . . ." The Superior gave one more furtive look at the room: the stained picture, the broken chair, the slanting shelf.

"A safe return," Father Paul said. "I will fetch Doctor Colin."

"No, no, this is his time for a siesta. M. Querry will explain to him how it is."

They walked down to the river-bank to see the last of him and Father Thomas carried his knapsack. By the gang-plank the Superior took it and slung it over his shoulder with something of a military gesture. He touched Father Thomas on the arm. "I think you'll find the accounts in good order. Leave next month's as late as you can . . . in case I'm back." He hesitated and said with a deprecating smile, "Be careful of yourself, Father Thomas. Not too much enthusiasm." Then the ship and the river took him away from them.

Father Joseph and Querry returned to the house together. Querry said, "Why has he chosen Father Thomas? He has been here a shorter time than any of you."

"It is as the Superior said. We all have our proper jobs, and to tell you the truth Father Thomas is the only one who has the least notion of book-keeping."

Querry lay down on his bed. At this hour of the day the heat made it impossible to work and almost as impossible to sleep except for brief superficial spells. He thought he was with the Superior on the boat going away, but in his dream the boat took the contrary direction to that of Luc. It went on down the narrowing river into the denser forest, and it was now the Bishop's boat. A corpse lay in the Bishop's cabin and the two of them were taking it to Pendélé for burial. It surprised him to think that he had been so misled as to believe that the boat had reached the furthest point of its journey into the interior when it reached the leproserie. Now he was in motion again, going deeper.

The scrape of a chair woke him. He thought it was the ship's bottom grinding across a snag in the river. He opened his eyes and saw Father Thomas sitting by his bedside.

"I had not meant to wake you," Father Thomas said.

"I was only half asleep."

"I have brought you messages from a friend of yours," Father Thomas said.

"I have no friends in Africa except those I have made here."

"You have more friends than you know. My message is from M. Rycker."

"Rycker is no friend of mine."

"I know he is a little impetuous, but he is a man with a great admiration for you. He feels, from something his wife has said, that he was perhaps wrong to speak of you to the English journalist."

"His wife has more sense than he has then."

"Luckily it has all turned out for the best," Father Thomas said, "and we owe it to M. Rycker."

"The best?"

"He has written about you and all of us here in the most splendid fashion."

"Already?"

"He telegraphed his first article from Luc. M. Rycker helped him at the post-office. He made it a condition that he should read the article first—M. Rycker, of course, would never have allowed anything damaging to us to pass. He has written a real appreciation of your work. It has already been translated in *Paris Dimanche*."

"That rag?"

"It reaches a very wide public," Father Thomas said.

"A scandal-sheet."

"All the more creditable then that your message should appear there."

"I don't know what you are talking about—I have no message." He turned impatiently away from Father Thomas's searching and insinuating gaze and lay facing the wall. He heard the rustle of paper—Father Thomas was drawing something from the pocket of his soutane. He said, "Let me read a little bit of it to you. I assure you that it will give you great pleasure. The article is called: 'An Architect of Souls. The Hermit of the Congo'."

"What nauseating rubbish. I tell you, father, nothing that man could write would interest me."

"You are really much too harsh. I am only sorry I had no time to show it to the Superior. He makes a slight mistake about the name of the Order, but you can hardly

150

expect anything different from an Englishman. Listen to the way he ends. 'When a famous French statesman once retired into the depths of the country, to avoid the burden of office, it was said that the world made a path to his door'."

"He can get nothing right," Querry said. "Nothing. It was an author, not a statesman. And the author was American, not French."

"These are trifles," Father Thomas said rebukingly. "Listen to this. 'The whole Catholic world has been discussing the mysterious disappearance of the great architect Querry. Querry whose range of achievement extended from the latest cathedral in the United States, a palace of glass and steel, to a little white Dominican chapel on the Côte d'Azur . . .' "

"Now he's confusing me with that amateur, Matisse," Querry said.

"Never mind small details."

"I hope for your sake that the gospels are more accurate in small details than M. Parkinson."

" 'Querry has not been seen for a long while in his usual haunts. I have tracked him all the way from his favourite restaurant, the l'Epaule de Mouton . . .' "

"This is absurd. Does he think I'm a gourmandising tourist?"

" 'To the heart of Africa. Near the spot where Stanley once pitched his camp among the savage tribes, I at last came on Querry . . .' " Father Thomas looked up. He said, "It is here that he writes a great many gracious things about our work. 'Selfless . . . devoted . . . in the white robes of their blameless lives.' Really, you know, he does have a certain sense of style.

" 'What is it that has induced the great Querry to abandon a career that brought him honour and riches to give up his life to serving the world's untouchables? I was in no position to ask him that when suddenly I found that my quest had ended. Unconscious and burning with fever, I was carried on shore from my pirogue, the frail bark in which I had penetrated what Joseph Conrad called the Heart of Darkness, by a few faithful natives who had followed me down the great river with the same fidelity their grandfathers had shown to Stanley'."

"He can't keep Stanley out of it," Querry said. "There have been many others in Central Africa, but I suppose the English would never have heard of them."

" 'I woke to find Querry's hand upon my pulse and Querry's eyes gazing into mine. Then I sensed the great mystery'."

"Do you really enjoy this stuff?" Querry asked. He sat up impatiently on his bed.

"I have read many lives of saints that were far worse written," Father Thomas said. "Style is not everything. The man's intentions are sound. Perhaps you are not the best judge. He goes on, 'It was from Querry's lips that I learned the meaning of the mystery. Though Querry spoke to me as perhaps he had never spoken to another human soul, with a burning remorse for a past as colourful and cavalier as that St. Francis once led in the dark alleys of the city by the Arno . . .' I wish I had been there," Father Thomas said wistfully, "when you spoke of that. I'm leaving out the next bit which deals mainly with the lepers. He seems to have noticed only the mutilated—a pity since it gives a rather too sombre impression of our home here." Father Thomas, as the acting Superior, was already taking a more favourable view of the mission than he had a month before.

"Here is where he reaches what he calls the heart of the matter. 'It was from Querry's most intimate friend, André Rycker, the manager of a palm-oil plantation, that I learned the secret. It is perhaps typical of Querry that what he keeps humbly hidden from the priests for whom he works he is ready to disclose to this planter—the last person you would expect to find on terms of close friendship with the great architect. "You want to know what makes him tick?" M. Rycker said to me. "I am sure that it is love, a completely selfless love without the barrier of colour or class. I have never known a man more deeply instructed in faith. I have sat at this very table late into the night discussing the nature of divine love with the great Querry." So the two strange halves of Querry meet—to me Querry had spoken of the women he had loved in the world of Europe, and to his obscure friend, in his factory in the bush, he had spoken of his love of God. The world in this atomic day has need of saints. When a famous French statesman once retired into the depths of the country, to avoid the burden of office, it was said that the world made a path to his door. It is unlikely that the world which discovered the way to Schweitzer at Lambaréné will fail to seek out the hermit of the Congo.' I think he might have left out the reference to St. Francis," Father Thomas said, "it might be mis-understood."

"What lies the man does tell," Querry exclaimed. He got up from his bed and stood near his drawing-board and the stretched sheet of blueprint. He said, "I won't allow that man . . ."

"He is a journalist, of course," Father Thomas said. "These are just professional exaggerations."

"I don't mean Parkinson. It's his job. I mean Rycker. I have never spoken to Rycker about Love or God."

"He told me that he once had an interesting discussion with you."

"Never. There was no discussion. All the talking, I assure you, was done by him."

Father Thomas looked down at the newspaper cutting. He said, "There's to be a second article, it appears, in a week's time. It says here, 'Next Sunday. A Saint's Past. Redemption by Suffering. The Leper Lost in the Jungle.' That will be Deo Gratias I imagine," Father Thomas said. "There's also a photograph of the Englishman talking to Rycker."

"Give it to me." Querry tore the paper into pieces and dropped them on the floor. He said, "Is the road open?"

"It was when I left Luc. Why?"

"I'm going to take a truck then."

"Where to?"

"To have a word with Rycker. Can't you see, father,

that I must silence him? This mustn't go on. I'm fighting for my life."

"Your life?"

"My life here. It's all I have." He sat wearily down on the bed. He said, "I've come a long way. There's nowhere else for me to go if I leave here."

Father Thomas said, "For a good man fame is always a problem."

"But, father, I'm not a good man. Can't you believe me? Must you too twist everything like Rycker and that man? I had no good motive in coming here. I am looking after myself as I have always done, but surely even a selfish man has the right to a little happiness?"

"You have a truly wonderful quality of humility," Father Thomas said.

PART VI

CHAPTER ONE

I

MARIE RYCKER stopped her reading of *The Imitation of Christ* as soon as she saw that her husband was asleep, but she was afraid to move in case she might wake him, and of course there was always the possibility of a trap. She could imagine how he would reproach her, "Could you not watch by me one hour?" for her husband was not afraid to carry imitation to great lengths. The hollow face was turned away from her so that she could not see his eyes. She thought that so long as he was ill she need not tell him her news, for one had no duty to give such unwelcome news as hers to a sick man. Through the net of the window there blew in the smell of stale margarine which she would always associate with marriage, and from where she sat she could see the corner of the engine-house, where they were feeding the ovens with the husks.

She felt ashamed of her fear and boredom and nausea. She had been bred a *colon* and she knew very well that this was not how a *colon* ought to behave. Her father had represented the same company as her husband, in a different, a roving capacity, but because his wife was delicate he had sent her home to Europe before his child's birth. Her mother had fought to stay with him, for she was a true *colon*, and in her turn the daughter of a *colon*. The word spoken in Europe so disparagingly was a badge of honour to them. Even in Europe on leave they lived in groups, went to the same restaurants and café-bars kept by former *colons* and took villas for the season at the same watering-places. Wives waited among the potted palms for their husbands to return from the land of palms; they played bridge and read aloud to each other their husbands' letters, which contained the gossip of the colony. The letters bore bright postage stamps of beasts and birds and flowers and the postmarks of exotic places. Marie began to collect them at six, but she always preserved the envelopes and the postmarks as well, so that she had to keep them in a box instead of an album. One of the postmarks was Luc. She did not foresee that one day she would begin to know Luc better than she knew the rue de Namur.

With the tenderness that came from a sense of guilt she wiped Rycker's face with a handkerchief soaked in eau-de-cologne, even at the risk of waking him. She knew that she was a false *colon*. It was like betraying one's country— all the worse because one's country was so remote and so maligned.

One of the labourers came out of the shed to make water against the wall. When he turned back he saw her watching him and they stared across the few yards at each other, but they were like people watching with telescopes over an immense distance. She remembered a breakfast, with the pale European sun on the water outside and bathers going in for an early dip, and her father teaching her the Mongo for "bread" and "coffee" and "jam". They were still the only three words in Mongo that she knew. But it was not enough to say coffee and bread and jam to the man outside. They had no means of communication: she couldn't even curse him, as her father or her husband could have done, in words that he understood. He turned and went into the shed and again she felt the loneliness of her treachery to this country of *colons*. She wanted to apologise to her old father at home; she couldn't blame him for the postmarks and the stamps. Her mother had yearned to remain with him. She had not realised how fortunate her weakness was. Rycker opened his eyes and said, "What time is it?"

"I think it's about three o'clock."

He was asleep again before he could have heard her reply, and she sat on. In the yard a lorry backed towards the shed. It was piled high with nuts for the presses and the ovens; they were like dried and withered heads, the product of a savage massacre. She tried to read, but the *Imitation of Christ* could not hold her attention. Once a month she received a copy of *Marie-Chantal*, but she had to read the serial in secret when Rycker was occupied, for he despised what he called women's fiction and spoke critically of daydreams. What other resources had she than dreams? They were a form of hope, but she hid them from him like a member of the Resistance used to hide his pill of cyanide. She refused to believe that this was the end, growing old in solitude with her husband and the smell of margarine and the black faces and the scrap-metal, in the heat and the humidity. She awaited day by day some radio-signal which would announce the hour of liberation. Sometimes she thought that there were no lengths to which she would not go for the sake of liberation.

Marie-Chantal came by surface-mail; it was always two months out-of-date, but that hardly mattered, since the serial story, as much as any piece of literature, had eternal values. In the story she was reading now a girl in the Salle Privée at Monte Carlo had placed 12,000 francs, the last money she had in the world, upon the figure 17, but a hand had reached over her shoulder while the ball ran and shifted her tokens to 19. Then the 19 socket caught the ball and she turned to see who her benefactor could be . . . but she would have to wait another three weeks before she discovered his identity. He was approaching her now down the West African coast, by mail-boat, but even when he arrived at Matadi, there was still the long river-journey ahead of him. The dogs began barking in the yard and Rycker woke.

"See who it is," he said, "but keep him away." She heard a car draw up. It was probably the representative of one of the two rival breweries. Each man made the tour of the out-stations three times a year and gave a party to the local chief and the villagers with his brand of beer gratis for everyone. In some mysterious way it was supposed to aid consumption.

They were shovelling the dried heads out of the *camion*

when she came into the yard. Two men sat in a small Peugeot truck. One of them was African, but she couldn't see who the other was because the sun on the windshield dazzled her, but she heard him say, "What I have to do here should take no time at all. We will reach Luc by ten." She came to the door of the car and saw that it was Querry. She recalled the shameful scene weeks before when she had run to her car in tears. Afterwards she had spent the night by the roadside bitten by mosquitoes rather than face another human being who might despise her husband too.

She thought gratefully, 'He has come of his own accord. What he said was just a passing mood. It was his *cafard* which spoke, not he.' She wanted to go in and see her husband and tell him, but then she remembered that he had told her, "Keep him away."

Querry climbed out of the truck and she saw that the boy with him was one of the *mutilés* from the leproserie. She said to Querry, "You've come to call on us? My husband will be so glad . . ."

"I am on my way to Luc," Querry said, "but I want to have a word with M. Rycker first." There was something in his expression which recalled her husband at certain moments. If *cafard* had dictated that insulting phrase the *cafard* still possessed him.

She said, "He is ill. I'm afraid you can't see him."

"I must. I have been three days on the road from the leproserie . . ."

"You will have to tell me." He stood by the door of the truck. She said, "Can't you give me your message?"

"I can hardly strike a woman," Querry said. A sudden rictus round the mouth startled her. Perhaps he was trying to soften the phrase with a smile, but it made his face all the uglier.

"Is that your message?"

"More or less," Querry said.

"Then you'd better come inside." She walked slowly away without looking back. He seemed to her like an armed savage from whom she must disguise her fear.

When she reached the house she would be safe. Violence in their class always happened in the open air; it was restrained by sofas and bric-à-brac. When she passed through the door she was tempted to escape to her room, leaving the sick man at Querry's mercy, but she steeled herself by the thought of what Rycker might say to her when he had gone, and with no more than a glance down the passage where safety lay she went to the verandah and heard Querry's steps following behind.

When she reached the verandah she put on the voice of a hostess as she might have done a clean frock. She said, "Can I get you something to drink?"

"It's a little early. Is your husband really sick?"

"Of course he is. I told you. The mosquitoes are bad here. We are too close to water. He hadn't been taking his paludrin. I don't know why. You know he has moods."

"I suppose it was here that Parkinson got his fever?"

"Parkinson?"

"The English journalist."

"That man," she said with distaste. "Is he still around?"

"I don't know. You were the last people to see him. After your husband had put him on my track."

"I am sorry if he troubled you. I wouldn't answer any of his questions."

Querry said, "I had made it quite clear to your husband that I had come here to be private. He forced himself on me in Luc. He sent you out to the leproserie after me. He sent Parkinson. He has been spreading grotesque stories about me in the town. Now there's this newspaper article and another one is threatened. I have come to tell your husband that this persecution has got to stop."

"Persecution?"

"Have you another name for it?"

"You don't understand. My husband was excited by your coming here. At finding you. There are not so many people he can talk to about what interests him. He's very alone." She was looking across at the river and the winding-gear of the ferry and the forest on the other side. "When he's excited by something he wants to possess it. Like a child."

"I have never cared for children."

"It's the only young thing about him," she said, the words coming quickly and unintentionally out, like the spurt from a wound.

He said, "Can't you persuade him to stop talking about me?"

"I have no influence. He doesn't listen to me. After all why should he?"

"If he loves you . . ."

"I don't know whether he does. He says sometimes that he only loves God."

"Then I must speak to him myself. A touch of fever is not going to stop him hearing what I have to say." He added, "I'm not sure of his room, but there aren't many in this house. I can find it."

"No. Please no. He'll think it's my fault. He'll be angry. I don't want him angry. I've got something to tell him. I can't if he's angry. It's ghastly enough as it is."

"What's ghastly?"

She looked at him with an expression of despair. Tears formed in her eyes and began to drip gracelessly like sweat. She said, "I think I have a baby on the way."

"But I thought women usually liked . . ."

"He doesn't want one. But he wouldn't allow me to be safe."

"Have you seen a doctor?"

"No. There's been no excuse for me to go to Luc, and we've only the one car. I didn't want him to be suspicious. He usually wants to know after a time if everything's all right."

"Hasn't he asked you?"

"I think he's forgotten that we did anything since the time before."

He was moved unwillingly by her humility. She was very young and surely she was pretty enough, yet it seemed never to occur to her that a man ought not to forget such an act. She said, as if that explained everything, "It was after the Governor's cocktail party."

"Are you sure about it?"

"I've missed twice."

"My dear, in this climate that often happens." He said, "I advise you—what's your name?"

"Marie." It was the commonest woman's name of all, but it sounded to him like a warning.

"Yes," she said eagerly, "you advise me . . .?"

"Not to tell your husband yet. We must find some excuse for you to go to Luc and see the doctor. But don't worry too much. Don't you want the child?"

"What would be the use of wanting it if *he* doesn't?"

"I would take you in with me now—if we could find you an excuse."

"If anybody can persuade him, you can. He admires you so much."

"I have some medicines to pick up for Doctor Colin at the hospital, and I was going to buy some surprise provisions for the fathers too, champagne for when the roof-tree goes up. But I wouldn't be able to deliver you back before tomorrow evening."

"Oh," she said, "his boy can look after him far better than I can. He's been with him longer."

"I meant that perhaps he mightn't trust me . . ."

"There hasn't been rain for days. The roads are quite good."

"Shall I talk to him then?"

"It isn't really what you came to say, is it?"

"I'll treat him as gently as I can. You've drawn my sting."

She said, "It will be fun—to go to Luc alone. I mean with you." She wiped her eyes dry with the back of her hand; she was no more ashamed of her tears than a child would have been.

"Perhaps the doctor will say you have nothing to fear. Which is his room?"

"Through the door at the end of the passage. You really won't be harsh to him?"

163

"No."

Rycker was sitting up in bed when he entered. He was wearing a look of grievance like a mask, but he took it off quickly and substituted another representing welcome when he saw his visitor. "Why, Querry? Was it you?"

"I came to see you on the way to Luc."

"It's good of you to visit me on a bed of sickness."

Querry said, "I wanted to see you about that stupid article by the Englishman."

"I gave it to Father Thomas to take to you." Rycker's eyes were bright with fever or pleasure. "There has never been such a sale in Luc for *Paris-Dimanche*, I can tell you that. The bookshop has sent for extra copies. They say they have ordered a hundred of the next issue."

"Did it never occur to you how detestable it would be to me?"

"I know the paper is not a very high-class one, but the article was highly laudatory. Do you realise that it's even been reprinted in Italy? The bishop, so I'm told, has had an enquiry from Rome."

"Will you listen to me, Rycker? I'm trying to speak gently because you are sick. But all this has to stop. I am not a Catholic, I am not even a Christian. I won't be adopted by you and your Church."

Rycker sat under the crucifix, wearing a smile of understanding.

"I have no belief whatever in a god, Rycker. No belief in the soul, in eternity. I'm not even interested."

"Yes. Father Thomas has told me how terribly you have been suffering from aridity."

"Father Thomas is a pious fool, and I came out here to escape fools, Rycker. Will you promise to leave me in peace or must I go again the way I came? I was happy before this started. I found I could work. I was feeling interested, involved in something . . ."

"It's a penalty of genius to belong to the world."

If he had to have a tormentor how gladly he would have chosen the cynical Parkinson. There were interstices in that cracked character where the truth might occasionally seed. But Rycker was like a wall so plastered over with church-announcements that you couldn't even see the brickwork behind. He said, "I'm no genius, Rycker. I am a man who had a certain talent, not a very great talent, and I have come to the end of it. There was nothing new I could do. I could only repeat myself. So I gave up. It's as simple and commonplace as that. Just as I have given up women. After all there are only thirty-two ways of driving a nail into a hole."

"Parkinson told me of the remorse you felt . . ."

"I have never felt remorse. Never. You all dramatise too much. We can retire from feeling just as naturally as we retire from a job. Are you sure that you still feel anything, Rycker, that you aren't pretending to feel? Would you greatly care if your factory were burnt down tomorrow in a riot?"

"My heart is not in that."

"And your heart isn't in your wife either. You made that clear to me the first time we met. You wanted someone to save you from St. Paul's threat of burning."

"There is nothing wrong in a Christian marriage," Rycker said. "It's far better than a marriage of passion. But if you want to know the truth, my heart has always been in my faith."

"I begin to think we are not so different, you and I. We don't know what love is. You pretend to love a god because you love no one else. But I won't pretend. All I have left me is a certain regard for the truth. It was the best side of the small talent I had. You are inventing all the time, Rycker, aren't you? There are men who talk about love to prostitutes—they daren't even sleep with a woman without inventing some sentiment to excuse them. You've even invented this idea of me to justify yourself. But I won't play your game, Rycker."

"When I look at you," Rycker said, "I can see a man tormented."

"Oh no you can't. I haven't felt any pain at all in

twenty years. It needs something far bigger than you to cause me pain."

"Whether you like it or not, you have set an example to all of us."

"An example of what?"

"Unselfishness and humility," Rycker said.

"I warn you, Rycker, that unless you stop spreading this rubbish about me . . ."

But he felt his powerlessness. He had been trapped into words. A blow would have been simpler and better, but it was too late now for blows.

Rycker said, "Saints used to be made by popular acclaim. I'm not sure that it wasn't a better method than a trial in Rome. We have taken you up, Querry. You don't belong to yourself any more. You lost yourself when you prayed with that leper in the forest."

"I didn't pray. I only . . ." He stopped. What was the use? Rycker had stolen the last word. Only after he had slammed the door shut did he remember that he had said nothing of Marie Rycker and of her journey to Luc.

And of course there she was waiting for him eagerly and patiently, at the other end of the passage. He wished that he had brought a bag of sweets with which to comfort her. She said excitedly, "Did he agree?"

"I never asked him."

"You promised."

"I got angry, and I forgot. I'm very sorry."

She said, "I'll come with you to Luc all the same."

"You'd better not."

"Were you very angry with him?"

"Not very. I kept most of the anger to myself."

"Then I'm coming." She left him before he had time to protest, and a few moments later she was back with no more than a Sabena night-bag for the journey.

He said, "You travel light."

When they reached the truck he asked, "Wouldn't it be better if I went back and spoke to him?"

"He might say no. Then what could I do?"

They left behind them the smell of the margarine and

the cemetery of old boilers, and the shadow of the forest fell on either side. She said politely in her hostess voice, "Is the hospital going well?"

"Yes."

"How is the Superior?"

"He is away."

"Did you have a heavy storm last Saturday? We did."

He said, "You don't have to make conversation with me."

"My husband says that I am too silent."

"Silence is not a bad thing."

"It is when you are unhappy."

"I'm sorry. I had forgotten . . ."

They drove a few more kilometres without words. Then she asked, "Why did you come here and not some other place?"

"Because it is a long way off."

"Other places are a long way off. The South Pole."

"When I was at the airport there was no plane leaving for the South Pole." She giggled. It was easy to amuse the young, even the unhappy young. "There was one going to Tokyo," he added, "but somehow this place seemed a lot further off. And I was not interested in geishas or cherry-blossom."

"You don't mean you really didn't know where . . .?"

"One of the advantages of having an air-credit card is that you don't need to make up your mind where you are going till the last moment."

"Haven't you any family to leave?"

"Not a family. There was someone, but she was better off without me."

"Poor her."

"Oh no. She's lost nothing of value. It's hard for a woman to live with a man who doesn't love her."

"Yes."

"There are always the times of day when one ceases to pretend."

"Yes." They were silent again until darkness began to fall and he switched the headlights on. They shone on a human effigy with a coconut-head, sitting on a rickety chair. She gave a gasp of fright and pressed against his shoulder. She said, "I'm scared of things I don't understand."

"Then you must be frightened of a great deal."

"I am."

He put his arm round her shoulders to reassure her. She said, "Did you say goodbye to her?"

"No."

"But she must have seen you packing."

"No. I travel light too."

"You came away without anything?"

"I had a razor and a toothbrush and a letter of credit from a bank in America."

"Do you really mean you didn't know where you were going?"

"I had no idea. So it wasn't any good taking clothes."

The track was rough and he needed both hands on the wheel. He had never before scrutinised his own behaviour. It had seemed to him at the time the only logical thing to do. He had eaten a larger breakfast than usual because he could not be certain of the hour of his next meal, and then he had taken a taxi. His journey began in the great all-but-empty airport built for a world-exhibition which had closed a long time ago. One could walk a mile through the corridors without seeing more than a scattering of human beings. In an immense hall people sat apart waiting for the plane to Tokyo. They looked like statues in an art-gallery. He had asked for a seat to Tokyo before he noticed an indicator with African names.

He had said, "Is there a seat on that plane too?"

"Yes, but there's no connection to Tokyo after Rome."

"I shall go the whole way." He gave the man his credit-card.

"Where is your luggage?"

"I have no luggage."

He supposed now that his conduct must have seemed a little odd. He said to the clerk, "Mark my ticket with my first name only, please. On the passenger list too. I don't want to be bothered by the Press." It was one of the few advantages which fame brought a man that he was not automatically regarded with suspicion because of unusual behaviour. Thus simply he had thought to cover his tracks, but he had not entirely succeeded or the letter signed *toute à toi* could never have reached him. Perhaps she had been to the airport herself to make enquiries. The man there must have had quite a story to tell her. Even so, at his destination, no one had known him, and at the small hotel he went to—without air-conditioning and with a shower which didn't work—no one knew his name. So it could have been no one but Rycker who had betrayed his whereabouts; the ripple of Rycker's interest had gone out across half the world like radio-waves, reaching the international Press. He said abruptly, "How I wish I'd never met your husband."

"So do I."

"It's done you no harm, surely?"

"I mean—I wish I hadn't met him either." The head-lamps caught the wooden poles of a cage high in the air. She said, "I hate this place. I want to go home."

"We've come too far to turn back now."

"That's not home," she said. "That's the factory."

He knew very well what she expected him to say, but he refused to speak. You uttered a few words of sympathy —however false and conventional—and experience taught him what nearly always followed. Unhappiness was like a hungry animal waiting beside the track for any victim. He said, "Have you friends in Luc to put you up?"

"We have no friends there. I'll go with you to the hotel."

"Did you leave a note for your husband?"

"No."

"It would have been better."

"Did you leave a note behind before you caught the plane?"

"That was different. I was not returning."

She said, "Would you lend me money for a ticket home —I mean, to Europe?"

169

"No."

"I was afraid you wouldn't." As if that settled everything and there was nothing more to do about it, she fell asleep. He thought rashly: poor frightened beast—this one was too young to be a great danger. It was only when they were fully grown you couldn't trust them with your pity.

2

It was nearly eleven at night before they drove into Luc past the little river-port. The Bishop's boat was lying at her moorings. A cat stopped halfway up the gang-plank and regarded them, and Querry swerved to avoid a dead piedog stretched in their track waiting for the morning-vulture. The hotel across the square from the Governor's house was decked out with the relics of gaiety. Perhaps the directors of the local brewery had been giving their annual party or some official, who thought himself lucky, had been celebrating his recall home. In the bar there were mauve and pink paper-chains hanging over the tubular steel chairs that gave the whole place the cheerless and functional look of an engine-room; shades which represented the man in the moon beamed down from the light-brackets.

There was no air-conditioning in the rooms upstairs, and the walls stopped short of the ceiling so that any privacy was impossible. Every movement was audible from the neighbouring room, and Querry could follow every stage of the girl's retirement—the zipping of the all-night bag, the clatter of a coat-hanger, the tinkle of a glass bottle on a porcelain basin. Shoes were dropped on bare boards, and water ran. He sat and wondered what he ought to do to comfort her if the doctor told her in the morning that she was pregnant. He was reminded of his long night's vigil with Deo Gratias. It had been fear then too that he had contended with. He heard the bed creak.

He took a bottle of whisky from his sack and poured himself a glass. Now it was his turn to tinkle, run water, clatter; he was like a prisoner in a cell answering by code the signals of a fellow-convict. An odd sound reached him through the wall—it sounded to him as though she were crying. He felt no pity, only irritation. She had forced herself on him and she was threatening now to spoil his night's sleep. He had not yet undressed. He took the bottle of whisky with him and knocked on her door.

He saw at once that he had been wrong. She was sitting up in bed reading a paper-back—she must have had time to stow that away too in the Sabena bag. He said, "I'm sorry—I thought I heard you crying."

"Oh no," she said. "I was laughing." He saw that it was a popular novel dealing with the life in Paris of an English major. "It's terribly funny."

"I brought this along in case you needed comfort."

"Whisky? I've never drunk it."

"You can begin. But you probably won't like it." He washed her toothmug out and poured her a weak drink.

"You don't like it?"

She said, "I like the idea. Drinking whisky at midnight in a room of my own."

"It's not midnight yet."

"You know what I mean. And reading in bed. My husband doesn't like me reading in bed. Especially a book like this."

"What's wrong with the book?"

"It's not serious. It's not about God. Of course," she said, "he has good reason. I'm not properly educated. The nuns did their best, but it simply didn't stick."

"I'm glad you're not worrying about tomorrow."

"There may be good news. I've got a bit of a stomach-ache at this moment. It can't be the whisky yet, can it? and it might be the curse." The hostess-phrases had gone to limbo where the nuns' learning lay, and she had reverted to the school-dormitory. It was absurd to consider that anyone so immature could be in any way a danger.

He asked, "Were you happy when you were at school?"

171

"It was bliss." She hunched her knees higher and said, "Why don't you sit down?"

"It's quite time you were asleep." He found it impossible not to treat her as a child. Rycker, instead of rupturing her virginity, had sealed it safely down once and for all.

She said, "What are you going to do? When the hospital's finished, I mean?" That was the question they were all asking him, but this time he did not evade it: there was a theory that one should always tell the direct truth to the young.

He said, "I am going to stay. I am never going back."

"You'll have to—sometime—on leave."

"The others perhaps, but not me."

"You'll get sick in the end if you stay."

"I'm very tough. Anyway what do I care? We all sooner or later get the same sickness, age. Do you see those brown marks on the backs of my hands—my mother used to call them grave-marks."

"They are only freckles," she said.

"Oh no, freckles come from the sunlight. These come from the darkness."

"You are very morbid," she said, speaking like the head of the school. "I don't really understand you. I have to stay here, but my God if I were free like you . . ."

"I will tell you a story," he said and poured himself out a second treble Scotch.

"That's a very large whisky. You aren't a heavy drinker, are you? My husband is."

"I'm only a steady one. This one is to help me with the story. I'm not used to telling stories. How does one begin?" He drank slowly. "Once upon a time."

"Really," she said, "you and I are much too old for fairy-stories."

"Yes. That in a way *is* the story as you'll see. Once upon a time there was a boy who lived in the deep country."

"Were you the boy?"

"No, you mustn't draw close parallels. They always

172

say a novelist chooses from his general experience of life, not from special facts. I have never lived out of cities until now."

"Go on."

"This boy lived with his parents on a farm—not a very large farm, but it was big enough for them and two servants and six labourers, a dog, a cat, a cow . . . I suppose there was a pig. I don't know much about farms."

"There seem to be an awful lot of characters. I shall fall asleep if I try to remember them all."

"That's exactly what I'm trying to make you do. His parents used to tell the boy stories about the King who lived in a city a hundred miles away—about the distance of the furthest star."

"That's nonsense. A star is billions and billions . . ."

"Yes, but the boy *thought* the star was a hundred miles away. He knew nothing about light-years. He had no idea that the star he was watching had probably been dead and dark before the world was made. They told him that, even though the King was far away, he was watching everything that went on everywhere. When a pig littered, the King knew of it, or when a moth died against a lamp. When a man and woman married, he knew that too. He was pleased by their marriage because when *they* came to litter it would increase the number of his subjects; so he rewarded them—you couldn't see the reward, for the woman frequently died in childbirth and the child was sometimes born deaf or blind, but, after all, you cannot see the air—and yet it exists according to those who know. When a servant slept with another servant in a haystack the King punished them. You couldn't always see the punishment—the man found a better job and the girl was more beautiful with her virginity gone and afterwards married the foreman, but that was only because the punishment was postponed. Sometimes it was postponed until the end of life, but that made no difference because the King was the King of the dead too and you couldn't tell what terrible things he might do to them in the grave.

"The boy grew up. He married properly and was rewarded by the King, although his only child died and he made no progress in his profession—he had always wanted to carve statues, as large and important as the Sphinx. After his child's death he quarrelled with his wife and he was punished by the King for it. Of course you couldn't have seen the punishment any more than you could the reward: you had to take both on trust. He became in time a famous jeweller, for one of the women whom he had satisfied gave him money for his training, and he made many beautiful things in honour of his mistress and of course the King. Lots of rewards began to come his way. Money too. From the King. Everyone agreed that it all came from the King. He left his wife and his mistress, he left a lot of women, but he always had a great deal of fun with them first. They called it love and so did he, he broke all the rules he could think of, and he must surely have been punished for breaking them, but you couldn't see the punishment nor could he. He grew richer and richer and he made better and better jewellery, and women were kinder and kinder to him. He had, everyone agreed, a wonderful time. The only trouble was that he became bored, more and more bored. Nobody ever seemed to say no to him. Nobody ever made him suffer—it was always other people who suffered. Sometimes just for a change he would have welcomed feeling the pain of the punishment that the King must all the time have been inflicting on him. He could travel wherever he chose and after a while it seemed to him that he had gone much further than the hundred miles that separated him from the King, further than the furthest star, but wherever he went he always came to the same place where the same things happened: articles in the papers praised his jewellery, women cheated their husbands and went to bed with him, and servants of the King acclaimed him as a loyal and faithful subject.

"Because people could only see the reward, and the punishment was invisible, he got the reputation of being a very good man. Sometimes people were a little perplexed that such a good man should have enjoyed quite so many women—it was, on the surface anyway, disloyal to the King who had made quite other rules. But they learnt in time to explain it; they said he had a great capacity for love and love had always been regarded by them as the highest of virtues. Love indeed was the greatest reward even the King could give, all the greater because it was more invisible than such little material rewards as money and success and membership of the Academy. Even the man himself began to believe that he loved a great deal better than all the so-called good people who obviously could not be so good if you knew all (you had only to look at the punishments they received —poverty, children dying, losing both legs in a railway accident and the like). It was quite a shock to him when he discovered one day that he didn't love at all."

"How did he discover that?"

"It was the first of several important discoveries which he made about that time. Did I tell you that he was a very clever man, much cleverer than the people around him? Even as a boy he had discovered all by himself about the King. Of course there were his parents' stories, but they proved nothing. They might have been old wives' tales. They loved the King, they said, but he went one better. He proved that the King existed by historical, logical, philosophical, and etymological methods. His parents told him that was a waste of time: they knew: they had seen the King. 'Where?' 'In our hearts of course.' He laughed at them for their simplicity and their superstition. How could the King possibly be in their hearts when he was able to prove that he had never stirred from the city a hundred miles away? His King existed objectively and there was no other King but his."

"I don't like parables much, and I don't like your hero."

"He doesn't like himself much, and that's why he's never spoken before—except in this way."

"What you said about 'no other king but his' reminds me a little of my husband."

"You mustn't accuse a story-teller of introducing real characters."

"When are you going to reach a climax? Has it a happy ending? I don't want to stay awake otherwise. Why don't you describe some of the women?"

"You are like so many critics. You want me to write your own sort of story."

"Have you read *Manon Lescaut*?"

"Years ago."

"We all loved it at the convent. Of course it was strictly forbidden. It was passed from hand to hand, and I pasted the cover of M. Lejeune's History of the Wars of Religion on it. I have it still."

"You must let me finish my story."

"Oh well," she said with resignation, leaning back against the pillows, "if you must."

"I have told you about my hero's first discovery. His second came much later when he realised that he was not born to be an artist at all: only a very clever jeweller. He made one gold jewel in the shape of an ostrich egg: it was all enamel and gold and when you opened it you found inside a little gold figure sitting at a table and a little gold and enamel egg on the table, and when you opened that there was a little figure sitting at a table and a little gold and enamel egg and when you opened that . . . I needn't go on. Everyone said he was a master-technician, but he was highly praised too for the seriousness of his subject-matter because on the top of each egg there was a gold cross set with clips of precious stones in honour of the King. The trouble was that he wore himself out with the ingenuity of his design, and suddenly when he was making the contents of the final egg with an optic glass—that was what they called magnifying glasses in the old days in which this story is set, for of course it contains no reference to our time and no likeness to any living character . . ." He took another long drink of whisky; he couldn't remember how long it was since he had experienced the odd elation he was feeling now. He said, "What am I saying? I think I am a lit-

176

tle drunk. The whisky doesn't usually affect me in this way."

"Something about an egg," her sleepy voice replied from under the sheet.

"Oh yes, the second discovery." It was, he began to think, a sad story, so that it was hard to understand this sense of freedom and release, like that of a prisoner who at last "comes clean," admitting everything to his inquisitor. Was this the reward perhaps which came sometimes to a writer? 'I have told all: you can hang me now.' "What did you say?"

"The last egg."

"Oh yes, that was it. Suddenly our hero realised how bored he was—he never wanted to turn his hand any more to mounting any jewel at all. He was finished with his profession—he had come to an end of it. Nothing could ever be so ingenious as what he had done already, or more useless, and he could never hear any praise higher than what he had received. He knew what the damned fools could do with their praise."

"So what?"

"He went to a house number 49 in a street called the rue des Remparts where his mistress had kept an apartment ever since she left her husband. Her name was Marie like yours. There was a crowd outside. He found the doctor and the police there because an hour before she had killed herself."

"How ghastly."

"Not for him. A long time ago he had got to the end of pleasure just as now he had got to the end of work, although it is true he went on practising pleasure like a retired dancer continues to rehearse daily at the bar, because he has spent all his mornings that way and it never occurs to him to stop. So our hero felt only relief: the bar had been broken, he wouldn't bother, he thought, to obtain another. Although, of course, after a month or two he did. However it was too late then—the morning habit had been broken and he never took it up again with quite the same zeal."

177

"It's a very unpleasant fairy-story," the voice said. He couldn't see her face because the sheet was pulled over it. He paid no attention to her criticism.

"I tell you it isn't easy leaving a profession any more than you would find it easy leaving a husband. In both cases people talk a lot to you about duty. People came to him to demand eggs with crosses (it was his duty to the King and the King's followers). It almost seemed from the fuss they made that no one else was capable of making eggs or crosses. To try and discourage them and show them how his mind had changed, he did cut a few more stones as frivolously as he knew how, exquisite little toads for women to wear in their navels—navel-jewels became quite a fashion for a time. He even fashioned little soft golden coats of mail, with one hollow stone like a knowing eye at the top, with which men might clothe their special parts—they came to be known for some reason as Letters of Marque and for a while they too were quite fashionable as gifts. (You know how difficult it is for a woman to find anything to give a man at Christmas.) So our hero received yet more money and praise, but what vexed him most was that even these trifles were now regarded as seriously as his eggs and crosses had been. He was the King's jeweller and nothing could alter that. People declared that he was a moralist and that these were serious satires on the age—in the end the idea rather spoilt the sale of the letters, as you can imagine. A man hardly wants to wear a moral satire in that place, and women were chary of touching a moral satire in the way they had liked touching a soft jewelled responsive coat.

"However the fact that his jewels ceased to be popular with people in general only made him more popular with the connoisseurs who distrust popular success. They began to write books about his art; especially those who claimed to know and love the King wrote about him. The books all said much the same thing, and when our hero had read one he had read them all. There was nearly always a chapter called The Toad in the Hole: the Art of Fallen

Man, or else there was one called From Easter Egg to Letters of Marque, the Jeweller of Original Sin."

"Why do you keep on calling him a jeweller?" the voice said from under the sheet. "You know very well he was an architect."

"I warned you not to attach real characters to my story. You'll be identifying yourself with the other Marie next. Although, thank God, you're not the kind to kill yourself."

"You'd be surprised what I could do," she said. "Your story isn't a bit like *Manon Lescaut*, but it's pretty miserable all the same."

"What none of these people knew was that one day our hero had made a startling discovery—he no longer believed all those arguments historical, philosophical, logical, and etymological that he had worked out for the existence of the King. There was left only a memory of the King who had lived in his parents' heart and not in any particular place. Unfortunately his heart was not the same as the one his parents shared: it was calloused with pride and success, and it had learned to beat only with pride when a building . . ."

"You said building."

"When a jewel was completed or when a woman cried under him, '*donne, donne, donne*'." He looked at the whisky in the bottle: it wasn't worth preserving the little that remained; he emptied it into his glass and he didn't bother to add water.

"You know," he said, "he had deceived himself, just as much as he had deceived the others. He had believed quite sincerely that when he loved his work he was loving the King and that when he made love to a woman he was at least imitating in a faulty way the King's love for his people. The King after all had so loved the world that he had sent a bull and a shower of gold and a son . . ."

"You are getting it all confused," the girl said.

"But when he discovered there was no such King as the one he had believed in, he realised too that anything that he had ever done must have been done for love of himself.

How could there be any point any longer in making jewels or making love for his own solitary pleasure? Perhaps he had reached the end of his sex and the end of his vocation before he made his discovery about the King or perhaps that discovery brought about the end of everything? I wouldn't know, but I'm told that there were moments when he wondered if his unbelief were not after all a final and conclusive proof of the King's existence. This total vacancy might be his punishment for the rules he had wilfully broken. It was even possible that this was what people meant by pain. The problem was complicated to the point of absurdity, and he began to envy his parents' simple and uncomplex heart, in which they had always believed that the King lived—and not in the cold palace as big as St. Peter's a hundred miles away."

"So then?"

"I told you, didn't I, that it's just as difficult to leave a profession as to leave a husband. If you left your husband there would be acres and acres of daylight you wouldn't know how to cross, and acres of darkness as well, and of course there would always be telephone calls and the kind enquiries of friends and the chance paragraphs in the newspapers. But that part of the story has no real interest."

"So he took an air-credit card . . ." she said.

The whisky was finished and the equatorial day broke outside the window like something smashed suddenly on the curb of the sky, flowing in a stream of pale green and pale yellow and flamingo pink along the horizon, leaving it afterwards just the plain grey colour of any other Thursday. He said, "I've kept you awake all night."

"I wish you'd told me a romantic story. All the same it took my mind off things." She giggled under the sheet. "I could almost say to him, couldn't I, that we'd spent the night together. Do you think that he'd divorce me? I suppose not. The Church won't allow divorce. The Church says, the Church orders . . ."

"Are you really so unhappy?" He got no reply. To the young sleep comes as quickly as day to the tropical town. He opened the door very quietly and went out into the passage that was still half dark with one all-night globe palely burning. Some late-sleeper or early-riser closed a door five rooms away: a flush choked and swallowed in the silence. He sat on his bed and the light grew around him—it was the hour of coolness. He thought: the King is dead, long live the King. Perhaps he had found here a country and a life.

CHAPTER TWO

I

QUERRY was out early to do as many as he could of the doctor's errands before the day became too hot. There was no sign of Marie Rycker at breakfast, and no sound over the partition of their rooms. At the Cathedral he collected the letters which had been waiting for the next boat—he was glad to find that not one of them was addressed to him. *Toute à toi* had made her one gesture towards his unknown region, and he hoped for her sake that it had been a gesture of duty and convention and not of love, for in that case his silence would do her no further hurt.

By midday he was feeling parched, and finding himself not far from the wharf he went down to the river and up the gang-plank of the Bishop's boat to see whether the captain were on board. He hesitated a moment at the foot of the ladder, surprised by his own action. It was the first time for a long while that he had voluntarily made a move towards companionship. He remembered how fearful he had been when he last set foot on board and the light was burning in the cabin. The crew had piled logs on the pontoons ready for another voyage, and a woman was hanging her washing between the companion-way and the boiler; he called "Captain," as he climbed the ladder, but the priest who sat at the saloon table going through the bills of lading was a stranger to him.

"May I come in?"

"I think I know who you are. You must be M. Querry. Shall we open a bottle of beer?"

Querry asked after the former captain. "He has been

sent to teach moral theology," his successor said, "at Wakanga."

"Was he sorry to go?"

"He was delighted. The river-life did not appeal to him."

"To you it does?"

"I don't know yet. This is my first voyage. It is a change from canon law. We start tomorrow."

"To the leproserie?"

"We shall end there. A week. Ten days. I'm not sure yet about the cargo."

Querry when he left the boat felt that he had aroused no curiosity. The captain had not even asked him about the new hospital. Perhaps *Paris-Dimanche* had done its worst; there was nothing more that Rycker or Parkinson could inflict on him. It was as though he were on the verge of acceptance into a new country; like a refugee he watched the consul lift his pen to fill in the final details of his visa. But the refugee remains apprehensive to the last; he has had too many experiences of the sudden afterthought, the fresh question of requirement, the strange official who comes into the room carrying another file. A man was in the hotel-bar, drinking below the man in the moon and the chains of mauve paper; it was Parkinson.

Parkinson raised a glass of pink gin and said, "Have one on me."

"I thought you had gone away, Parkinson."

"Only as far as Stanleyville for the riots. Now I've filed my story and I'm a free man again until something turns up. What's yours?"

"How long are you staying here?"

"Until I get a cable from home. Your story has gone over well. They may want a third instalment."

"You didn't use what I gave you."

"It wasn't family reading."

"You can get no more from me."

"You'd be surprised," Parkinson said, "what sometimes comes one's way by pure good luck." He chinked the ice against the side of his glass. "Quite a success that first article had. Full syndication, even the Antipodes—except of course behind the curtain. The Americans are lapping it up. Religion and an anti-colonialist angle—you couldn't have a better mixture for them. There's just one thing I do rather regret—you never took that photograph of me carried ashore with fever. I had to make do with a photograph which Mme. Rycker took. But now I've got a fine one of myself in Stanleyville, beside a burnt-out car. Wasn't it you who contradicted me about Stanley? He must have been there or they wouldn't have called the place after him. Where are you going?"

"To my room."

"Oh yes, you are number six, aren't you, in my corridor?"

"Number seven."

Parkinson stirred the ice round with his finger. "Oh, I see. Number seven. You aren't vexed with me, are you? I assure you those angry words the other day, they didn't mean a thing. It was just a way to get you talking. A man like me can't afford to be angry. The darts the picador sticks into the bull are not the real thing."

"What is?"

"The next instalment. Wait till you read it."

"I hardly expect to find the moment of truth.

"*Touché*," Parkinson said. "It's a funny thing about metaphors—they never really follow through. Perhaps you won't believe me, but there was a time when I was interested in style." He looked into his glass of gin as though into a well. "What the hell of a long life it is, isn't it?"

"The other day you seemed afraid to lose it."

"It's all I've got," Parkinson said.

The door opened from the blinding street and Marie Rycker walked in. Parkinson said in a jovial voice, "Well, fancy, look who's here."

"I gave Mme. Rycker a lift from the plantation."

"Another gin," Parkinson said to the barman.

"I do not drink gin," Marie Rycker told him in her stilted phrase-book English.

184

"What *do* you drink? Now that I come to think of it, I don't remember ever seeing you with a glass in your hand all the time I stayed with you. Have an *orange pressée*, my child?"

"I am very fond of whisky," Marie Rycker said with pride.

"Good for you. You are growing up fast." He went down the length of the bar to give the order and on his way he made a little jump, agile in so fat a man, and set the paper-chains rocking with the palm of his hand.

"Any news?" Querry asked.

"He can't tell me—not until the day-after-tomorrow. He thinks . . ."

"Yes."

"He thinks I'm caught," she said gloomily and then Parkinson was back beside them holding the glass. He said, "I heard your old man had the fever."

"Yes."

"Don't I know what it feels like!" Parkinson said. "He's lucky to have a young wife to look after him."

"He does not need me for a nurse."

"Are you staying here long?"

"I do not know. Two days perhaps."

"Time for a meal with me then?"

"Oh no. No time for that," she said without hesitation.

He grinned without mirth. "*Touché* again."

When she had drained her whisky she said to Querry, "We're lunching together, aren't we, you and I? Give me just a minute for a wash. I'll fetch my key."

"Allow *me*," Parkinson said, and before she had time to protest, he was already back at the bar, swinging her key on his little finger. "Number six," he said, "so we are all three on the same floor."

Querry said, "I'll come up with you."

She looked into her room and came quickly back to his. She asked, "Can I come in? You can't think how squalid it is in mine. I got up too late and they haven't made the bed." She wiped her face with his towel, then looked ruefully at the marks which her powder had left. "I'm sorry. What a mess I've made. I didn't mean to."

"It doesn't matter."

"Women are disgusting, aren't they?"

"In a long life I haven't found them so."

"See what I've landed you with now. Twenty-four more hours in a hole like this."

"Can't the doctor write to you about the result?"

"I can't go back until I know. Don't you see how impossible that would be? If the answer's yes, I've got to tell him right away. It was my only excuse for coming anyway."

"And if the answer's no?"

"I'll be so happy then I won't care about anything. Perhaps I won't even go back." She asked him, "What *is* a rabbit test?"

"I don't know exactly. I believe they take your urine, and cut the rabbit open . . ."

"Do they do *that*?" she asked with horror.

"They sew the rabbit up again. I think it survives for another test."

"I wonder why we all have to know the worst so quickly. At a poor beast's expense."

"Haven't you any wish at all for a child?"

"For a young Rycker? No." She took the comb out of his brush and without examining it pushed it through her hair. "I didn't trap you into lunch, did I? You weren't eating with anyone else?"

"No."

"It's just that I can't stand that man out there."

But it was impossible to get far away from him in Luc. There were only two restaurants in the town and they chose the same one. The three of them were the only people there; he watched them between bites from his table by the door. He had slung his Rolleiflex on the chair-back beside him much as civilians slung their revolvers in these uncertain days. At least you could say of him that he went hunting with a camera only.

Marie Rycker gave herself a second helping of potatoes.

"Don't tell me," she said, "that I'm eating enough for two."

"I won't."

"It's the stock *colon* joke, you know, for someone with worms."

"How is your stomach-ache?"

"Alas, it's gone. The doctor seemed to think that it had no connection."

"Hadn't you better telephone to your husband? Surely he'll be anxious if you don't come back today."

"The lines are probably down. They usually are."

"There hasn't been a storm."

"The Africans are always stealing the wire."

She finished off a horrible mauve dessert before she spoke again. "I expect you are right. I'll telephone," and she left him alone with his coffee. His cup and Parkinson's clinked in unison over the empty tables.

Parkinson called across, "The mail's not in. I've been expecting a copy of my second article. I'll drop it in your room if it comes. Let me see. Is it six or seven? It wouldn't do to get the wrong room, would it?"

"You needn't bother."

"You owe me a photograph. Perhaps you and Mme. Rycker would oblige."

"You'll get no photograph from me, Parkinson."

Querry paid the bill and went to find the telephone. It stood on a desk where a woman with blue hair and blue spectacles was writing her accounts with an orange pen. "It's ringing," Marie Rycker said, "but he doesn't answer."

"I hope his fever's not worse."

"He's probably gone across to the factory." She put the telephone down and said, "I've done my best, haven't I?"

"You could try again this evening before we have dinner."

"You *are* stuck with me, aren't you?"

"No more than you with me."

"Have you any more stories to tell?"

"No. I only know the one."

She said, "It's an awful time till tomorrow. I don't know what to do until I know."

"Lie down awhile."

"I can't. Would it be very stupid if I went to the cathedral and prayed?"

"Nothing is stupid that makes the time pass."

"But if the thing is here," she said, "inside me, it couldn't suddenly disappear, could it, if I prayed?"

"I wouldn't think so." He said reluctantly, "Even the priests don't ask you to believe that. They would tell you, I suppose, to pray that God's will be done. But don't expect me to talk to you about prayer."

"I'd want to know what his will was before I prayed anything like that," she said. "All the same, I think I'll go and pray. I could pray to be happy, couldn't I?"

"I suppose so."

"That would cover almost everything."

2

Querry too found the hours hanging heavily. Again he walked down to the river. Work had stopped upon the Bishop's boat, and there was no one on board. In the little square the shops were shuttered. It seemed as though all the world were asleep except himself and the girl who, he supposed, was still praying. But when he returned to the hotel he found that Parkinson at least was awake. He stood under the mauve-and-pink streamers, with his eyes upon the door. After Querry had crossed the threshold, he came tiptoeing forward and said with sly urgent importance, "I must have a word with you quietly before you go to your room."

"What about?"

"The general situation," Parkinson said. "Storm over Luc. Do you know who's up there?"

"Up where?"

"On the first floor."

"You seem very anxious to tell me. Go ahead."

"The husband," Parkinson said heavily.

"What husband?"

"Rycker. He's looking for his wife."

"I think he'll find her in the Cathedral."

"It's not as simple as all that. He knows you're with her."

"Of course he does. I was at his house yesterday."

"All the same I don't think he expected to find you here in adjoining rooms."

"You think like a gossip-writer," Querry said. "What difference does it make whether rooms adjoin? You can sleep together from opposite ends of a passage just as easily."

"Don't underrate the gossip-writers. They write history. From Fair Rosamund to Eva Braun."

"I don't think history will be much concerned with the Ryckers." He went to the desk and said, "My bill, please. I'm leaving now."

"Running away?" Parkinson asked.

"Why running away? I was only staying here to give her a lift back. Now I can leave her with her husband. She's his responsibility."

"You *are* a cold-blooded devil," Parkinson said. "I begin to believe some of the things you told me."

"Print them instead of your pious rubbish. It might be interesting to tell the truth for once."

"But which truth? You aren't as simple-minded as you make out, Querry, and there weren't any lies of fact in what I wrote. Leaving out Stanley, of course."

"And your *pirogue* and your faithful servants."

"Anyway, what I wrote about *you* was true."

"No."

"You have buried yourself here, haven't you? You are working for the lepers. You did pursue that man into the forest . . . It all adds up, you know, to what people like to call goodness."

"I know my own motives."

"Do you? And did the saints? What about 'most miserable sinner' and all that crap?"

"You talk—almost—as Father Thomas does. Not quite, of course."

189

"History's just as likely to take my interpretation as your own. I told you I was going to build you up, Querry. Unless, of course, as now seems likely, I find it makes a better story if I pull you down."

"Do you really believe you have all that power?"

"Montagu Parkinson has a very wide syndication."

The woman with blue hair said, "Your bill, M. Querry," and he turned to pay. "Isn't it worth your while," Parkinson said, "to ask me a favour?"

"I don't understand."

"I've been threatened often in my time. I've had my camera smashed twice. I've spent a night in a police-cell. Three times in a restaurant somebody hit me." For a moment he sounded like St. Paul: 'Three times I was beaten with rods, once I was stoned: I have been ship-wrecked three times . . .' He said, "The strange thing is that no one has ever appealed to my better nature. It might work. It's probably there, you know, some-where . . ." It was like a genuine grief.

Querry said gently, "Perhaps I would, Parkinson, if I cared at all."

Parkinson said, "I can't bear that damned indifference of yours. Do you know what he found up there? But you wouldn't ask a journalist for information, would you? There's a towel in your room. I showed it him myself. And a comb with long hair in it." The misery of being Parkinson for a moment looked out of his wounded eyes. He said, "I'm disappointed in you, Querry. I'd begun to believe my own story about you."

"I'm sorry," Querry said.

"A man's got to believe a bit or contract out altogether."

Somebody stumbled at the turn of the stairs. It was Rycker coming down. He had a book of some kind in his hand in a pulpy scarlet cover. The fingers on the rail shook as he came, from the remains of fever or from nerves. He stopped and the fat-boy mask of the man in the moon grinned at him from a neighbouring light-bracket. He said, "Querry."

"Hello, Rycker, are you feeling better?"

"I can't understand it," Rycker said. "You of all men in the world . . ." He seemed to be searching desperately for clichés, the clichés from the *Marie-Chantal* serials rather than the clichés he was accustomed to from his reading in theology. "I thought you were my friend, Querry."

The orange pen was suspiciously busy behind the desk and the blue head was unconvincingly bent. "I don't know what you are talking about, Rycker," Querry said. "You'd better come into the bar. We'll be more alone there." Parkinson prepared to follow them, but Querry blocked the door. He said, "No, Parkinson, there isn't a story for the *Post*."

"I have nothing to hide from Mr. Parkinson," Rycker said in English.

"As you wish." The heat of the afternoon had driven away even the barman. The paper streamers hung down like old man's beard. Querry said, "Your wife tried to telephone to you at lunch-time, but there was no reply."

"What do you suppose? I was on the road by six this morning."

"I'm glad you've come. I shall be able to leave now."

Rycker said, "It's no good denying anything, Querry, anything at all. I've been to my wife's room, number six, and you've got the key of number seven in your pocket."

"You needn't jump to stupid conclusions, Rycker. Even about towels and combs. What if she did wash in my room this morning? As for rooms they were the only ones prepared when we arrived."

"Why did you take her away without so much as a word . . . ?"

"I meant to tell you, but you and I talked about other things." He looked at Parkinson leaning on the bar. He was watching their mouths closely as though in that way he might come to understand the language they were using.

"She went and left me ill with a high fever . . ."

"You had your boy. There were things she had to do in town."

"What things?"

"I think that's for her to tell you, Rycker. A woman can have her secrets."

"You seem to share them all right. Hasn't a husband got the right . . . ?"

"You are too fond of talking about rights, Rycker. She has her rights too. But I'm not going to stand and argue . . ."

"Where are you going?"

"To find my boy. I want to start for home. We can do nearly four hours before dark."

"I've got a lot more to talk to you about."

"What? The love of God?"

"No," Rycker said, "about this." He held the book open at a page headed with a date. Querry saw that it was a diary with ruled lines and between them the kind of careful script girls learn to write at school. "Go on," Rycker said, "read it."

"I don't read other people's diaries."

"Then I'll read it to you. 'Spent night with Q'."

Querry smiled. He said, "It's true—in a way. We sat drinking whisky and I told her a long story."

"I don't believe a word you're saying."

"You deserve to be a cuckold, Rycker, but I never went in for seducing children."

"I can imagine what the Courts would say to this."

"Be careful, Rycker. Don't threaten me. I might change my mind."

"I could make you pay," Rycker said, "pay heavily."

"I doubt whether any court in the world would take your word against hers and mine. Goodbye, Rycker."

"You can't walk out of here as though nothing had happened."

"I would have liked to leave you in suspense, but it wouldn't be fair to her. Nothing has happened, Rycker. I haven't even kissed your wife. She doesn't attract me in that way."

"What right have you to despise us as you do?"

"Be a sensible man. Put that diary back where you found it and say nothing."

" 'Spent the night with Q' and say nothing?"

Querry turned to Parkinson. "Give your friend a drink and talk some sense into him. You owe him an article."

"A duel would make a good story," Parkinson said wistfully.

"It's lucky for her I'm not a violent man," Rycker said. "A good thrashing . . ."

"Is that a part of Christian marriage, too?"

He felt an extraordinary weariness; he had lived a lifetime in the middle of some such scene as this, he had been born to such voices, and if he were not careful, he would die with them in his ears. He walked out on the two of them, paying no attention at all to the near scream of Rycker, "I've got a right to demand . . ." In the cabin of the truck sitting beside Deo Gratias he was at peace again. He said, "You've never been back, have you, into the forest, and I know you'll never take me there . . . All the same, I wish . . . Is Pendélé very far away?"

Deo Gratias sat with his head down, saying nothing.

"Never mind."

Outside the Cathedral Querry stopped the truck and got out. It would be wiser to warn her. The doors were open for ventilation, and the hideous windows through which the hard light glared in red and blue made the sun more clamorous than outside. The boots of a priest going to the sacristy squealed on the tiled floor, and a mammy chinked her beads. It was not a church for meditation; it was as hot and public as a market-place, and in the side-chapels stood plaster stallholders, offering a baby or a bleeding heart. Marie Rycker was sitting under a statue of Ste. Thérèse of Lisieux. It seemed a less than suitable choice. The two had nothing in common but youth.

He asked her, "Still praying?"

"Not really. I didn't hear you come."

"Your husband's at the hotel."

"Oh," she said flatly, looking up at the saint who had disappointed her.

"He's been reading a diary you left in your room. You oughtn't to have written what you did—'Spent the night with Q'."

"It was true, wasn't it? Besides I put in an exclamation mark to show."

"Show what?"

"That it wasn't serious. The nuns never minded if you put an exclamation mark. 'Mother Superior in a tearing rage!' They always called it the 'exaggeration mark'."

"I don't think your husband knows the convent code."

"So he really believes . . . ?" she asked and giggled.

"I've tried to persuade him otherwise."

"It seems such a waste, doesn't it, if he believes that. We might just as well have really done it. Where are you going now?"

"I'm driving home."

"I'd come with you if you liked. Only I know you don't like."

He looked up at the plaster face with its simpering and holy smile. "What would she say?"

"I don't consult her about everything. Only *in extremis*. Though this is pretty *extremis* now, I suppose, isn't it? What with this and that. Have I got to tell him about the baby?"

"It would be better to tell him before he finds out."

"And I prayed to her so hard for happiness," she said disdainfully. "What a hope. Do you believe in prayer at all?"

"No."

"Did you never?"

"I suppose I believed once. When I believed in giants." He looked around the church, at the altar, the tabernacle, the brass candles, and the European saints, pale like albinos in the dark continent. He could detect in himself a dim nostalgia for the past, but everyone always felt that, he supposed, in middle age, even for a past of pain, when pain was associated with youth. If there were a place called Pendélé, he thought, I would never bother to find my way back.

"You think I've been wasting my time, don't you, praying?"

"It was better than lying on your bed brooding."

"You don't believe in prayer at all—or in God?"

"No." He said gently, "Of course, I may be wrong."

"And Rycker does," she said, calling him by his sur-name as though he were no longer her husband. "I wish it wasn't always the wrong people who believed."

"Surely the nuns . . ."

"Oh, they are professionals. They believe anything. Even the Holy House of Loretto. They ask us to believe too much and then we believe less and less." Perhaps she was talking in order to postpone the moment of return. She said, "Once I got into trouble drawing a picture of the Holy House in full flight with jet-engines. How much did you believe—when you believed?"

"I suppose, like the boy in the story I told you, I persuaded myself to believe almost everything with arguments. You can brainwash yourself into anything you want—even into marriage or a vocation. Then the years pass and the marriage or the vocation fails and its better to get out. It's the same with belief. People hang on to a marriage for fear of a lonely old age or to a vocation for fear of poverty. It's not a good reason. And it's not a good reason to hang on to the Church for the sake of some mumbo-jumbo when you come to die."

"And what about the mumbo-jumbo of birth?" she asked. "If there's a baby inside me now, I'll have to have it christened, won't I? I'm not sure that I'd be happy if it wasn't. Is that dishonest? If only it hadn't *him* for a father."

"Of course it isn't dishonest. You mustn't think your marriage has failed yet."

"Oh but it has."

"I didn't mean with Rycker, I meant . . ." He said sharply. "For God's sake, don't start taking me for an example, too."

CHAPTER THREE

I

THE rather sweet champagne was the best that Querry had been able to find in Luc, and it had not been improved by the three-day drive in the truck and a breakdown at the first ferry. The nuns provided tinned pea-soup, four lean roast chickens, and an ambiguous sweet omelette which they had made with guava jelly: the omelette had sat down halfway between their house and the fathers'. But on this day, when the ceremony of raising the roof-tree was over at last, no one felt in a mood to criticise. An awning had been set up outside the dispensary, and at long trestle tables the priests and nuns had provided a feast for the lepers who had worked on the hospital and their families, official and unofficial; beer was there for the men and fizzy fruit drinks and buns for the women and children. The nuns' own celebration had been prepared in strict privacy, but it was rumoured to consist mainly of extra strong coffee and some boxes of *petits fours* that had been kept in reserve since the previous Christmas and had probably turned musty in the interval.

Before the feast there was a service. Father Thomas trapesed round the new hospital, supported by Father Joseph and Father Paul, sprinkling the walls with holy water, and several hymns were sung in the Mongo language. There had been prayers and a sermon from Father Thomas which went on far too long—he had not yet learned enough of the native tongue to make himself properly understood. Some of the younger lepers grew impatient and wandered away, and a child was found by Brother Philippe arrosing the new walls with his own form of water.

Nobody cared that a small dissident group who had nothing to do with the local tribe sang their own hymns apart. Only the doctor, who had once worked in the Lower Congo, recognised them for what they were, trouble-makers from the coast more than a thousand kilometres away. It was unlikely that any of the lepers could understand them, so he let them be. The only sign of their long journey by path and water and road was an unfamiliar stack of bicycles up a sidepath into the bush which he had happened to take that morning.

"*E ku Kinshasa ka bazeyi ko:*
E ku Luozi ka bazeyi ko. . . ."
"In Kinshasa they know nothing:
In Luozi they know nothing."
The proud song of superiority went on: superiority to their own people, to the white man, to the Christian god, to everyone beyond their own circle of six, all of them wearing the peaked caps that advertised Polo beer.
"In the Upper Congo they know nothing:
In heaven they know nothing:
Those who revile the Spirit know nothing:
The Chiefs know nothing:
The whites know nothing."
Nzambe had never been humiliated as a criminal: he was an exclusive god. Only Deo Gratias moved some way towards them; he squatted on the ground between them and the hospital, and the doctor remembered that as a child he had come west from the Lower Congo too.
"Is that the future?" Querry said. He couldn't understand the words, only the aggressive slant of the Polo-beer caps.
"Yes."
"Do you fear it?"
"Of course. But I don't want my own liberty at the expense of anyone else."
"They do."
"We taught them."
What with one delay and another it was nearly sunset before the tree was raised on to the roof and the feast

197

began. By that time the awning outside the dispensary was no longer needed to shelter the workmen from the heat, but judging from the black clouds massing beyond the river, Father Joseph decided that it might yet serve to protect them from the rain.

Father Thomas's decision to raise the roof-tree had not been made without argument. Father Joseph wished to wait a month in the hope that the Superior would return, and Father Paul had at first supported him, but when Doctor Colin agreed with Father Thomas they had withdrawn their opposition. "Let Father Thomas have his feast and his hymns," the doctor said to them. "I want the hospital."

Doctor Colin and Querry left the group from the east and turned back to the last of the ceremony. "We were right, but all the same," the doctor said, "I wish the Superior were here. He would have enjoyed the show and at least he would have talked to these people in a language they can understand."

"More briefly too," Querry said. The hollow African voices rose around them in another hymn.

"And yet you stay and watch," the doctor said.

"Oh yes, I stay."

"I wonder why."

"Ancestral voices. Memories. Did you ever lie awake when you were a child listening to them talking down below? You couldn't understand what they were saying, but it was a noise that somehow comforted. So it is now with me. I am happy listening, saying nothing. The house is not on fire, there's no burglar lurking in the next room: I don't want to understand or believe. I would have to think if I believed. I don't want to think any more. I can build you all the rabbit-hutches you need without thought."

Afterwards at the mission there was a great deal of raillery over the champagne. Father Paul was caught pouring himself a glass out of turn; somebody—Brother Philippe seemed an unlikely culprit—filled an empty bottle with soda-water, and the bottle had circulated half around the table before anyone noticed. Querry remembered an occasion months ago: a night at a seminary on the river when the priests cheated over their cards. He had walked out into the bush unable to bear their laughter and their infantility. How was it that he could sit here now and smile with them? He even found himself resenting the strict face of Father Thomas who sat at the end of the table unamused.

The doctor proposed the toast of Father Joseph and Father Joseph proposed the toast of the doctor. Father Paul proposed the toast of Brother Philippe, and Brother Philippe lapsed into confusion and silence. Father Jean proposed the toast of Father Thomas who did not respond. The champagne had almost reached an end, but someone disinterred from the back of the cupboard a half-finished bottle of Sandeman's port and they drank it out of liqueur glasses to make it go further. "After all the English drink port at the end of a meal," Father Jean said. "An extraordinary custom. Protestant perhaps, but nevertheless . . ."

"Are you sure there's nothing against it in moral theology?" Father Paul asked.

"Only in canon law. *Lex contra Sandemanium*, but even that, of course, was interpreted by that eminent Benedictine, Dom . . ."

"Father Thomas, won't you have a glass of port?"

"No thank you, father. I have drunk enough."

The darkness outside the open door suddenly drew back and for a moment they could see the palm trees bending in a strange yellow light the colour of old photographs. Then everything went dark again, and the wind blew in, rustling the pages of Father Jean's film magazines. Querry got up to close it against the coming storm, but on a second thought he stepped outside and shut it behind him. The northern sky lightened again, in a long band above the river. From where the lepers were celebrating came the sound of drums and the thunder answered like the reply of a relieving force. Somebody moved on the verandah. When the lightning flashed he saw that it was Deo Gratias.

"Why aren't you at the feast, Deo Gratias?" Then he remembered that the feast was only for the non-mutilated, for the masons and carpenters and bricklayers. He said, "Well, they've done a good job on the hospital." The man made no reply. Querry said, "You aren't planning to run away again, are you?" and he lit a cigarette and put it between the man's lips.

"No," Deo Gratias said.

In the darkness Querry felt himself prodded by the man's stump. He said, "What's troubling you, Deo Gratias?"

"You will go," Deo Gratias said, "now that the hospital is built."

"Oh no, I won't. This is where I'm going to end my days. I can't go back where I came from, Deo Gratias. I don't belong there any more."

"Have you killed a man?"

"I have killed everything." The thunder came nearer, and then the rain: first it was like skirmishers rustling furtively among the palm tree fans, creeping through the grass; then it was the confident tread of a great watery host beating a way from across the river to sweep up the verandah steps. The drums of the lepers were extinguished like flames; even the thunder could be heard only faintly behind the great charge of rain.

Deo Gratias hobbled closer. "I want to go with you," he said.

"I tell you I'm staying here. Why won't you believe me? For the rest of my life. I shall be buried here."

Perhaps he had not made himself heard through the rain, for Deo Gratias repeated, "I will go with you." Somewhere a telephone began to ring—a trivial human sound persisting like an infant's cry through the rain.

2

After Querry had left the room Father Thomas said, "We seem to have toasted everyone except the man to whom we owe most."

Father Joseph said, "He knows well enough how grateful we are. Those toasts were not very seriously meant, Father Thomas."

"I think I ought to express the gratitude of the community, formally, when he comes back."

"You'll only embarrass him," Doctor Colin said. "All he wants of any of us is to be left alone." The rain pounded on the roof; Brother Philippe began to light candles on the dresser in case the electric current failed.

"It was a happy day for all of us when he arrived here," Father Thomas said. "Who could have foreseen it? The great Querry."

"An even happier day for him," the doctor replied. "It's much more difficult to cure the mind than the body, and yet I think the cure is nearly complete."

"The better the man the worse the aridity," Father Thomas said.

Father Joseph looked guiltily at his champagne and then at his companions; Father Thomas made them all feel as though they were drinking in church. "A man with little faith doesn't feel the temporary loss of it." His sentiments were impeccable. Father Paul winked at Father Jean.

"Surely," the doctor said, "you assume too much. His case may be much simpler than that. A man can believe for half his life on insufficient reason, and then he discovers his mistake."

"You talk, doctor, like all atheists, as though there were no such thing as grace. Belief without grace is unthinkable, and God will never rob a man of grace. Only a man himself can do that—by his own actions. We have seen Querry's actions here, and they speak for themselves."

"I hope you won't be disappointed," the doctor said. "In our treatment we get burnt-out cases, too. But we don't say they are suffering from aridity. We only say the disease has run its course."

"You are a very good doctor, but all the same I think we are better judges of a man's spiritual condition."

"I dare say you are—if such a thing exists."

"You can detect a patch on the skin where we see nothing at all. You must allow us to have a nose for— well . . ." Father Thomas hesitated and then said ". . . heroic virtue." Their voices were raised a little against the storm. The telephone began to ring.

Doctor Colin said, "That's probably the hospital. I'm expecting a death tonight." He went to the sideboard where the telephone stood and lifted the receiver. He said, "Who is it? Is that Sister Clare?" He said to Father Thomas, "It must be one of your sisters. Will you take it? I can't hear what she is saying."

"Perhaps they have got at our champagne," Father Joseph said.

Doctor Colin surrendered the receiver to Father Thomas and came back to the table. "She sounded agitated, whoever she was," he said.

"Please speak more slowly," Father Thomas said. "Who is it? Sister Hélène? I can't hear you—the storm is too loud. Say that again. I don't understand."

"It's lucky for us all," Father Joseph said, "that the sisters don't have a feast every day of the week."

Father Thomas turned furiously from the telephone. He said, "Be quiet, father. I can't hear if you talk. This is no joke. A terrible thing seems to have happened."

"Is somebody ill?" the doctor asked.

"Tell Mother Agnes," Father Thomas said, "that I'll be over as soon as I can. I had better find him and bring him with me." He put the receiver down and stood bent like a question-mark over the telephone.

"What is it, father?" the doctor said. "Can I be of use?"

"Does anyone know where Querry's gone?"

"He went outside a few minutes ago."

"How I wish the Superior were here." They looked at Father Thomas with astonishment. He could not have given a more extreme signal of distress.

"You had better tell us what it's all about," Father Paul said.

Father Thomas said, "I envy you your skin-test, doctor.

202

You were right to warn me against disappointment. The Superior too. He said much the same thing as you. I have trusted too much to appearances."

"Has Querry done something?"

"God forbid one should condemn any man without hearing all the facts . . ."

The door opened and Querry entered. The rain splashed in behind him and he had to struggle with the door. He said, "The gauge outside shows nearly half a centimetre already."

Nobody spoke. Father Thomas came a little way towards him.

"M. Querry, is it true that when you went into Luc you went with Mme. Rycker?"

"I drove her in. Yes."

"Using *our* truck?"

"Of course."

"While her husband was sick?"

"Yes."

"What is this all about?" Father Joseph asked.

"Ask M. Querry," Father Thomas replied.

"Ask me what?"

Father Thomas drew on his rubber boots and fetched his umbrella from the coat-rack.

"What am I supposed to have done?" Querry said and he looked first to Father Joseph and then to Father Paul. Father Paul made a gesture with his hand of non-comprehension.

"You had better tell us what is going on, father," Doctor Colin said.

"I must ask you to come with me, M. Querry. We will discuss what has to be done next with the sisters. I had hoped against hope that there was some mistake. I even wish you had tried to lie. It would have been less brazen. I don't want you found here by Rycker if he should arrive."

"What would Rycker want here?" Father Jean said.

"He might be expected to want his wife, mightn't he? She's with the sisters now. She arrived half an hour ago.

203

After three days by herself on the road. She is with child," Father Thomas said. The telephone began to ring again. "Your child."

Querry said, "That's nonsense. She can't have told anyone that."

"Poor girl. I suppose she hadn't the nerve to tell him to his face. She came from Luc to find you."

The telephone rang again.

"It seems to be my turn to answer it," Father Joseph said, approaching the telephone with trepidation.

"We gave you a warm welcome here, didn't we? We asked you no questions. We didn't pry into your past. And in return you present us with this—scandal. Weren't there enough women for you in Europe?" Father Thomas said. "Did you have to make our little community here a base for your operations?" Suddenly he was again the nervy and despairing priest who couldn't sleep and was afraid of the dark. He began to weep, clinging to his umbrella as an African might cling to a totem-pole. He looked as though he had been left out all night like a scarecrow.

"Hullo, hullo," Father Joseph called into the telephone. "In the name of all the known saints, can't you speak up, whoever you are?"

"I'll go and see her with you right away," Querry said.

"It's your right," Father Thomas said. "She's in no condition to argue, though. She's had nothing but a packet of chocolate to eat the last three days. She hadn't even a boy with her when she arrived. If only the Superior . . . Mme. Rycker of all people. Such kindness to the mission. For God's sake, what is it now, Father Joseph?"

"It's only the hospital," Father Joseph said with relief. He gave the receiver to Doctor Colin. "It is the death I was expecting," the doctor said. "Thank goodness something tonight seems to be following a normal course."

Father Thomas walked silently ahead below his great umbrella. The rain had stopped for a while, but the aftermath dripped from the ribs. Father Thomas was only visible at intervals when the lightning flared. He had no torch, but he knew the path by heart in the dark. Many omelettes and soufflés had come to grief along this track, eggs broken in vain. The nuns' white house was suddenly close to them in a simultaneous flash and roar—the lightning had struck a tree somewhere close by and all the lights of the mission fused at once.

One of the sisters met them at the door carrying a candle. She looked at Querry over Father Thomas's shoulder as though he were the devil himself—with fear, distaste, and curiosity. She said, "Mother's sitting with Mme. Rycker."

"We'll go in," Father Thomas said gloomily.

She led them to a white-painted room, where Marie Rycker lay in a white-painted bed under a crucifix, with a night-light burning beside her. Mother Agnes sat by the bed with a hand touching Marie Rycker's cheek. Querry had the impression of a daughter who had come safely home, after a long visit to a foreign land.

Father Thomas said in an altar-whisper, "How is she?"

"She's taken no harm," Mother Agnes said, "not in the body, that is."

Marie Rycker turned in the bed and looked up at them. Her eyes had the transparent honesty of a child who has prepared a cast-iron lie. She smiled at Querry and said, "I am sorry. I had to come. I was scared."

Mother Agnes withdrew her hand and watched Querry closely as though she feared a violent act against her charge.

Querry said gently, "You mustn't be frightened. It was the long journey which scared you—that's all. Now you are safe among friends you will explain, won't you . . ." He hesitated.

"Oh yes," she whispered, "everything."

"They haven't understood what you told them. About our visit to Luc together. And the baby. There's going to be a baby?"

"Yes."

"Just tell them whose baby it is."

"I have told them," she said. "It's yours. Mine, too, of course," she added, as though by adding that qualification she were making everything quite clear and beyond blame.

Father Thomas said, "You see."

"Why are you telling them that? You know it's not true. We have never been in each other's company except in Luc."

"That first time," she said, "when my husband brought you to the house."

It would have been easier if he had felt anger, but he felt none: to lie is as natural at a certain age as to play with fire. He said, "You know what you are saying is all nonsense. I'm certain you don't want to do me any harm.'

"Oh no," she said, "never. *Je t'aime, chéri. Je suis toute à toi.*"

Mother Agnes wrinkled her nose with distaste.

"That's why I've come to you," Marie Rycker said.

"She ought to rest now," Mother Agnes said. "All this can be discussed in the morning."

"You must let me talk to her alone."

"Certainly not," Mother Agnes said. "That would not be right. Father Thomas, you won't permit him . . ."

"My good woman, do you think I'm going to beat her? You can come to her rescue at her first scream."

Father Thomas said, "We can hardly say no if Mme. Rycker wishes it."

"Of course I wish it," she said. "I came here only for that." She put her hand on Querry's sleeve. Her smile of sad and fallen trust was worthy of Bernhardt's Marguerite Gauthier on her death bed.

When they were alone she gave a happy sigh. "That's that."

"Why have you told them these lies?"

"They aren't all lies," she said. "I do love you."

"Since when?"

"Since I spent a night with you."

"You know very well that was nothing at all. We drank some whisky. I told you a story to send you to sleep."

"Yes. Once upon a time. That was when I fell in love. No, it wasn't. I'm afraid I'm lying again," she said with unconvincing humility. "It was when you came to the house the first time. *Un coup de foudre.*"

"The night you told them we slept together?"

"That was really a lie too. The night I slept with you properly was after the Governor's party."

"What on earth are you talking about now?"

"I didn't want him. The only way I could manage was to shut my eyes and think it was you."

"I suppose I ought to thank you," Querry said, "for the compliment."

"It was then that the baby must have started. So you see it wasn't a lie that I told them."

"Not a lie?"

"Only half a lie. If I hadn't thought all the time of you, I'd have been all dried up and babies don't come so easily then, do they? So in a way it is your child."

He looked at her with a kind of respect. It would have needed a theologian to appreciate properly the tortuous logic of her argument, to separate good from bad faith, and only recently he had thought of her as someone too simple and young to be a danger. She smiled up at him winningly, as though she hoped to entice him into yet another of his stories to postpone the hour of bed. He said, "You'd better tell me exactly what happened when you saw your husband in Luc."

She said, "It was ghastly. Really ghastly. I thought once he was going to kill me. He wouldn't believe about the diary. He went on and on all that night until I was tired out and I said, 'All right. Have it your own way then. I did sleep with him. Here and there and everywhere.' Then he hit me. He would have hit me again, I think, if M. Parkinson hadn't interfered."

"Was Parkinson there too, then?"

"He heard me cry and came along."

"To take some photographs, I suppose."

"I don't think he took any photographs."

"And then what happened?"

"Well, of course, he found out about things in general. You see, he wanted to go home right away, and I said no, I had to stay in Luc until I knew. 'Know?' he said. And then it all came out. I went and saw the doctor in the morning and when I knew the worst I just took off without going back to the hotel."

"Rycker thinks the baby is mine?"

"I tried very hard to convince him it was his—because of course, you could say in a way that it was." She stretched herself down in the bed with a sigh of comfort and said, "Goodness, I'm glad to be here. It was really scary driving all the way alone. I didn't wait in the house to get any food and I forgot a bed and I just slept in the car."

"In his car?"

"Yes. But I expect M. Parkinson will have given him a lift home."

"Is it any use asking you to tell Father Thomas the truth?"

"Well, I've rather burned my boats, haven't I?"

"You've burned the only home I have," Querry said.

"I just had to escape," she exclaimed apologetically. For the first time he was confronted by an egoism as absolute as his own. The other Marie had been properly avenged: as for *toute à toi* the laugh was on her side now.

"What do you expect me to do?" Querry said. "Love you in return?"

"It would be nice if you could, but if you can't, they'll have to send me home, won't they?"

He went to the door and opened it. Mother Agnes was lurking at the end of the passage. He said, "I've done all I can."

208

"I suppose you've tried to persuade the poor girl to protect you."

"Oh, she admits the lie to me, of course, but I have no tape-recorder. What a pity the Church doesn't approve of hidden microphones."

"May I ask you, M. Querry, from now on to stay away from our house?"

"You don't need to ask me that. Be very careful yourselves of that little packet of dynamite in there."

"She's a poor, innocent young . . ."

"Oh, innocent . . . I daresay you are right. God preserve us from all innocence. At least the guilty know what they are about."

The electric fuses had not yet been repaired, and only the feel of the path under his feet guided him towards the mission buildings. The rain had passed to the south, but the lightning flapped occasionally above the forest and the river. Before he reached the mission he had to pass the doctor's house. An oil lamp burned behind the window and the doctor stood beside it, peering out. Querry knocked on the door.

Colin asked, "What has happened?"

"She'll stick to her lies. They are her only way of escape."

"Escape?"

"From Rycker and Africa."

"Father Thomas is talking to the others now. It was no concern of mine, so I came home."

"They want me to go away, I suppose?"

"I wish to God the Superior were here. Father Thomas is not exactly a well-balanced man."

Querry sat down at the table. The Atlas of Leprosy was open at a gaudy page of swirling colour. He said, "What's this?"

"We call these 'the fish swimming upstream'. The bacilli—those coloured spots there—are swarming along the nerves."

"I thought I had come far enough," Querry said, "when I reached this place."

"It may blow over. Let them talk. You and I have more important things to do. Now that the hospital's finished we can get down to the mobile units and the new lavatories I talked to you about."

"We are not dealing with your sick people, doctor, and your coloured fish. They are predictable. These are normal people, healthy people with unforeseeable reactions. It looks as though I shall get no nearer to Pendélé than Deo Gratias did."

"Father Thomas has no authority over me. You can stay in my house from now on if you don't mind sleeping in the workroom."

"Oh no. You can't risk quarrelling with them. You are too important to this place. I shall have to go away."

"Where will you go to?"

"I don't know. It's strange, isn't it, how worried I was when I came here, because I thought I had become incapable of feeling pain. I suppose a priest I met on the river was right. He said one only had to wait. You said the same to me too."

"I'm sorry."

"I don't know that I am. You said once that when one suffers, one begins to feel part of the human condition, on the side of the Christian myth, do you remember? 'I suffer, therefore I am'. I wrote something like that once in my diary, but I can't remember what or when, and the word wasn't 'suffer'."

"When a man is cured," the doctor said, "we can't afford to waste him."

"Cured?"

"No further skin-tests are required in your case."

4

Father Joseph absent-mindedly wiped a knife with the skirt of his soutane; he said, "We mustn't forget that it's only her word against his."

"Why should she invent such a shocking story like

that?" Father Thomas asked. "In any case the baby is presumably real enough."

"Querry has been of great use to us here," Father Paul said. "We've reason to be grateful . . ."

"Grateful? Can you really think that, father, after he's made us a laughing stock? The Hermit of the Congo. The Saint with a Past. All those stories the papers printed. What will they print now?"

"You were more pleased with the stories than he was," Father Jean said.

"Of course I was pleased. I believed in him. I thought his motives for coming here were good. I even defended him to the Superior when he warned me . . . But I hadn't realised then what his true motives were."

"If you know them tell us what they were," Father Jean said. He spoke in the dry precise tones that he was accustomed to use in discussions on moral theology so as to rob of emotion any question dealing with sexual sin.

"I can only suppose he was flying from some woman-trouble in Europe."

"Woman-trouble is not a very exact description, and aren't we all supposed to run away from it? St. Augustine's wish to wait awhile is not universally recommended."

"Querry is a very good builder," Father Joseph said obstinately.

"What do you propose then, that he should stay here in the mission, living in sin with Mme. Rycker?"

"Of course not," Father Jean said. "Mme Rycker must leave tomorrow. From what you have told us he has no wish to go with her."

"The matter will not end there," Father Thomas said. "Rycker will want a separation. He may even sue Querry for divorce, and the newspapers will print the whole edifying story. They are interested enough as it is in Querry. Do you suppose the General will be pleased when he reads at his breakfast-table the scandal at our leproserie?"

"The roof-tree is safely up," Father Joseph said,

rubbing away at his knife, "but a great deal still remains to be done."

"There is no possible harm in simply waiting," Father Paul said. "The girl may be lying. Rycker may take no action. The newspapers may print nothing, it's not the picture of Querry they wanted to give the world. The story may not even reach the General's ears—or eyes."

"Do you suppose the Bishop won't hear of it? It will be all over Luc by this time. In the absence of the Superior I am responsible . . ."

Brother Philippe spoke for the first time. "There's a man outside," he said. "Had I better unlock the door?"

It was Parkinson, sodden and speechless. He had been walking very fast. He ran his hand back and forth over his heart as though he were trying to soothe an animal that he carried like a Spartan under his shirt.

"Give him a chair," Father Thomas said.

"Where's Querry?" Parkinson asked.

"I don't know. In his room perhaps."

"Rycker's looking for him. He went to the sisters' house, but Querry had gone."

"How did you know where to look?"

"She had left a note for Rycker at home. We would have caught her up, but we had car-trouble at the last ferry."

"Where's Rycker now?"

"God knows. It's so pitch-dark out there. He may have walked into the river for all I know."

"Did he see his wife?"

"No—an old nun pushed us both out and locked the door. That made him madder than ever, I can tell you. We haven't had six hours' sleep since Luc, and that was more than three days ago."

He rocked backwards and forwards on the chair. "Oh that this too too solid flesh. Quote. Shakespeare. I've got a weak heart," he explained to Father Thomas who was finding it difficult with his inadequate English to follow the drift of Parkinson's thoughts. The others watched closely and understood little. The situation seemed to all of them to have got hopelessly out of control.

"Please give me a drink," Parkinson said. Father Thomas found that there was a little champagne left at the bottom of one of the many bottles which still littered the table among the carcasses of the chickens and the remains of the mutilated uneaten soufflé.

"Champagne?" Parkinson exclaimed. "I'd rather have had a spot of gin." He looked at the glasses and the bottles: one glass still held an inch of port. He said, "You do yourselves pretty well here."

"It was a very special day," Father Thomas said with some embarrassment, seeing the table for a moment with the eyes of a stranger.

"A special day—I should think it has been. I never thought we'd make the ferry, and now with this storm I suppose we may be stuck here. How I wish I'd never come to this damned dark continent. Quoth the raven never more. Quote. Somebody."

Outside a voice shouted unintelligibly.

"That's him," Parkinson said, "roaming around. He's fighting mad. I said to him I thought Christians were supposed to forgive, but it's no use talking to him now."

The voice came nearer. "Querry," they heard it cry, "Querry. Where are you, Querry?"

"What a damned fuss about nothing. And I wouldn't be surprised if there had been no hanky-panky after all. I told him that. 'They talked all night,' I said, 'I heard them. Lovers don't talk all night. There are intervals of silence'."

"Querry. Where are you, Querry?"

"I think he *wants* to believe the worst. It makes him Querry's equal, don't you see, when they fight over the same girl." He added with a somewhat surprising insight, "He can't bear not being important."

The door opened yet again and a tousled, rain-soaked Rycker stood in the doorway, an over-watered bathroom plant; he looked from one father to another as though among them he expected to find Querry, perhaps in the disguise of a priest.

"M. Rycker," Father Thomas began.

"Where's Querry?"

"Please come in and sit down and talk things . . ."

"How can I sit?" Rycker said. "I am a man in agony." He sat down, nonetheless, on the wrong chair—the weak back splintered. "I'm suffering from a terrible shock, father. I opened my soul to that man, I told him my inmost thoughts, and this is my reward."

"Let us talk quietly and sensibly . . ."

"He laughed at me and despised me," Rycker said. "What right had he to despise me? We are all equal in the sight of God. Even a poor plantation manager and *the* Querry. Breaking up a Christian marriage." He smelt very strongly of whisky. He said, "I'll be retiring in a couple of years. Does he think I'm going to keep his bastard on my pension?"

"You've been on the road for three days, Rycker. You need a night's sleep. Afterwards . . ."

"She never wanted to sleep with me. She always made her excuses, but then the first time he comes along, just because he's famous . . ."

Father Thomas said, "We all want to avoid scandal."

"Where's the doctor?" Rycker said sharply. "They were as thick as thieves."

"He's at home. He has nothing to do with this."

Rycker made for the door. He stood there for a moment as though he were on a stage and had forgotten his exit line. "There isn't a jury that would convict me," he said and went out again into the dark and rain. For a moment nobody spoke and then Father Joseph asked them all, "What did he mean by that?"

"We shall laugh at this in the morning," Father Jean said.

"I don't see the humour of the situation," Father Thomas replied.

"What I mean is it's a little like one of those Palais Royal farces that one has read . . . The injured husband pops in and out."

"I don't read Palais Royal farces, father."

"Sometimes I think God was not entirely serious when he gave man the sexual instinct."

"If that is one of the doctrines you teach in moral theology . . ."

"Nor when he invented moral theology. After all, it was St. Thomas Aquinas who said that he made the world in play."

Brother Philippe said, "Excuse me . . ."

"You are lucky not to have my responsibility, Father Jean. I can't treat the affair as a Palais Royal farce whatever St. Thomas may have written. Where are you going, Brother Philippe?"

"He said something about a jury, father, and it occurred to me that, well, perhaps he's carrying a gun. I think I ought to warn . . ."

"This is too much," Father Thomas said. He turned to Parkinson and asked him in English, "Has he a gun with him?"

"I'm sure I don't know. A lot of people are carrying them nowadays, aren't they? But he wouldn't have the nerve to use it. I told you, he only wants to seem important."

"I think, if you will excuse me, father, I had better go over to Doctor Colin's," Brother Philippe said.

"Be careful, brother," Father Paul said.

"Oh, I know a great deal about firearms," Brother Philippe replied.

5

"Was that someone shouting?" Doctor Colin asked.

"I heard nothing." Querry went to the window and looked into the dark. He said, "I wish Brother Philippe would get the lights back. It's time I went home, and I haven't a torch."

"They won't start the current now. It's gone ten o'clock."

"They'll want me to go as soon as I can, won't they? But the boat's unlikely to be here for at least a week. Perhaps someone can drive me out . . ."

"I doubt if the road will be passable now after the rain, and there's more to come."

"Then we have a few days, haven't we, for talking about those mobile units you dream of. But I'm no engineer, doctor. Brother Philippe will be able to help you more than I could ever do."

"This is a makeshift life we lead here," Doctor Colin said. "All I want is a kind of pre-fab on wheels. Something we can fit onto the chassis of a half-ton truck. What did I do with that sheet of paper? There's an idea I wanted to show you . . ." The doctor opened the drawer in his desk. Inside was the photograph of a woman. She lay there in wait, unseen by strangers, gathering no dust, always present when the drawer opened.

"I shall miss this room—wherever I am. You've never told me about your wife, doctor. How she came to die."

"It was sleeping-sickness. She used to spend a lot of time out in the bush in the early days trying to persuade the lepers to come in for treatment. We didn't have such effective drugs for sleeping-sickness as we have now. People die too soon."

"It was my hope to end up in the same patch of ground as you and she. We would have made an atheist corner between us."

"I wonder if you would have qualified for that."

"Why not?"

"You're too troubled by your lack of faith, Querry. You keep on fingering it like a sore you want to get rid of. I am content with the myth; you are not—you have to believe or disbelieve."

Querry said, "Somebody is calling out there. I thought for a moment it was my name . . . But one always seems to hear one's own name, whatever anyone really calls. It only needs a syllable to be the same. We are such egoists."

"You must have had a lot of belief once to miss it the way you do."

"I swallowed their myth whole, if you call that a belief. This is my body and this is my blood. Now when

216

I read that passage it seems so obviously symbolic, but how can you expect a lot of poor fishermen to recognise symbols? Only in moments of superstition I remember that I gave up the sacrament before I gave up the belief and the priests would say there was a connection. Rejecting grace Rycker would say. Oh well, I suppose belief is a kind of vocation and most men haven't room in their brains or hearts for two vocations. If we really believe in something we have no choice, have we, but to go further. Otherwise life slowly whittles the belief away. My architecture stood still. One can't be a half-believer or a half-architect."

"Are you saying that you've ceased to be even a half?"

"Perhaps I hadn't a strong enough vocation in either, and the kind of life I lived killed them both. It needs a very strong vocation to withstand success. The popular priest and the popular architect—their talents can be killed easily by disgust."

"Disgust?"

"Disgust of praise. How it nauseates, doctor, by its stupidity. The very people who ruined my churches were loudest afterwards in their praise of what I'd built. The books they have written about my work, the pious motives they've attributed to me—they were enough to sicken me of the drawing-board. It needed more faith than I possessed to withstand all that. The praise of priests and pious people—the Ryckers of the world."

"Most men seem to put up with success comfortably enough. But you came here."

"I think I'm cured of pretty well everything, even disgust. I've been happy here."

"Yes, you were learning to use your fingers pretty well, in spite of the mutilation. Only one sore seems to remain, and you rub it all the time."

"You are wrong, doctor. Sometimes you talk like Father Thomas."

"Querry," a voice unmistakably called. "Querry."

"Rycker," Querry said. "He must have followed his

wife here. I hope to God the sisters didn't let him in to see her. I'd better go and talk . . ."

"Let him cool off first."

"I've got to make him see reason."

"Then wait till morning. You can't see reason at night."

"Querry. Querry. Where are you, Querry?"

"What a grotesque situation it is," Querry said. "That this should happen to me. The innocent adulterer. That's not a bad title for a comedy." His mouth moved in the effort of a smile. "Lend me the lamp."

"You'd do much better to keep out of it, Querry."

"I must do something. He's making so much noise . . . It will only add to what Father Thomas calls the scandal."

The doctor reluctantly followed him out. The storm had come full circle and was beating up towards them again, from across the river. "Rycker," Querry called, holding the lamp up, "I'm here." Somebody came running towards them, but when he reached the area of light, they saw that it was Brother Philippe. "Please go back into the house," Brother Philippe said, "and shut the door. We think that Rycker may be carrying a gun."

"He wouldn't be mad enough to use it," Querry said.

"All the same . . . to avoid unpleasantness . . ."

"Unpleasantness . . . you have a wonderful capacity, Brother Philippe, for understatement."

"I don't know what you mean."

"Never mind. I'll take your advice and hide under Doctor Colin's bed."

He had walked a few steps back when Rycker's voice said, "Stop. Stop where you are." The man came unsteadily out of the dark. He said in a tone of trivial complaint, "I've been looking everywhere for you."

"Well, here I am."

All three looked where Rycker's right hand was hidden in his pocket.

"I've got to talk to you, Querry."

"Then talk, and when you've finished, I'd like a word too with you." Silence followed. A dog barked somewhere in the leproserie. Lightning lit them all like a flash-bulb.

"I'm waiting, Rycker."

"You—you renegade."

"Are we here for a religious argument? I'll admit you know much more than I do about the love of God."

Rycker's reply was partly buried under the heavy fall of the thunder. The last sentence stuck out like a pair of legs from beneath the rubble.

". . . persuade me what she wrote meant nothing, and all the time you must have known there was a child coming."

"Your child. Not mine."

"Prove it. You'd better prove it."

"It's difficult to prove a negative, Rycker. Of course, the doctor can make a test of my blood, but you'll have to wait six months for the . . ."

"How dare you laugh at me?"

"I'm not laughing at you, Rycker. Your wife has done us both an injury. I'd call her a liar if I thought she even knew what a lie was. She thinks the truth is anything that will protect her or send her home to her nursery."

"You sleep with her and then you insult her. You're a coward, Querry."

"Perhaps I am."

"Perhaps. Perhaps. Nothing that I can say would ever anger *the* Querry, would it? He's so infernally important, how could he care what the mere manager of a palm-oil factory—I've got an immortal soul as much as you, Querry."

"I don't make any claims to one. You can be God's important man, Rycker, for all I care. I'm not *the* Querry to anyone but you. Certainly not to myself."

"Please come to the mission, M. Rycker," Brother Philippe pleaded. "We'll put up a bed for you there. We shall all of us feel better after a night's sleep. And a cold shower in the morning," he added, and as though to illustrate his words, a waterfall of rain suddenly descended on them. Querry made an odd awkward sound

219

which the doctor by now had learned to interpret as a laugh, and Rycker fired twice. The lamp fell with Querry and smashed; the burning wick flared up once under the deluge of rain, lighting an open mouth and a pair of surprised eyes, and then went out.

The doctor plumped down on his knees in the mud and felt for Querry's body. Rycker's voice said, "He laughed at me. How dare he laugh at me?" The doctor said to Brother Philippe, "I have his head. Can you find his legs? We've got to get him inside." He called to Rycker, "Put down that gun, you fool, and help!"

"Not at Rycker," Querry said. The doctor leant down closer: he could hardly hear him. He said, "Don't speak. We are going to lift you now. You'll be all right."

Querry said, "Laughing at myself."

They carried him onto the verandah and laid him down out of the rain. Rycker fetched a cushion for his head. He said, "He shouldn't have laughed."

"He doesn't laugh easily," the doctor said, and again there was a noise that resembled a distorted laugh.

"Absurd," Querry said, "this is absurd or else . . ." but what alternative, philosophical or psychological, he had in mind they never knew.

6

The Superior had returned a few days after the funeral, and he visited the cemetery with Doctor Colin. They had buried Querry not far from Mme. Colin's grave, but with enough space left for the doctor in due course. Under the special circumstances Father Thomas had given way in the matter of the cross—only a piece of hard wood from the forest was stuck up there, carved with Querry's name and dates. Nor had there been a Catholic ceremony, though Father Joseph had said unofficially a prayer at the grave. Someone—it was probably Deo Gratias—had put an old jam-pot beside the mound filled with twigs and plants curiously twined. It looked more like an offering to Nzambe than a funeral wreath. Father Thomas would have thrown it away, but Father Joseph dissuaded him.

"It's a very ambiguous offering," Father Thomas protested, "for a Christian cemetery."

"He was an ambiguous man," Father Joseph replied.

Parkinson had procured in Luc a formal wreath which was labelled "From three million readers of the *Post*. Nature I loved and next to Nature Art. Robert Browning." He had photographed it for future use, but with unexpected modesty he refused to be taken beside it.

The Superior said to Colin, "I can't help regretting that I wasn't here. I might have been able to control Rycker."

"Something was bound to happen sooner or later," Colin said. "They would never have let him alone."

"Who do you mean by 'they'?"

"The fools, the interfering fools, they exist everywhere, don't they? He had been cured of all but his success; but you can't cure success, any more than I can give my *mutilés* back their fingers and toes. I return them to the town, and people look at them in the stores and watch them in the street and draw the attention of others to them as they pass. Success is like that too—a mutilation of the natural man. Are you coming my way?"

"Where are you going?"

"To the dispensary. Surely we've wasted enough time on the dead."

"I'll come a little way with you." The Superior felt in the pocket of his soutane for a cheroot, but there wasn't one there.

"Did you see Rycker before you left Luc?" Colin asked.

"Of course. They've made him quite comfortable at the prison. He has been to confession and he intends to go to communion every morning. He's working very hard at Garrigou-Lagrange. And of course he's quite a hero in Luc. M. Parkinson has already telegraphed an interview with him and the metropolitan journalists will soon begin to pour in. I believe M. Parkinson's article was headed 'Death of a Hermit. The Saint who Failed.'

Of course, the result of the trial is a foregone conclusion."

"Acquittal?"

"Naturally. *Le crime passionnel*. Everybody will have got what they wanted—it's really quite a happy ending, isn't it? Rycker feels he has become important both to God and man. He even spoke to me about the possibility of the Belgian College at Rome and an annulment. I didn't encourage him. Mme. Rycker will soon be free to go home and she will keep the child. M. Parkinson has a much better story than he had ever hoped to find. I'm glad, by the way, that Querry never read his second article."

"You can hardly say it was a happy ending for Querry."

"Wasn't it? Surely he always wanted to go a bit further." The Superior added shyly. "Do you think there was anything between him and Mme. Rycker?"

"No."

"I wondered. Judging from Parkinson's second article he would seem to have been a man with a great capacity— well—for love."

"I'm not so sure of that. Nor was he. He told me once that all his life he had only made use of women, but I think he saw himself always in the hardest possible light. I even wondered sometimes whether he suffered from a kind of frigidity. Like a woman who changes partners constantly in the hope that one day she will experience the true orgasm. He said that he always went through the motions of love efficiently, even towards God in the days when he believed, but then he found that the love wasn't really there for anything except his work, so in the end he gave up the motions. And afterwards, when he couldn't even pretend that what he felt was love, the motives for work failed him. That was like the crisis of a sickness— when the patient has no more interest in life at all. It is then that people sometimes kill themselves, but he was tough, very tough."

"You spoke just now as though he had been cured."

"I really think he was. He'd learned to serve other people, you see, and to laugh. An odd laugh, but it was

222

a laugh all the same. I'm frightened of people who don't laugh."

The Superior said shyly, "I thought perhaps you meant that he was beginning to find his faith again."

"Oh no, not that. Only a reason for living. You try too hard to make a pattern, father."

"But if the pattern's there . . . you haven't a cheroot have you?"

"No."

The Superior said, "We all analyse motives too much. I said that once to Father Thomas. You remember what Pascal said, that a man who starts looking for God has already found him. The same may be true of love—when we look for it, perhaps we've already found it."

"He was inclined—I only know what he told me himself—to confine his search to a woman's bed."

"It's not so bad a place to look for it. There are a lot of people who only find hate there."

"Like Rycker?"

"We don't know enough about Rycker to condemn him."

"How persistent you are, father. You never let anyone go, do you? You'd like to claim even Querry for your own."

"I haven't noticed that you relax much before a patient dies."

They had reached the dispensary. The lepers sat on the hot cement steps waiting for something to happen. At the new hospital the ladders leant against the roof, and the last work was in progress. The roof-tree had been battered and bent by the storm, but it was held in place still by its strong palm-fibre thongs.

"I see from the accounts," the Superior said, "that you've given up using vitamin tablets. Is that a wise economy?"

"I don't believe the anaemia comes from the D.D.S. treatment. It comes from hookworm. It's cheaper to build lavatories than to buy vitamin tablets. That's our next project. I mean it was to have been. How many patients have turned up today?" he asked the dispenser. "About sixty."

"Your god must feel a bit disappointed," Doctor Colin said, "when he looks at this world of his."

"When you were a boy they can't have taught you theology very well. God cannot feel disappointment or pain."

"Perhaps that's why I don't care to believe in him."

The doctor sat down at the table and drew forward a blank chart. "Number one," he called.

It was a child of three, quite naked, with a little pot-belly and a dangling tassel and a finger stuck in the corner of his mouth. The doctor ran his fingers over the skin of the back while the child's mother waited.

"I know that little fellow," the Superior said. "He always came to me for sweets."

"He's infected all right," Doctor Colin said. "Feel the patches here and here. But you needn't worry," he added in a tone of suppressed rage, "we shall be able to cure him in a year or two, and I can promise you that there will be no mutilations."